# VISUALIZED GEOMETRY

## A van Hiele Level Approach

**Ernest Woodward**
**Thomas Hamel**

J. WESTON
WALCH
PUBLISHER

PORTLAND, MAINE

1    2    3    4    5    6    7    8    9    10

ISBN 0-8251-2599-5

Copyright © 1990
J. Weston Walch, Publisher
P. O. Box 658 • Portland, Maine 04104-0658

Printed in the United States of America

# Acknowledgments

*The authors want to thank Eugene Stewart and Marilyn Woodward for their editorial assistance in the preparation of this book. We also want to thank Betty Leimer, who typed the manuscript and drew the various figures and illustrations.*

# Table of Contents

# Chapter 6   Congruence and Line Symmetry *(continued)*

# Chapter 7   Similarity . . . . . . . . . . . . . . . . . . . . . . . . . . . . . . . . . . . .**363**

# Appendix . . . . . . . . . . . . . . . . . . . . . . . . . . . . . . . . . . . . . . . .**421**

# Introduction

The process of reforming mathematics curricula has led many math educators to recognize the importance of instruction that matches students' cognitive development. This book, *Visualized Geometry: A van Hiele Level Approach,* is a supplementary program of lessons designed to facilitate this important instructional goal. It is a resource of teaching notes and reproducible blackline masters all tailor-made to meet students on their initial level of geometrical thinking—**visualization.** Further, the lessons are designed to move students to more advanced levels. This is accomplished through a variety of manipulative techniques as suggested in the NCTM publication *Curriculum and Evaluation Standards for School Mathematics.* Students are asked to visualize, analyze, draw, compare, represent, model, construct, generalize, and eventually make simple deductions.

## *The van Hiele Model*

In the late 1950's a Dutch couple, Dina van Hiele-Geldof and Pierre van Hiele, investigated the way students learn geometry. They found that there were five distinct geometry learning levels which have subsequently been named van Hiele levels. These levels are described below:

1. **Visualization**—At this level, the student views geometric figures in terms of their physical appearance and not in terms of their individual parts. For example, a student at this level will recognize a square but when asked why that figure is a square, the student will respond that it looks like a square.

2. **Analysis**—At this level, the student becomes aware of characteristics of geometric figures but is unable to understand the significance of minimal conditions and definitions.

3. **Informal Deduction**—At this level, the student becomes aware of the relationships between properties of geometric figures and minimal conditions, and definitions become meaningful. Informal arguments can be understood but the significance of axioms is not understood.

4. **Formal Deduction**—At this level, the student recognizes the significance of an axiomatic system and can construct geometric proofs.

5. **Rigor**—At this level, geometry is seen as abstract and various non-Euclidean geometries can be understood and appreciated.

Information concerning the van Hiele model did not reach the United States until the late 1970's. Since that time, leaders in the mathematics education community have been recommending a geometry curriculum which recognizes the existence of the learning levels.

## Properties of the van Hiele Model

The van Hiele geometry learning model is characterized by the following properties:

a. The levels are sequential. To function at a particular level, the learner must have passed through the preceding levels.

b. A student progresses from level to level primarily because of the instruction received rather than the chronological age of that student.

c. When the instruction on a geometry topic is on one level and the student is operating at a lower level, the student is usually not able to follow the thought process used, and often very little real learning takes place.

## The van Hiele Model and This Book

A significant amount of research has been conducted concerning the van Hiele model. The van Hiele model itself, and the implications of the model as described above, are generally accepted by researchers in the field. Several studies have shown that most beginning American high school geometry students are at the first or second level while the instruction is generally at the third or fourth level. *This mismatch between the level of the learner and the level of instruction is at least a partial explanation for the frustration which often occurs in high school geometry courses.*

This book is written with the general purpose of increasing the van Hiele level of the learner. Specific sequences of lessons are designed to raise the student from the first to the third level. Most lessons include exploratory, laboratory-type activities which are consistent with the van Hiele model. In many instances the students are given dot paper representations of geoboards and are asked to identify the figure pictured or to draw a figure with certain properties. The dot paper approach is significant because the student can easily identify the properties of a figure from a dot paper picture. The lessons in this book can be used with students who are initially at the first level without respect to age. Specifically, the lessons can be used in middle school mathematics classes or in the first semester of a high school geometry course and should prepare the student for formal geometric proofs.

## Using This Book

This book contains 82 lessons, most of which are exploratory, laboratory-type lessons. Each lesson begins with a description of the materials needed for that lesson. Most lessons involve the use of transparencies and student worksheets. These must be made from master pages provided with the lesson. Occasionally the teacher and/or student will need other materials such as index cards, marking pencils, blank transparencies, and scissors. Also, each lesson contains a "Directions to the Teacher" section which gives specific suggestions on how the lesson should be taught.

A lesson is not necessarily designed to last an entire class period. In most instances, several of these lessons can be covered in one day or one lesson can be used to supplement other teacher-determined activities for a particular day. The student worksheet pages can be completed in class or used as homework.

Generally speaking, the lessons in each chapter should be taught sequentially but the chapters can be taught in any order. For example, Chapter 7 can easily be taught before Chapter 4. However, Lesson 1–5 and Lesson 2–7 are prerequisites for many lessons in later chapters.

The appendix contains three pages of paper strips. These strips are to be punched out and are used for several lessons. Also included in the appendix is a page of regular dot paper and a page of special (isometric) dot paper. The teacher may wish to provide each student with a copy of these two pages.

# CHAPTER 1

# General Concepts

## Comments and Suggestions

In this chapter, students are introduced to basic vocabulary of lines, segments, angles, and polygons. They learn about right, acute, and obtuse angles by comparing given angles to an index card angle. Dot paper representations of geoboards are introduced and students learn to recognize congruent, parallel, and perpendicular dot paper segments.

# Lesson 1-1
# Vocabulary—Lines, Segments, Rays, and Angles

## *Materials Needed:*

One copy of page 4 for each student.

## *Directions for the Teacher:*

The purpose of this short lesson is to review the concepts of line, ray, segment, and angle. Draw a picture like the following on the chalkboard or the overhead projector.

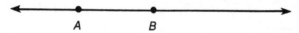

Indicate that this is a picture of a line and the arrows mean that the line goes on indefinitely in both directions.

Write

$$\overleftrightarrow{AB}$$

on the chalkboard. Indicate that this is read "line *A, B.*" Also write "$\overleftrightarrow{BA}$" and indicate this is another name for the line pictured.

Next, draw a picture like the following on the chalkboard.

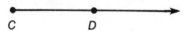

Indicate that this is a picture of a ray and *C* is the endpoint of this ray. Write "$\overrightarrow{CD}$" and tell students this is read "ray *C, D.*"

Now draw a picture like the following on the chalkboard.

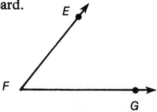

Tell your students that this is a picture of an angle. Point out that there are two rays, $\overrightarrow{FE}$ and $\overrightarrow{FG}$; that the two rays have the common endpoint *F*; and that *F* is called the vertex of the angle. Write "∠*EFG*" and read this "angle *E, F, G.*" Also write "∠*GFE*" and indicate this is another name for the angle pictured. Finally, write "∠*F*" and tell your students that when only one angle is pictured with a given vertex, it is permissible to use only the angle symbol and the letter indicating the vertex.

Finally draw a picture like the following on the chalkboard.

Indicate this is a segment. Write "$\overline{HI}$" and tell your students to read this "segment H, I." Point out that H and I are called endpoints of the segment. Also write "$\overline{IH}$" and indicate this is another name for the segment pictured.

As you conclude this discussion, point out that a segment has two endpoints, a ray has one endpoint, and a line has zero endpoints. Additionally, some of your students may notice or you may choose to emphasize that an angle, a segment, or a line will generally have more than one name while a ray may have just one name. A ray is always named by listing its endpoint first.

Distribute the worksheet and tell the students to complete it.

## Correct Answers for Worksheet 1–1–1:

1. $\angle BCA$ (or $\angle ACB$ or $\angle C$)

2. $\overrightarrow{DE}$

3. $\overline{GH}$ (or $\overline{HG}$)

4. $\overleftrightarrow{IJ}$ (or $\overleftrightarrow{JI}$)

# WORKSHEET 1-1-1
## Vocabulary—Lines, Segments, Rays, and Angles

Name the figure pictured.

1.

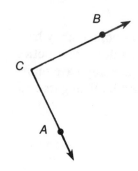

3.

2.

4.

# Lesson 1–2
# General Congruence Concepts

## *Materials Needed:*

One copy of each of the following pages for each student: pages 8 and 9.

One transparency of page 7.

An overhead projector pen and a blank transparency for each student.

## *Directions for the Teacher:*

Place the prepared transparency on the overhead projector. Place the blank transparency on top of it and trace $\overline{AB}$. Tell the students that two segments are congruent when the segments are the same length. Place the copy of $\overline{AB}$ on $\overline{CD}$—they should match—and conclude that $\overline{CD}$ is congruent to $\overline{AB}$. Then write $\overline{CD} \cong \overline{AB}$ and indicate that the symbol $\cong$ means "is congruent to." Place the copy of $\overline{AB}$ on $\overline{EF}$ and conclude that these segments are not the same length and thus are not congruent. In a similar way conclude that $\overline{GH}$ is not congruent to $\overline{AB}$ and $\overline{IJ} \cong \overline{AB}$.

Proceed with Problem II. Tell the students that two angles are congruent when they are the same size. On the blank transparency, copy $\angle A$ and place this copy of $\angle A$ on $\angle B$. They should see that the two angles are the same size even though the rays are drawn with different lengths. It is important for students to realize that rays are of infinite length even though their models are of finite length. Congruent angles have the same "amount of opening" between the rays that are their sides and this is the only criteria that is used in testing congruence of angles. Write $\angle B \cong \angle A$. Next place the copy of $\angle A$ on $\angle C$. They should conclude that $\angle C$ is larger than $\angle A$ so they are not congruent. Proceeding in a similar way they should conclude that $\angle D \cong \angle A$.

Finally, proceed to Problem III. Tell the students that two triangles are congruent if a copy of one triangle can be made to fit on the other triangle. Fit the copy of $\triangle ABC$ on $\triangle DFE$ (rotate $\triangle ABC$ until it matches $\triangle DFE$) and conclude that $\triangle DFE \cong \triangle ABC$. Attempt to fit the copy of $\triangle ABC$ on $\triangle GHI$ (it is not possible) and conclude that those triangles are not congruent. Proceed in a similar way with $\triangle JKL$ and conclude that $\triangle JKL \cong \triangle ABC$. Observe that $\triangle ABC$ must be flipped as well as rotated to fit on $\triangle JKL$.

Distribute the worksheet (pages 8 and 9), a blank transparency, and an overhead projector pen to each student. Point out that two quadrilaterals are congruent when a copy of one quadrilateral can be made to fit on the other quadrilateral. Provide individual assistance as needed.

**Correct Answers for Worksheet 1–2–1:**

1. $\overline{CD} \cong \overline{AB}$
   $\overline{IJ} \cong \overline{AB}$

2. $\angle B \cong \angle A$
   $\angle E \cong \angle A$
   $\angle G \cong \angle A$
   $\angle H \cong \angle A$

3. A "C" should be written in $\triangle DEF$ and $\triangle JKL$.

4. A "C" should be written in quadrilateral *FEHG* and quadrilateral *PONM*.

I. Which of the segments are congruent to $\overline{AB}$?

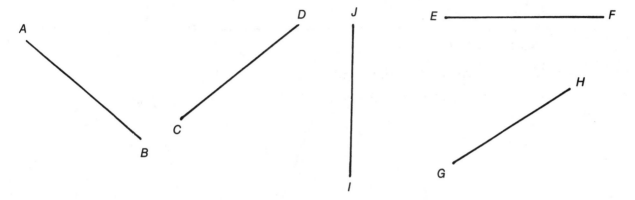

II. Which of the angles are congruent to $\angle A$?

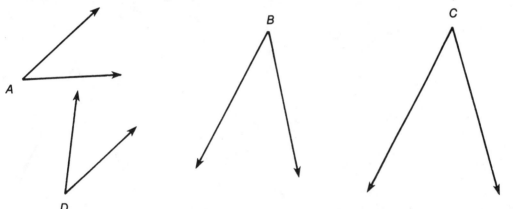

III. Which of the following triangles are congruent to $\triangle ABC$?

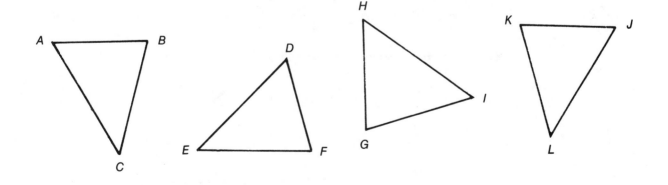

# WORKSHEET 1-2-1
## General Congruence Concepts

1. Which segments are congruent to $\overline{AB}$?

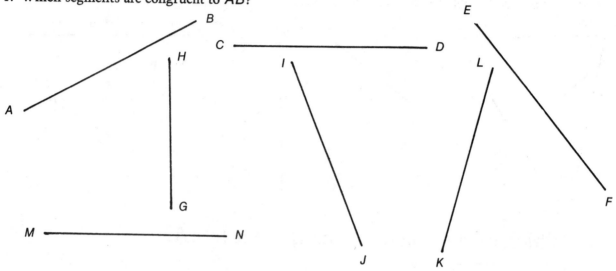

2. Which of the angles pictured are congruent to $\angle A$?

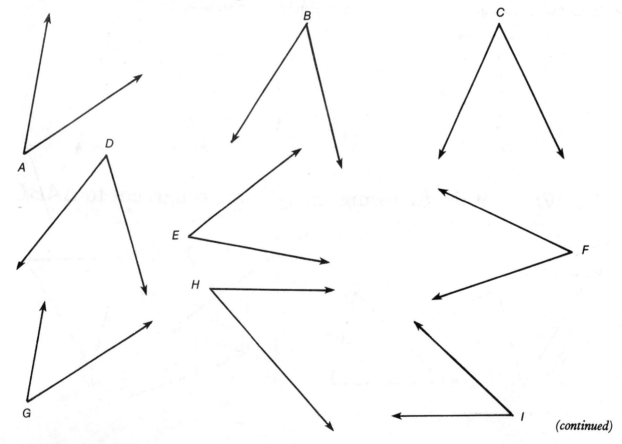

*(continued)*

*Visualized Geometry*

# WORKSHEET 1-2-1
## General Congruence Concepts (*continued*)

3. Write "C" in each triangle which is congruent to △*ABC*.

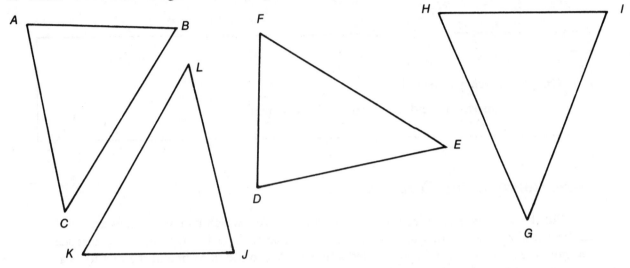

4. Write "C" in each quadrilateral which is congruent to quadrilateral *ABCD*.

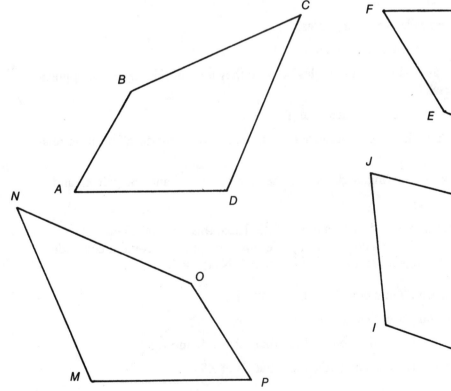

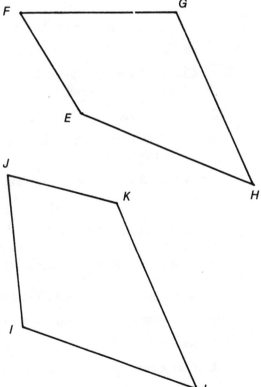

*Visualized Geometry*

## Lesson 1–3
# Angles Involved with Parallel Lines

## *Materials Needed:*

One copy of page 13 for each student.

One transparency of page 12.

A blank transparency and an overhead projector pen.

## *Directions for the Teacher:*

Put the transparency on your overhead projector. Ask which two of the lines are parallel. Tell students that a line which intersects two coplanar (lines in the same plane in space but not necessarily parallel) lines is called a transversal, so the third line in the picture is a transversal of the other two lines. Indicate that this transversal forms four angles with each of the parallel lines for a total of eight angles. Identify the eight angles by number. Discuss the following terminology:

a. $\angle 1$, $\angle 2$, $\angle 7$, and $\angle 8$ are called exterior angles.

b. $\angle 3$, $\angle 4$, $\angle 5$, and $\angle 6$ are called interior angles.

c. $\angle 3$ and $\angle 6$ are called alternate interior angles because they are interior angles on opposite sides of the transversal.

d. $\angle 4$ and $\angle 5$ are also called alternate interior angles.

e. $\angle 2$ and $\angle 6$ are corresponding angles because they are in a "corresponding" position relative to the transversal.

f. $\angle 4$ and $\angle 8$ are also corresponding angles as are the pair $\angle 1$ and $\angle 5$ and the pair $\angle 3$ and $\angle 7$.

Take the blank transparency and make a copy of $\angle 3$. Place this copy of $\angle 3$ on $\angle 6$. Thus conclude that $\angle 3 \cong \angle 6$. Make a copy of $\angle 4$, place this copy of $\angle 4$ on $\angle 5$ and conclude that $\angle 4 \cong \angle 5$. Point out that this illustrates generalization I. Next:

a. place your copy of $\angle 3$ on $\angle 7$ and conclude that $\angle 3 \cong \angle 7$;

b. place your copy of $\angle 4$ on $\angle 8$ and conclude that $\angle 4 \cong \angle 8$;

c. make a copy of $\angle 2$, place it on $\angle 6$, and conclude that $\angle 2 \cong \angle 6$; and finally

d. make a copy of $\angle 1$, place it on $\angle 5$, and conclude that $\angle 1 \cong \angle 5$.

Point out that this illustrates generalization II.

Provide each student with a copy of the worksheet (page 13). Provide individual assistance as needed.

**Correct Answers for Worksheet 1-3-1:**

1a. ∠4

 b. yes

2a. ∠5

 b. yes

3a. ∠2

 b. yes

4a. ∠3

 b. yes

# Transparency 1-3-1

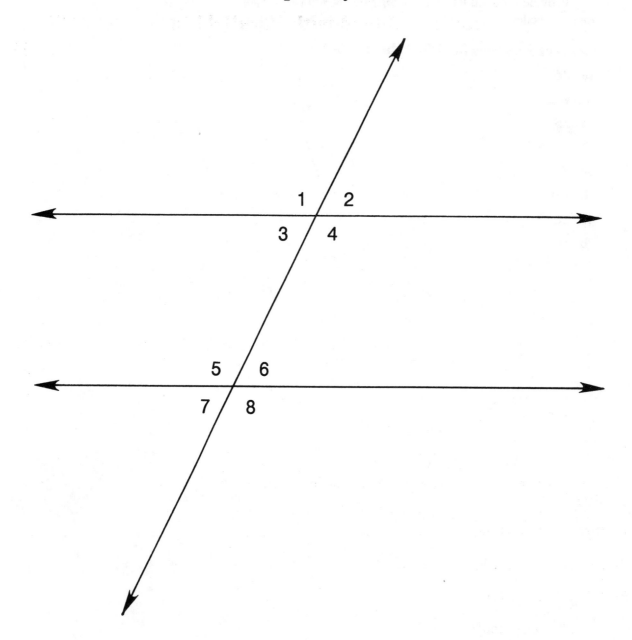

I. When a transversal intersects two parallel lines the alternate interior angles are congruent.

II. When a transversal intersects two parallel lines the corresponding angles are congruent.

*Visualized Geometry*

Name: _____   Date: _____

# WORKSHEET 1-3-1
## Angles Involved with Parallel Lines

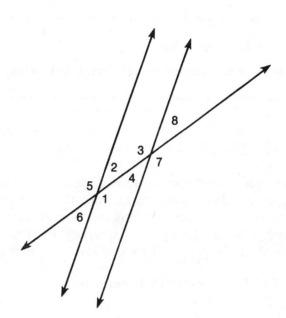

In the picture above, two lines are parallel and the third line is a transversal. Answer the following questions.

1a. Which is the angle which corresponds to ∠6? _____

 b. Are these angles congruent? _____

2a. Which is the angle which corresponds to ∠3? _____

 b. Are these angles congruent? _____

3a. Which angle is the alternate interior angle to ∠4? _____

 b. Are these angles congruent? _____

4a. Which angle is the alternate interior angle to ∠1? _____

 b. Are these angles congruent? _____

           *Visualized Geometry*

## Lesson 1–4
# Congruence of Dot Paper Segments

## *Materials Needed:*

One copy of page 18 for each student.

One transparency of each of the following pages: pages 16 and 17.

## *Directions for the Teacher:*

This is an important lesson because in succeeding lessons, the students will be required to know when dot paper segments are congruent. Place the first transparency on the overhead projector. Mention that dot paper segments are segments in which both endpoints occur at dots. Go through the first transparency carefully. Proceed to the second transparency, and with your students' help, answer the questions for problem 1, then for problem 2.

**Correct Answers for Transparency 1-4-2:**

1. $\overline{AB}$ is a (2, –2) segment
   $\overline{CD}$ is a (1, 2) segment
   $\overline{EF}$ is a (1, –3) segment
   $\overline{GH}$ is a (4, 0) segment
   $\overline{IJ}$ is a (0, 2) segment
   $\overline{KL}$ is a (3, 1) segment

2a. (4, 2)

b.

| SEGMENT NAME | TYPE OF SEGMENT | CONGRUENT TO $\overline{AB}$? |
| --- | --- | --- |
| $\overline{CD}$ | (2, –4) | yes |
| $\overline{EF}$ | (2, 4) | yes |
| $\overline{GH}$ | (3, 3) | no |
| $\overline{IJ}$ | (4, –2) | yes |
| $\overline{KL}$ | (1, 5) | no |
| $\overline{MN}$ | (4, 2) | yes |

If the students have difficulty accepting the entries in the third column of the table, you may want to copy $\overline{AB}$ on a blank transparency and compare its length with the lengths of the other segments. Point out that the only segments which are congruent to $\overline{AB}$ are (2, –4), (4, –2), (2, 4), and other (4, 2) segments.

3. (2, 3), (3, 2), (3, –2), and other (2, –3) segments. If your students understand about variables, you might suggest that segments of the type (*a*, *b*), (*b*, *a*), (*b*, –*a*), and (*a*, –*b*), are all congruent.

Distribute the worksheet. Provide individual assistance as needed.

### Correct Answers for Worksheet 1–4–1:

1. $\overline{AB}$ is a (3, –2) segment
   $\overline{CD}$ is a (1, 2) segment
   $\overline{EF}$ is a (1, –3) segment
   $\overline{GH}$ is a (0, 2) segment
   $\overline{IJ}$ is a (2, 0) segment
   $\overline{KL}$ is a (2, –3) segment

2. $\overline{CD}, \overline{GH}, \overline{IJ}$

3. (2, 1), (1, 2), (2, –1) and (1, –2)

4.

Segments can be classified in terms of the position of their endpoints. For example, $\overline{AB}$ pictured below is called a (3, 1) segment because you can get from the left endpoint, *A*, to the right endpoint, *B*, by moving to the right 3 units and then moving 1 unit up.

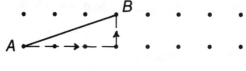

On the other hand, $\overline{CD}$ is called a (2, –3) segment because you can get from the left endpoint, *C*, to the right endpoint, *D*, by moving 2 units to the right and then moving 3 units down.

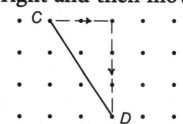

Vertical segments do not have a single left endpoint. When that is the case, start at the bottom endpoint and indicate how you could get to the top endpoint. For example, $\overline{EF}$ pictured below is a (0, 3) segment because if you start at the bottom endpoint you can get to the top endpoint by moving 0 units to the right and 3 units up.

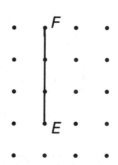

         *Visualized Geometry*

1. Classify the following segments.

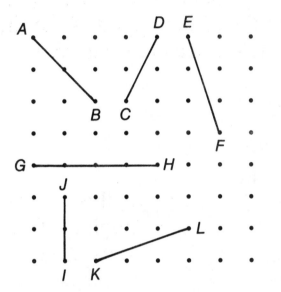

$\overline{AB}$ is a _____ segment.

$\overline{CD}$ is a _____ segment.

$\overline{EF}$ is a _____ segment.

$\overline{GH}$ is a _____ segment.

$\overline{IJ}$ is a _____ segment.

$\overline{KL}$ is a _____ segment.

2a. What kind of a segment is $\overline{AB}$?

b. Complete the table below. (Remember that segments are congruent when the segments are the same length.)

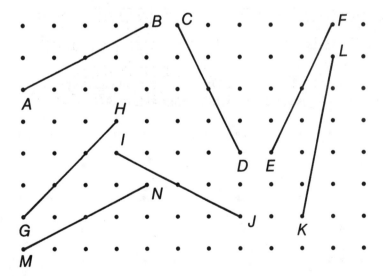

| Segment name | Type of segment | Congruent to AB? |
|---|---|---|
| $\overline{CD}$ | | |
| $\overline{EF}$ | | |
| $\overline{GH}$ | | |
| $\overline{IJ}$ | | |
| $\overline{KL}$ | | |
| $\overline{MN}$ | | |

3. What type segments are congruent to a (2, –3) segment?

 *Visualized Geometry*

# WORKSHEET 1-4-1
## Congruence of Dot Paper Segments

1. Classify the following segments.

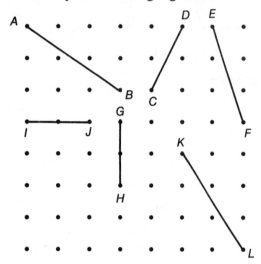

$\overline{AB}$ is a _____ segment.

$\overline{CD}$ is a _____ segment.

$\overline{EF}$ is a _____ segment.

$\overline{GH}$ is a _____ segment.

$\overline{IJ}$ is a _____ segment.

$\overline{KL}$ is a _____ segment.

2. Which segments are congruent to $\overline{AB}$?

_____

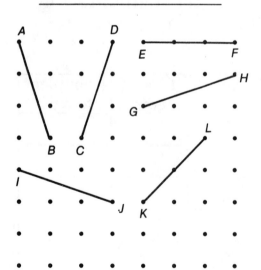

3. $\overline{AB}$ is a (1, –2) segment. List all the types (four) of segments that are congruent to $\overline{AB}$.

_____

4. $\overline{AB}$ is (2, 3). Draw a picture of each type of segment which is congruent to $\overline{AB}$.

## Lesson 1–5
# Right, Acute, and Obtuse Angles

## *Materials Needed:*

One copy of each of the following pages for each student: pages 24 and 25.

One transparency of each of the following pages: pages 22 and 23.

A standard 3″ x 5″ index card for each student.

## *Directions for the Teacher:*

In this lesson the students will learn to classify angles (right, obtuse, and acute). They may have had some previous experience with measuring angles and may respond that a right angle is an angle of 90° or something like that. Measurement of angles is not important in this lesson. Instead tell the students that the angle formed by two adjacent sides of a 3″ x 5″ index card is a right angle and that they are to find out if an angle is a right angle by comparing it with an angle of an index card.

Place the first transparency (page 22) on the overhead projector. Direct the students' attention to ∠1. Place the index card on ∠1 as shown below.

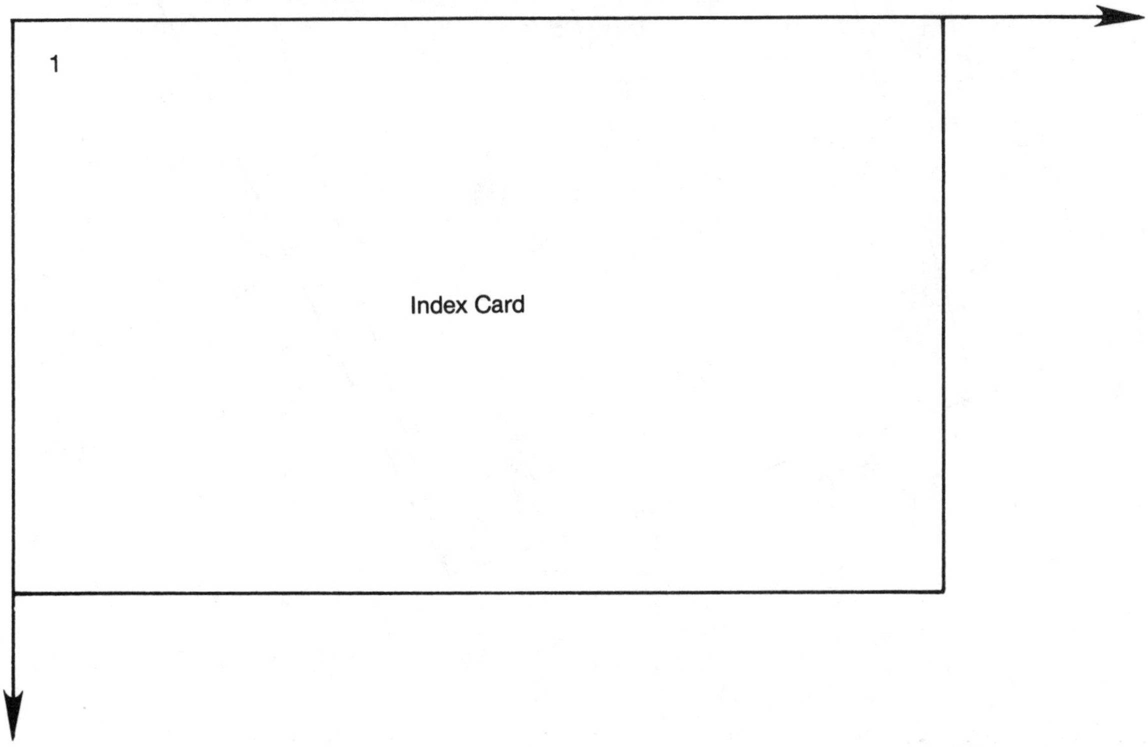

1

Index Card

Point out that since the sides of the card fall along the rays, the angle of the card is congruent to ∠1 and so ∠1 is a right angle. You may need to remind them that the "lengths" of the sides of the angle are not important.

Next direct your students' attention to ∠2. Place the index card as shown below.

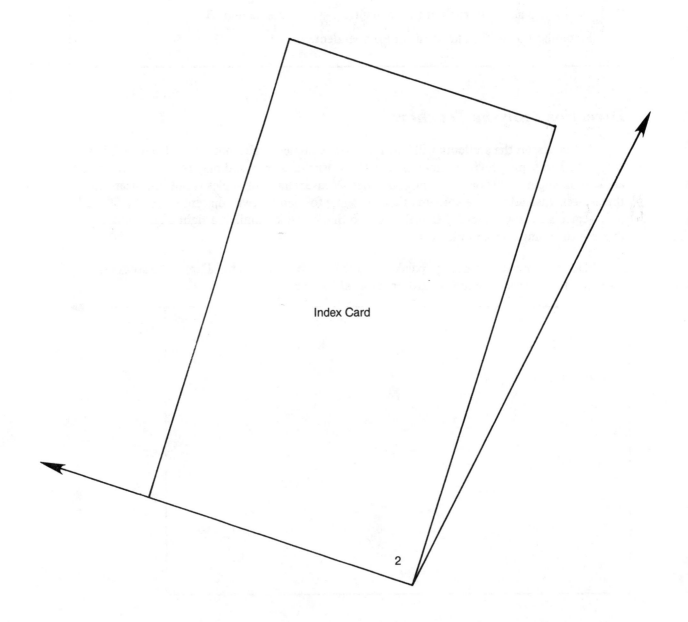

Point out that ∠2 is larger than a right angle.

Finally investigate ∠3. You will find that it is a right angle.

Next, place the second transparency (page 23) on your overhead projector. Go over definitions of obtuse and acute angles. Use your index card to find out which angles are right angles, which angles are obtuse angles, and which angles are acute angles.

## Correct Answers for Transparency 1-5-2:

| | |
|---|---|
| ∠1—obtuse | ∠4—right |
| ∠2—acute | ∠5—acute |
| ∠3—right | ∠6—obtuse |

Finally, distribute the worksheets and direct the students to complete the exercise using an index card.

## Correct Answers for Worksheet 1-5-1:

| | |
|---|---|
| 1a. acute | 2 a. right |
| b. obtuse | b. acute |
| c. right | c. right |
| d. obtuse | d. obtuse |
| e. right | e. right |
| f. acute | f. right |
| | g. obtuse |
| | h. right |

# Which angles are right angles?

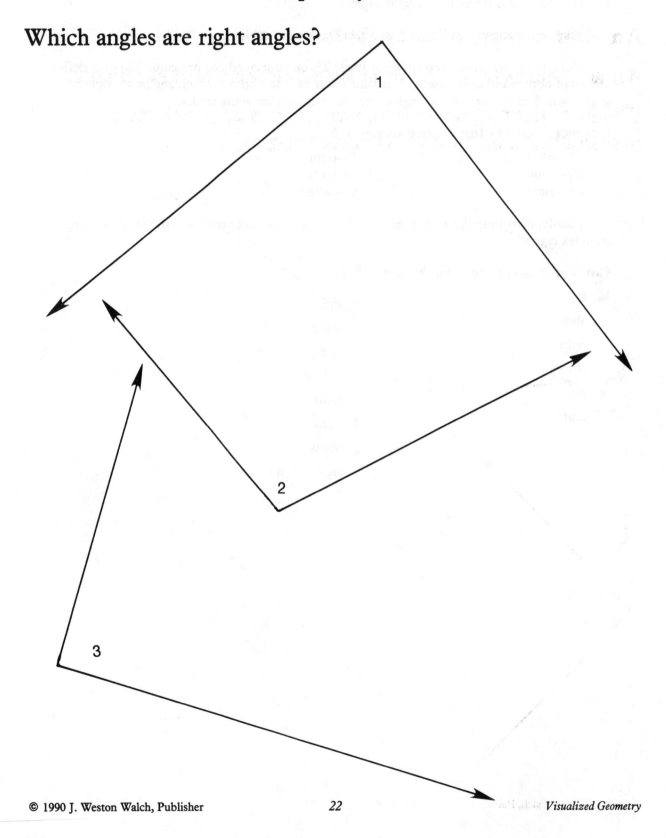

# An obtuse angle is an angle larger than a right angle.

# An acute angle is an angle smaller than a right angle.

Which of the following angles are right angles, which are obtuse angles, and which are acute angles?

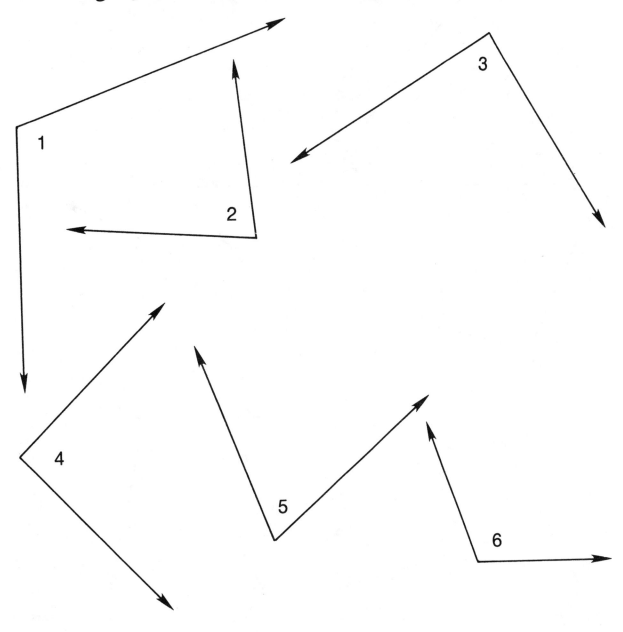

Name: _____ Date: _____

# WORKSHEET 1–5–1
## Right, Acute, and Obtuse Angles

1. Write "right" in the blank if the angle is a right angle, "obtuse" if the angle is an obtuse angle, and "acute" if the angle is an acute angle.

a. _____

d. _____

b. _____

e. _____

c. _____

f. _____

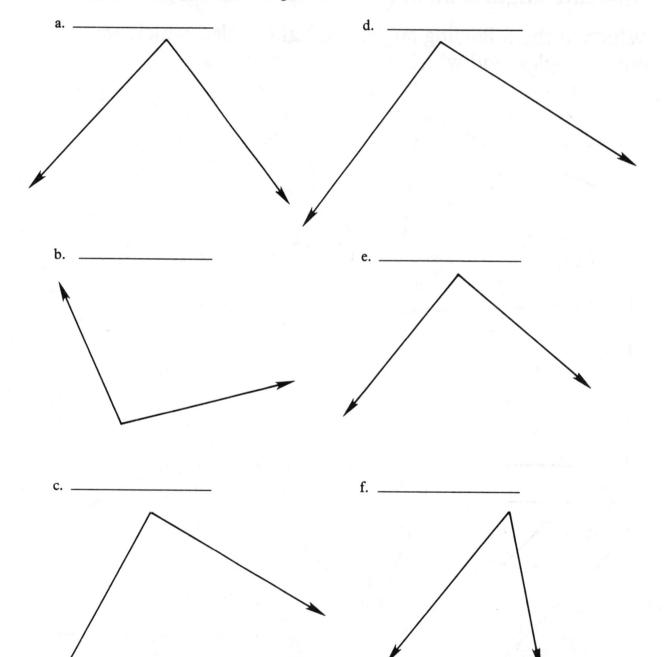

*(continued)*

*Visualized Geometry*

# WORKSHEET 1-5-1
## Right, Acute, and Obtuse Angles *(continued)*

2. Write "right" in the blank if the angle is a right angle, "obtuse" if the angle is an obtuse angle, and "acute" if the angle is an acute angle.

a. _____

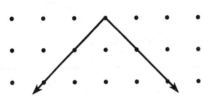

b. _____

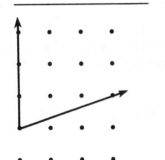

c. _____

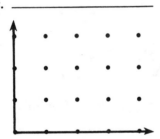

d. _____

e. _____

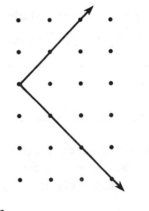

f. _____

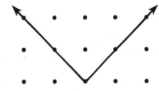

g. _____

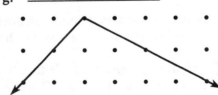

h. _____

## Lesson 1-6
# Slopes of Segments and Parallel Segments

## *Materials Needed:*

One copy of page 34 for each student.

One transparency of each of the following pages: pages 29, 30, 31, 32, and 33.

## *Directions for the Teacher:*

Lesson 1-4 is a prerequisite for this lesson. Place the first transparency (page 29) on the overhead projector. Read the definition and proceed with problems 1-7. Encourage the students to participate in the solutions.

### Correct Answers for Transparencies 1-6-1 through 1-6-4:

1. $\frac{-3}{4}$   2. $\frac{3}{1}$ or 3   3. 0   4. $\frac{-3}{2}$   5. $\frac{1}{3}$   6. 0

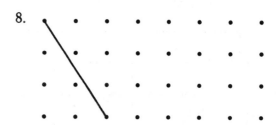

9.  Indicate that the stated definition does not apply (since the slope is undefined) in this situation and this segment does not have a slope.

10. The students should conclude that the slope of $\overline{AB}$ is $\frac{2}{4}$ or $\frac{1}{2}$ while the slope of $\overline{AC}$ is $\frac{1}{2}$. Point out that the slopes of $\overline{AB}$ and $\overline{AC}$ are the same. Mention that it is possible to find the slope of a segment without using both endpoints. In this case we could find the slope of $\overline{AB}$ by using the points *A* and *C* rather than *A* and *B*. Indicate that the slope of a segment describes its direction.

11. and 12. Mention that in each case the slopes of the parallel segments are the same ($\frac{-2}{7}$ for problem 11 and $\frac{1}{4}$ for problem 12).

13.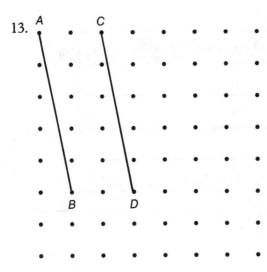

Point out that these two segments have the same slope (–5).

14. Any horizontal segment will be parallel to $\overline{AB}$. Mention that any horizontal line has slope 0.

15. Any vertical segment will be parallel to $\overline{AB}$. Indicate that vertical segments have undefined slopes.

16. With the students' assistance, take the information from problems 12–15 and complete the problem.

| Problem | Slope of $\overline{AB}$ | Slope of a segment parallel to $\overline{AB}$ |
|---------|--------------------------|-----------------------------------------------|
| 12 | $\frac{1}{4}$ | $\frac{1}{4}$ |
| 13 | –5 | –5 |
| 14 | 0 | 0 |
| 15 | Undefined slope | Undefined slope |

Finally, distribute the worksheet. Provide individual assistance as needed.

## Correct Answers for Worksheet 1-6-1:

1. The slope of $\overline{AB}$ is $\frac{-2}{3}$.

   The slope of $\overline{CD}$ is $\frac{2}{3}$.

   The slope of $\overline{EF}$ is 4.

   The slope of $\overline{GH}$ is 0.

   The slope of $\overline{IJ}$ is $\frac{-1}{3}$.

2.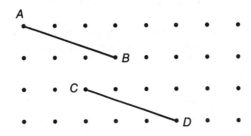

3.

| Slope of $\overline{AB}$ | Slope of a segment parallel to $\overline{AB}$ |
|:---:|:---:|
| $\frac{2}{3}$ | $\frac{2}{3}$ |
| $-4$ | $-4$ |
| $0$ | $0$ |
| $\frac{-3}{7}$ | $\frac{-3}{7}$ |

**Definition:** Suppose $\overline{AB}$ is classified as an $(a, b)$ segment. Then as long as $a \neq 0$ the slope of $\overline{AB}$ is $\frac{b}{a}$ .

1. Find the slope of $\overline{AB}$ where $\overline{AB}$ is a $(4, -3)$ segment.

2. Find the slope of $\overline{AB}$ where $\overline{AB}$ is a $(1, 3)$ segment.

3. Find the slope of $\overline{AB}$ where $\overline{AB}$ is a $(5, 0)$ segment.

4. What is the slope of the segment pictured?

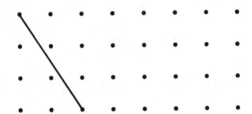

5. What is the slope of the segment pictured?

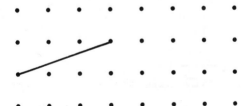

6. What is the slope of the segment pictured?

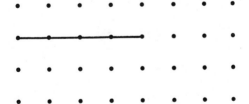

*Visualized Geometry*

7. Draw a picture of a segment with slope $\frac{2}{3}$ .

8. Draw a picture of a segment with slope $\frac{-3}{2}$ .

9. What is the slope of the segment pictured?

10. Find the slope of $\overline{AB}$ and $\overline{AC}$.

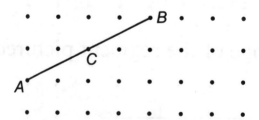

*Visualized Geometry*

11. Find the slope of $\overline{AB}$ and $\overline{CD}$.

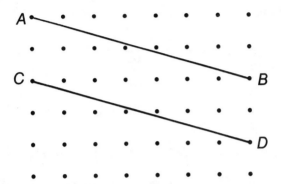

12. Find the slope of $\overline{AB}$ and $\overline{CD}$.

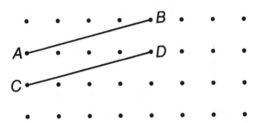

13. Draw a segment, $\overline{CD}$, that is parallel to $\overline{AB}$. What is the slope of $\overline{CD}$?

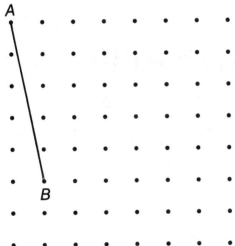

*Visualized Geometry*

14. Draw a segment, $\overline{CD}$, that is parallel to $\overline{AB}$. What is the slope of $\overline{CD}$?

15. Draw a segment, $\overline{CD}$, that is parallel to $\overline{AB}$. What is the slope of $\overline{CD}$?

16. Complete the following table.

| Problem | Slope of $\overline{AB}$ | Slope of a segment parallel to $\overline{AB}$ |
|---|---|---|
| 12 | $\frac{1}{4}$ | |
| 13 | –5 | |
| 14 | 0 | |
| 15 | Undefined slope | |

*Visualized Geometry*

# WORKSHEET 1-6-1
## Slopes of Segments and Parallel Segments

1. Find the slope of each segment pictured.

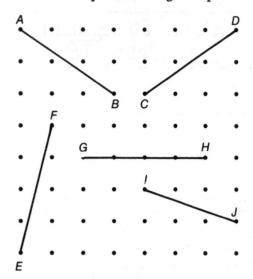

The slope of $\overline{AB}$ is _____ .

The slope of $\overline{CD}$ is _____ .

The slope of $\overline{EF}$ is _____ .

The slope of $\overline{GH}$ is _____ .

The slope of $\overline{IJ}$ is _____ .

2. Draw a segment, $\overline{CD}$, that is parallel to $\overline{AB}$.

3. Complete the following table.

| Slope of $\overline{AB}$ | Slope of a segment parallel to $\overline{AB}$ |
|---|---|
| $\frac{2}{3}$ | |
| $-4$ | |
| $0$ | |
| $\frac{-3}{7}$ | |

*Visualized Geometry*

# Lesson 1-7
# Perpendicular Segments on Dot Paper

## *Materials Needed:*

One copy of each of the following pages for each student: pages 40 and 41.

One transparency of each of the following pages: pages 37, 38, and 39.

## *Directions for the Teacher:*

This is a rather difficult lesson. It should only be used with students who can calculate the product of positive and negative rational numbers. Place the first transparency (page 37) on the overhead projector. Remind the students that two lines are perpendicular when they intersect to form right angles. Use an index card to see whether the segments are perpendicular. Answer the questions individually and record the information in the table (problem 7, third transparency).

## Correct Answers for Transparencies 1-7-1 through 1-7-3:

| Problem number | Slope of $\overline{AB}$ | Slope of other segment ($\overline{BC}$ or $\overline{CD}$) | Are the segments perpendicular? |
|---|---|---|---|
| 1 | $\frac{2}{3}$ | $\frac{-3}{2}$ | yes |
| 2 | $\frac{-4}{3}$ | $\frac{3}{4}$ | yes |
| 3 | 1 | –1 | yes |
| 4 | $\frac{-3}{2}$ | $\frac{2}{3}$ | yes |
| 5 | $\frac{1}{2}$ | –1 | no |
| 6 | $\frac{-2}{3}$ | $\frac{3}{2}$ | yes |

Direct the students' attention to this table. Ask them to describe the relationship between the slopes of two segments that are perpendicular. If the students are comfortable with variables, they may suggest that the segments are perpendicular and when the slope of one segment is $\frac{a}{b}$ the slope of the other segment is $\frac{-b}{a}$.

Another way to describe the relationship between slopes of perpendicular lines is that the product of their slopes is –1. In any event some generalization should be made.

Distribute the worksheets. Provide individual assistance as needed.

### Correct Answers for Worksheet 1–7–1:

1a. $\frac{-6}{5}, \frac{5}{6}$, yes          b. $\frac{-3}{2}, \frac{2}{3}$, yes          c. $\frac{2}{3}, \frac{-2}{3}$, no

2.  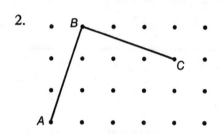          3.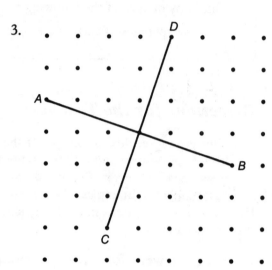

*Note:* With respect to problem 3, there are other segments that are perpendicular to $\overline{AB}$ but none contain a dot paper point that is also on $\overline{AB}$. There are several segments with a slope of $\frac{6}{2}$ (or $\frac{3}{1}$) that constitute correct answers.

**1.**

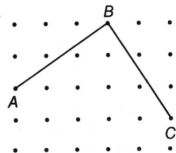

a. Is $\overline{AB}$ perpendicular to $\overline{BC}$?

b. What is the slope of $\overline{AB}$?

c. What is the slope of $\overline{BC}$?

**3.**

a. Is $\overline{AB}$ perpendicular to $\overline{CD}$?

b. What is the slope of $\overline{AB}$?

c. What is the slope of $\overline{CD}$?

**2.**

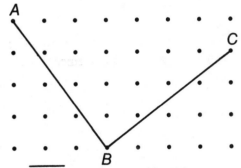

a. Is $\overline{AB}$ perpendicular to $\overline{BC}$?

b. What is the slope of $\overline{AB}$?

c. What is the slope of $\overline{BC}$?

**4.**

a. Is $\overline{AB}$ perpendicular to $\overline{BC}$?

b. What is the slope of $\overline{AB}$?

c. What is the slope of $\overline{BC}$?

*Visualized Geometry*

5.

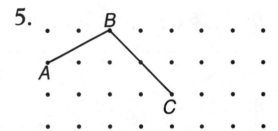

a.  Is $\overline{AB}$ perpendicular to $\overline{BC}$?

b.  What is the slope of $\overline{AB}$?

c.  What is the slope of $\overline{BC}$?

6.

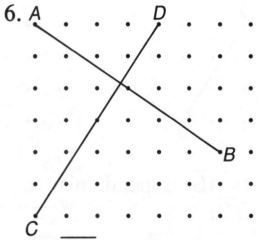

a.  Is $\overline{AB}$ perpendicular to $\overline{CD}$?

b.  What is the slope of $\overline{AB}$?

c.  What is the slope of $\overline{CD}$?

7.  Complete the table below from the results of problems 1–6.

| Problem number | Slope of $\overline{AB}$ | Slope of other segment ($\overline{BC}$ or $\overline{CD}$) | Are the segments perpendicular? |
|---|---|---|---|
| 1 | | | |
| 2 | | | |
| 3 | | | |
| 4 | | | |
| 5 | | | |
| 6 | | | |

*Visualized Geometry*

# WORKSHEET 1-7-1
## Perpendicular Segments on Dot Paper

1. Calculate the slopes and determine whether the segments are perpendicular.

a.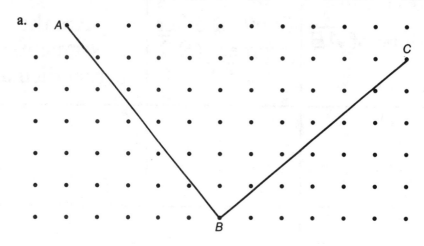

The slope of $\overline{AB}$ is _____ .

The slope of $\overline{BC}$ is _____ .

Are the segments perpendicular? _____

b.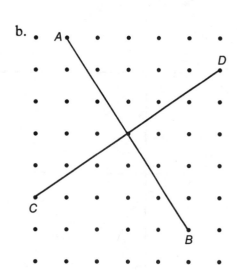

The slope of $\overline{AB}$ is _____ .

The slope of $\overline{BC}$ is _____ .

Are the segments perpendicular? _____

c.

The slope of $\overline{AB}$ is _____ .

The slope of $\overline{BC}$ is _____ .

Are the segments perpendicular?

_____

(continued)

       *Visualized Geometry*

# WORKSHEET 1-7-1
## Perpendicular Segments on Dot Paper *(continued)*

2. Draw $\overline{BC}$ so that $\overline{BC}$ is perpendicular to $\overline{AB}$.

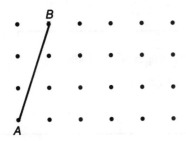

3. Draw $\overline{CD}$ so that $\overline{CD}$ is perpendicular to $\overline{AB}$.

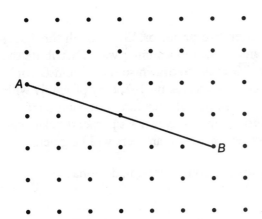

# Lesson 1-8
# Segments—Perpendicular and Bisecting

## *Materials Needed:*

One copy of each of the following pages for each student: pages 45 and 46.

One transparency of each of the following pages: pages 43 and 44.

Possibly an index card for each student.

## *Directions for the Teacher:*

Place the first transparency (page 43) on the overhead projector. Go through the discussion of each example. Proceed with the second transparency in a similar way. Distribute the worksheets and tell the students that in each case $\overline{CD}$ must be drawn so that C and D correspond to dot paper dots. If your students have completed Lesson 1-7, they probably will be able to find perpendicular segments using ideas of slopes. If they have not completed Lesson 1-7, you may want to allow them to use index cards to construct perpendicular segments. Since each problem has a variety of correct responses, no answers will be given.

This lesson is a prerequisite for several Chapter 3 lessons involving diagonals of quadrilaterals.

I.

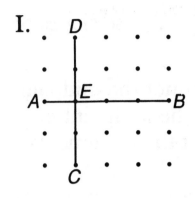

1. Notice that $\overline{AB}$ and $\overline{CD}$ form right angles. This means that $\overline{AB}$ and $\overline{CD}$ are perpendicular to each other. We denote this by $\overline{AB} \perp \overline{CD}$.

2. Notice that E is the midpoint of $\overline{CD}$. This means that $\overline{AB}$ bisects $\overline{CD}$. Thus $\overline{AB}$ is a perpendicular bisector of $\overline{CD}$.

3. Also notice that E is not the midpoint of $\overline{AB}$. Thus $\overline{CD}$ is not a bisector of $\overline{AB}$.

II.

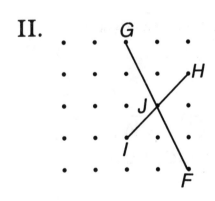

1. Notice that the angles formed by $\overline{FG}$ and $\overline{HI}$ are not right angles. Thus $\overline{FG}$ and $\overline{HI}$ are not perpendicular to each other.

2. Notice that J is the midpoint of $\overline{FG}$. Thus $\overline{HI}$ is a bisector of $\overline{FG}$ but not a perpendicular bisector of $\overline{FG}$.

3. Also J is the midpoint of $\overline{HI}$ and thus $\overline{FG}$ is a bisector of $\overline{HI}$. Thus $\overline{FG}$ and $\overline{HI}$ bisect each other.

*Visualized Geometry*

**III.**

M   L

K

O.

N

1. Notice that $\overline{KL} \perp \overline{MN}$. (Use slopes or index card to verify.)

2. Also notice that O is not the midpoint of $\overline{KL}$ and O is not the midpoint of $\overline{MN}$. Thus neither of these segments bisects the other.

**IV.**

Q

R · · · · · · · · ·S

P

1. Notice that the segments are not perpendicular nor does either segment bisect the other.

**V.**

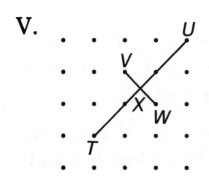

U

V

X

W

T

1. Notice that $\overline{TU} \perp \overline{VW}$. (Use slopes or index card to verify.)

2. Also notice that X is the midpoint of each of those segments. Thus each segment is a perpendicular bisector of the other.

Name: _____    Date: _____

# WORKSHEET 1-8-1
## Segments—Perpendicular and Bisecting

1. Draw $\overline{CD}$ so that $\overline{CD}$ and $\overline{AB}$ are perpendicular bisectors of each other.

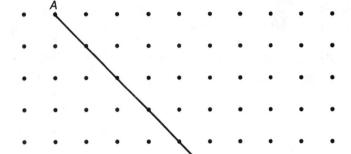

2. Draw $\overline{CD}$ so that $\overline{CD}$ is a perpendicular bisector of $\overline{AB}$ but $\overline{AB}$ is not a bisector of $\overline{CD}$.

3. Draw $\overline{CD}$ so that $\overline{CD}$ is perpendicular to $\overline{AB}$ but neither $\overline{AB}$ nor $\overline{CD}$ bisects the other.

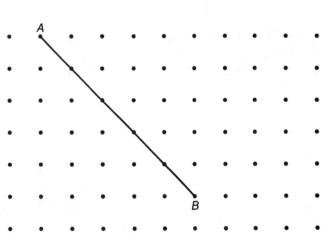

*(continued)*

*Visualized Geometry*

# WORKSHEET 1-8-1
## Segments—Perpendicular and Bisecting *(continued)*

4. Draw $\overline{CD}$ so that it bisects $\overline{AB}$ but $\overline{AB}$ does not bisect $\overline{CD}$ and so that $\overline{AB}$ and $\overline{CD}$ are not perpendicular.

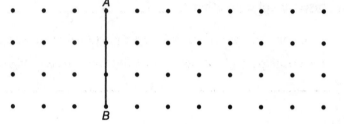

5. Draw $\overline{CD}$ so that $\overline{CD}$ does not bisect $\overline{AB}$, $\overline{AB}$ does not bisect $\overline{CD}$, and $\overline{AB}$ and $\overline{CD}$ are not perpendicular.

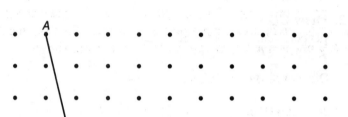

6. Draw $\overline{CD}$ so that $\overline{CD}$ and $\overline{AB}$ bisect each other but are not perpendicular to each other.

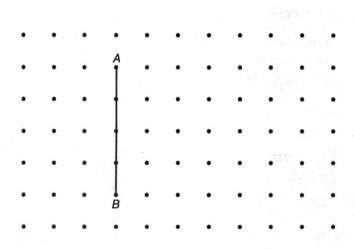

     *Visualized Geometry*

# Lesson 1-9
# Polygons

## *Materials Needed:*

One copy of each of the following pages for each student: pages 50 and 51.

One transparency of each of the following pages: pages 48 and 49.

## *Directions for the Teacher:*

Place the first transparency (page 48) on the overhead projector. Proceed with the figures indicating why figures are or are not simple or closed. Place the second transparency on your projector. Proceed as you did with the first transparency. Particularly emphasize that the last three figures are not polygons because the first one does not consist of segments, the second one is not closed and the third one is not simple.

Distribute the worksheet.

## Correct Answers for Worksheet 1-9-1:

1a. S          2a. N

  b. C            b. N

  c. SC           c. P

  d. N            d. N

              e. N

3a. quadrilateral

  b. pentagon

  c. triangle

  d. quadrilateral

  e. triangle

  f. hexagon

  g. quadrilateral

  h. pentagon

  i. hexagon

A closed figure is one which can be traced, beginning and finishing at the same point. The following figures are closed.

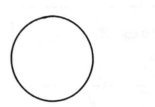   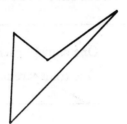

The following figures are not closed.

A simple figure is a curve which does not cross itself. The following figures are simple.

The following figures are not simple.

*Visualized Geometry*

A polygon is a simple closed figure consisting entirely of segments. The following are polygons.

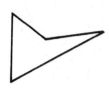  

The following are not polygons.

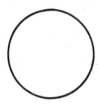 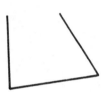 

*Visualized Geometry*

# WORKSHEET 1-9-1
## Polygons

1. Write "SC" in the blank for each simple closed figure, "S" for each simple figure which is not closed, "C" for each figure which is closed but not simple, and "N" for each figure which is not simple and not closed.

a. _____

c. _____

b. _____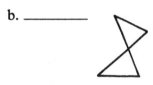

d. _____

2. Write "P" in the blank if the figure is a polygon and write "N" if the figure is not a polygon.

a. _____

d. _____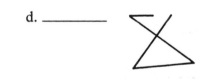

b. _____

e. _____

c. _____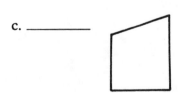

*(continued)*

*Visualized Geometry*

Name: _____  Date: _____

# WORKSHEET 1-9-1
## Polygons *(continued)*

**A triangle is a polygon with three sides.**

**A quadrilateral is a polygon with four sides.**

**A pentagon is a polygon with five sides.**

**A hexagon is a polygon with six sides.**

3. Which of the figures are triangles, quadrilaterals, pentagons, and hexagons?

a.

_____

d.

_____

g.

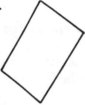

_____

b.

_____

e.

_____

h.

_____

c.

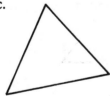

_____

f.

_____

i.

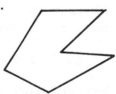

_____

*Visualized Geometry*

## Lesson 1-10
# Convex and Concave Figures

### *Materials Needed:*

One copy of page 54 for each student.

One transparency of page 53.

### *Directions for the Teacher:*

Place the first transparency (page 53) on the overhead projector. Read the material above the first three figures. Select points inside these figures and draw the segments as shown.

Proceed to the discussion of convex. Select points inside these figures and draw the corresponding segments. Point out that no matter which points are selected inside a figure, the entire segment is entirely inside that figure.

Distribute the worksheet.

### Correct Answers for Worksheet 1-10-1:

1. convex

2. convex

3. concave

4. concave

Look at the simple closed figures below. In each case it is possible to select two points inside the figure but the segment with these points as endpoints is not entirely inside the figure.

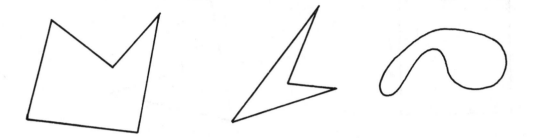

Such figures are said to be **concave**.

Look at the simple closed figures below. This time if you select any two points inside the curve, the resulting segment is entirely inside the curve.

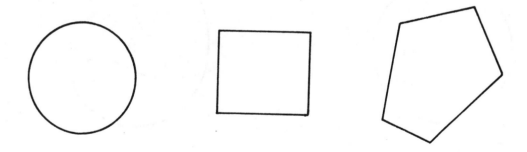

Such figures are said to be **convex**.

# WORKSHEET 1-10-1
## Convex and Concave Figures

Which of the following figures are convex and which are concave?

1.

3.

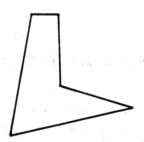

2.

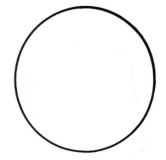

4.

# CHAPTER 2

# Triangles

## Comments and Suggestions

In this chapter, students learn to classify triangles, but more importantly they are asked to draw (on dot paper) triangles with particular properties. Also in a series of laboratory activities, they learn to find medians, altitudes, angle bisectors, and perpendicular bisectors of sides of triangles. They also learn that if the lengths of the three sides of a triangle are $a$, $b$, and $c$, where $c > a$ and $c > b$, then

    a.  in a right triangle, $c^2 = a^2 + b^2$,

    b.  in an obtuse triangle, $c^2 > a^2 + b^2$, and

    c.  in an acute triangle, $c^2 < a^2 + b^2$.

# Lesson 2–1
# Right, Acute, and Obtuse Triangles

## *Materials Needed:*

One copy of each of the following pages for each student: pages 60, 61, and 62.

One transparency of each of the following pages: pages 57, 58, and 59.

A standard 3″ x 5″ index card for each student.

## *Directions for the Teacher:*

Place the first transparency (page 57) on the overhead projector. Let the students predict what it means for a triangle to be a right triangle. They should conclude that a right triangle is a triangle with one right angle. Use an index card to show that each triangle pictured on the top half of the transparency does indeed have one right angle and that none of the triangles on the bottom half of the transparency has a right angle.

Place the second transparency (page 58) on the projector and proceed with obtuse triangles as you did with right triangles. The students should conclude that an obtuse triangle is a triangle with one obtuse angle. With an index card show that the triangles on the top half of the transparency all have an obtuse angle while none of those at the bottom half has one.

Place the third transparency (page 59) on the projector and proceed as before. The students should conclude that an acute triangle has three acute angles.

Distribute the worksheets and provide individual assistance as needed. Students should use an index card for these worksheets.

### Correct Answers for Worksheet 2–1–1:

1a. right

  b. obtuse

  c. obtuse

  d. acute

  e. acute

  f. right

There are many possible answers for problems 2, 3, and 4.

# The following triangles are right triangles.

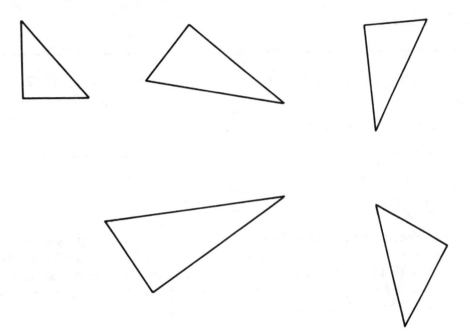

# The following triangles are not right triangles.

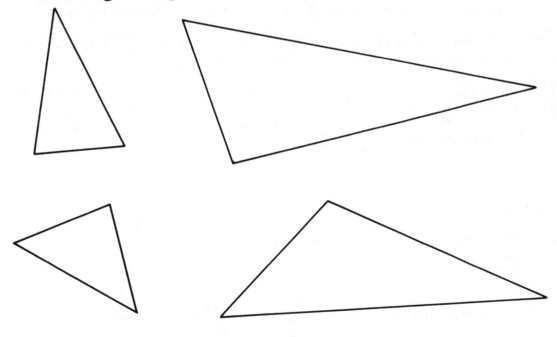

 *Visualized Geometry*

The following triangles are obtuse triangles.

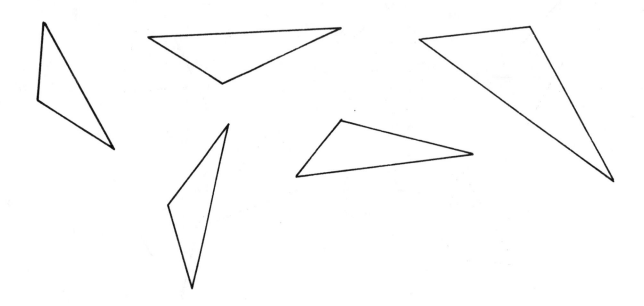

The following triangles are not obtuse triangles.

*Visualized Geometry*

The following triangles are acute triangles.

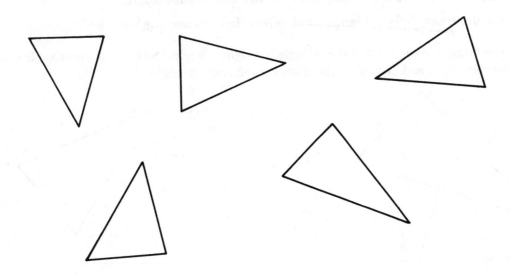

The following triangles are not acute triangles.

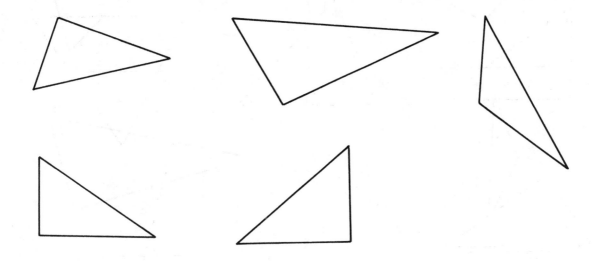

Name: _____ Date: _____

# WORKSHEET 2-1-1
## Right, Acute, and Obtuse Triangles

**A right triangle is a triangle which has one right angle.**

**An obtuse triangle is a triangle which has one obtuse angle.**

**An acute triangle is a triangle which has three acute angles.**

1. Write "right" in the blank if the triangle is a right triangle, "obtuse" if the triangle is an obtuse triangle, and "acute" if the triangle is an acute triangle.

a.

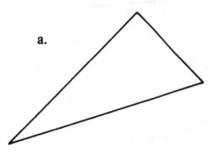

_____

b.

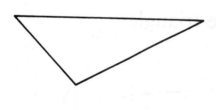

_____

c.

_____

d.

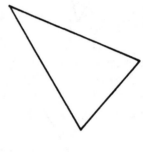

_____

e.

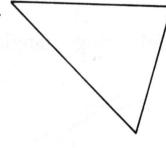

_____

f.

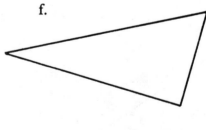

_____

*(continued)*

*Visualized Geometry*

# WORKSHEET 2-1-1
## Right, Acute, and Obtuse Triangles *(continued)*

2. One acute triangle is drawn on the dot paper below. Draw three other acute triangles. Next draw a triangle which is not an acute triangle and write "N" inside this triangle.

3. One right triangle is drawn on the dot paper below. Draw three other right triangles. Next draw a triangle which is not a right triangle and write "N" inside this triangle.

*(continued)*

*Visualized Geometry*

# WORKSHEET 2-1-1
## Right, Acute, and Obtuse Triangles *(continued)*

4. One obtuse triangle is drawn on the dot paper below. Draw three more obtuse triangles. Next draw a triangle which is not an obtuse triangle and write "N" inside this triangle.

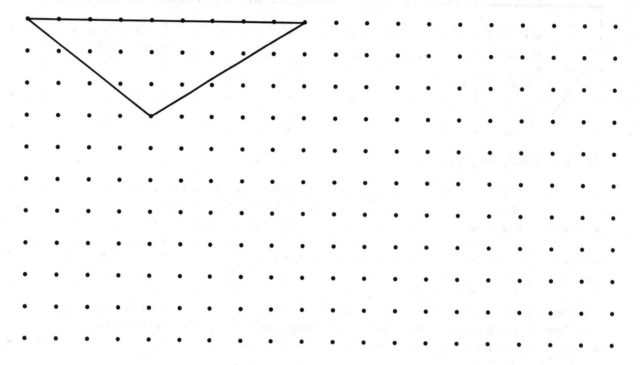

62                                *Visualized Geometry*

# Lesson 2–2
# Equilateral, Isosceles, and Scalene Triangles

## *Materials Needed:*

One copy of each of the following pages for each student: pages 67, 68, and 69.

One transparency of each of the following pages: pages 64, 65, and 66.

One blank transparency and an overhead projector pen.

## *Directions for the Teacher:*

Place the first transparency (page 64) on the overhead projector. Let the students predict what it means for a triangle to be an equilateral triangle. They should conclude that an equilateral triangle has three sides of equal length (congruent). Copy each triangle on the blank transparency and rotate to show that, indeed, each triangle on the upper half of the sheet has three sides of equal length while no triangle on the lower half of the sheet has three sides of equal length. Proceed with the second transparency. Now the students should see that an isosceles triangle has two (at least two) sides which are the same length (congruent). Copy each isosceles triangle and show that each of these triangles has two sides which are the same length. Likewise, show that none of the triangles on the lower half of the page has two or more sides of equal length. Finally, proceed to the third transparency. The students should conclude that a scalene triangle has three sides of different lengths. They may also conclude that non-scalene triangles are either isosceles or equilateral.

Distribute the worksheets and provide individual assistance as needed.

## Correct Answers for Worksheet 2–2–1:

1a.  isosceles

 b.  scalene

 c.  isosceles

 d.  isosceles and equilateral

There are many possible answers for problems 2, 3, 4, and 5, except that 5c is not possible on a 4 x 4 grid.

*Note:* A special kind of dot paper is provided for problems 1d and 4. It is impossible to make an equilateral triangle on ordinary dot paper.

# Each of the following triangles is equilateral.

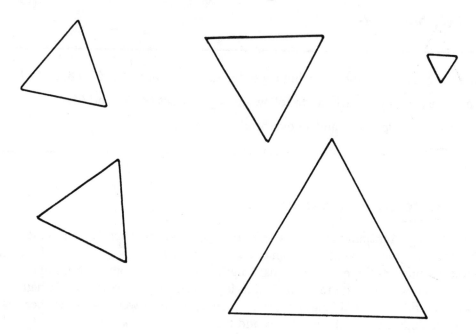

# None of the following triangles is equilateral.

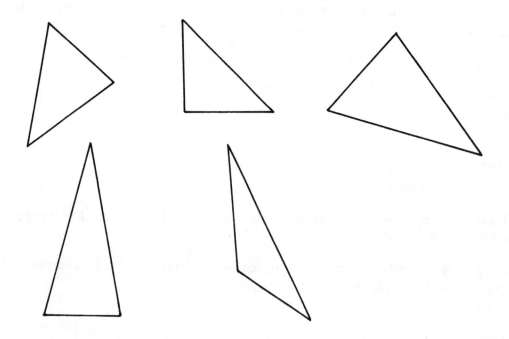

*Visualized Geometry*

# Each of the following triangles is isosceles.

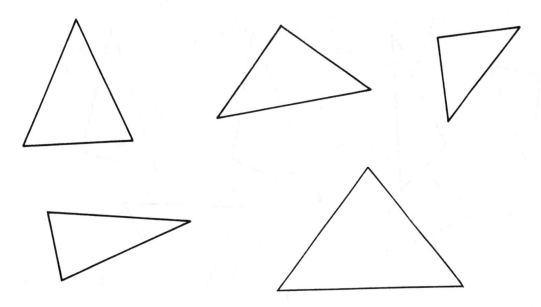

# None of the following triangles is isosceles.

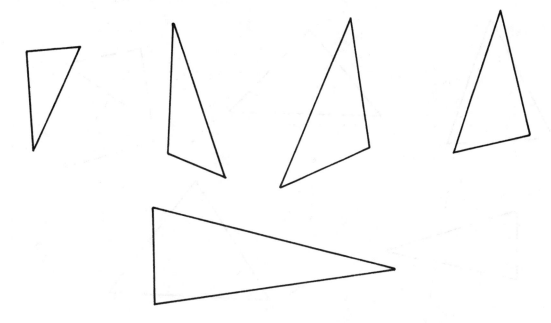

*Visualized Geometry*

Each of the following triangles is scalene.

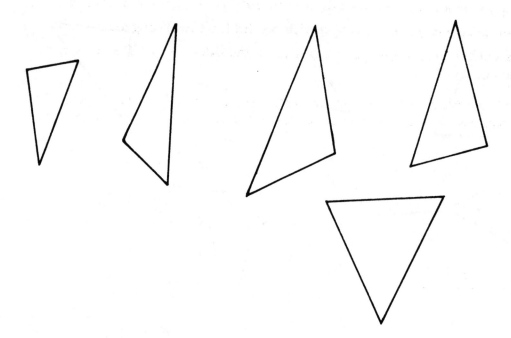

None of the following triangles is scalene.

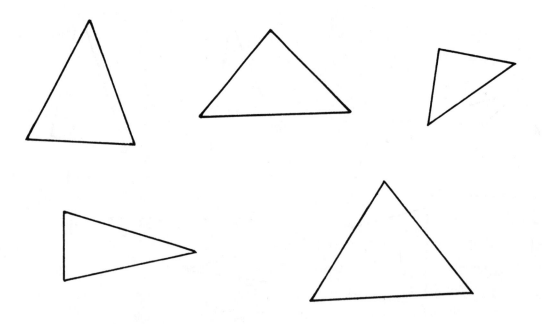

*Visualized Geometry*

# WORKSHEET 2-2-1
## Equilateral, Isosceles, and Scalene Triangles

**An equilateral triangle is a triangle with three congruent (same length) sides.**

**An isosceles triangle is a triangle with two (at least two) congruent sides.**

**A scalene triangle is a triangle in which all the sides are of different lengths (noncongruent).**

1. Write "equilateral" in the blank if the triangle is an equilateral triangle, "isosceles" if the triangle is an isosceles triangle, and "scalene" if the triangle is a scalene triangle.

a.

_____

c.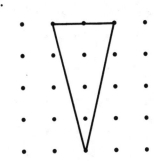

_____

b.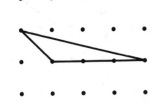

_____

d.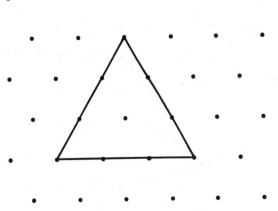

_____

*(continued)*

# WORKSHEET 2-2-1
## Equilateral, Isosceles, and Scalene Triangles *(continued)*

2. One scalene triangle is pictured on the dot paper below. Draw four other scalene triangles.

3. One isosceles triangle is pictured on the dot paper below. Draw four other isosceles triangles.

*(continued)*

# WORSHEET 2-2-1
## Equilateral, Isosceles, and Scalene Triangles *(continued)*

4. One equilateral triangle is pictured on the special dot paper below. Draw three other equilateral triangles.

5. On the dot paper below, draw the indicated triangles if possible. If not possible, write "NP."

a. an isosceles right triangle

c. an isosceles obtuse triangle

e. a scalene acute triangle

b. an isosceles acute triangle

d. a scalene right triangle

f. a scalene obtuse triangle

# Lesson 2-3
# Medians of a Triangle

## Materials Needed:

One copy of page 72 for each student.

One transparency of page 71.

One ruler (straightedge) for yourself and one for each student.

## Directions for the Teacher:

Put the transparency on the overhead projector. Point out that the dots on sides of the triangle are midpoints. Tell your students that a median of a triangle is a segment from a vertex to the midpoint of the opposite side. Using your ruler, draw in all three medians. Then tell your students to complete the worksheet. They will need a ruler or some kind of a straightedge to do this. The lesson is short. They should finish problems 1–4 with very little difficulty, but they will probably be unable to answer the question (problem 5) without assistance.

### Correct Answers for Worksheet 2-3-1:

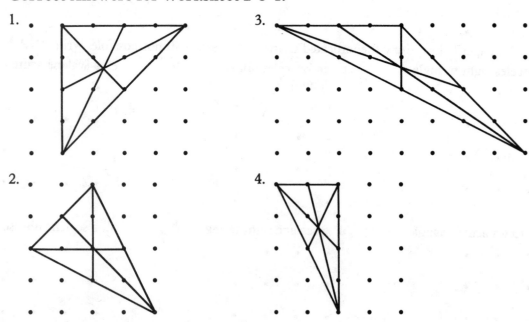

5. In each case the three medians intersect in a single point.

# Transparency 2-3-1

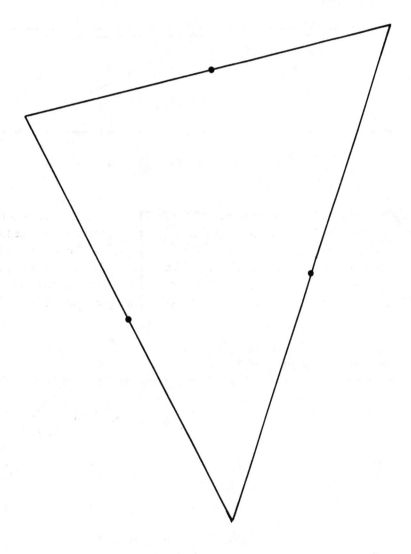

71

Name: _____     Date: _____

# WORKSHEET 2-3-1
## Medians of a Triangle

A median of a triangle is a segment from a vertex to the midpoint of the opposite side. Draw all medians. (Each triangle has three medians.)

1.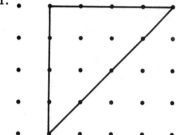

3.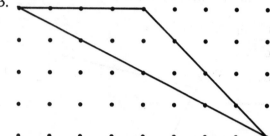

2.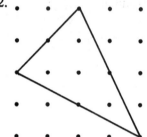

4.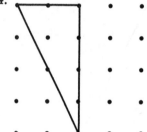

5. What do you notice in each triangle?

# Lesson 2–4
# Altitudes of a Triangle

## *Materials Needed:*

One copy of page 78 for each student.

One transparency of page 77.

One 3″ x 5″ index card for each student.

## *Directions for the Teacher:*

Place the transparency on the overhead projector. Direct your students' attention to the definition of an altitude of a triangle. Place an index card on the first triangle (on the transparency) as shown.

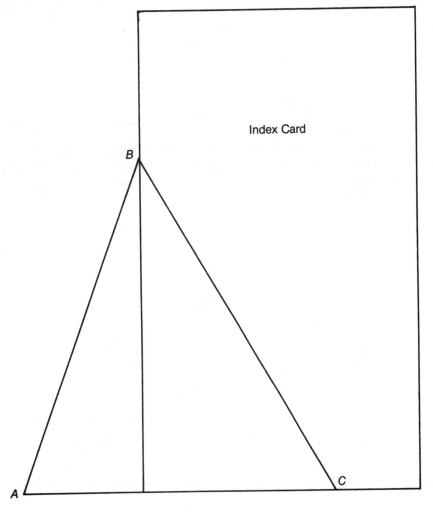

Note that the bottom of the index card is along one side of the triangle. Also note that the upper vertex is at one side of the index card. Now draw a segment along the side of the card so that this segment has the upper vertex of the triangle as one endpoint and a point of the bottom side as the other endpoint. The angles formed are right angles since the angles of the index card are right angles. Construct the other altitudes in a similar way.

**Correct Answers for Transparency 2–4–1:**

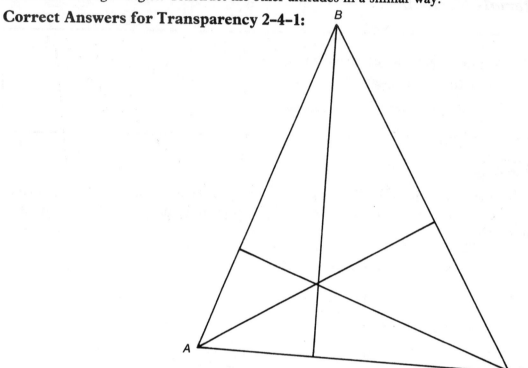

For $\triangle ABC$, the three altitudes are fairly easy to draw. When the triangle is obtuse, altitudes are harder to construct. For $\triangle DEF$ it is impossible to draw a segment from $F$ perpendicular to $\overline{DE}$ so you need to extend $\overline{DE}$ (dotted). Now place the index card as shown.

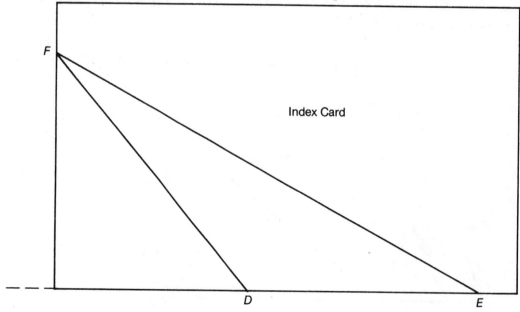

Now draw a segment along the side of the card so that *F* is one endpoint and the point on the extension of $\overline{DE}$ is the other endpoint. This segment is an altitude of $\triangle DEF$. The altitude from *D* is easy to draw. However, to draw the altitude from *E* is hard. In this case you must extend $\overline{FD}$, as shown below.

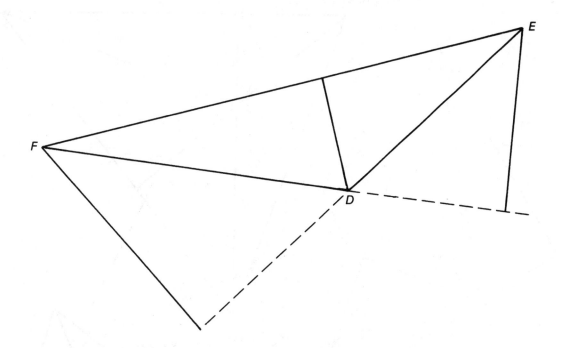

Proceed to $\triangle GHI$. This is a right triangle. When you attempt to draw an altitude from *G* to $\overline{HI}$ you will find this altitude is actually $\overline{GH}$. Also the altitude from *I* to $\overline{GH}$ is actually $\overline{IH}$. Then draw the altitude from *H* to $\overline{GI}$, as shown below. Point out that in the case of right triangles, two sides are also altitudes.

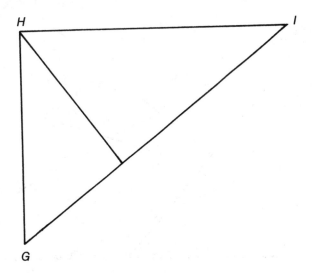

Distribute the worksheet and direct the students to work on it.

**Correct Answers for Worksheet 2–4–1:**

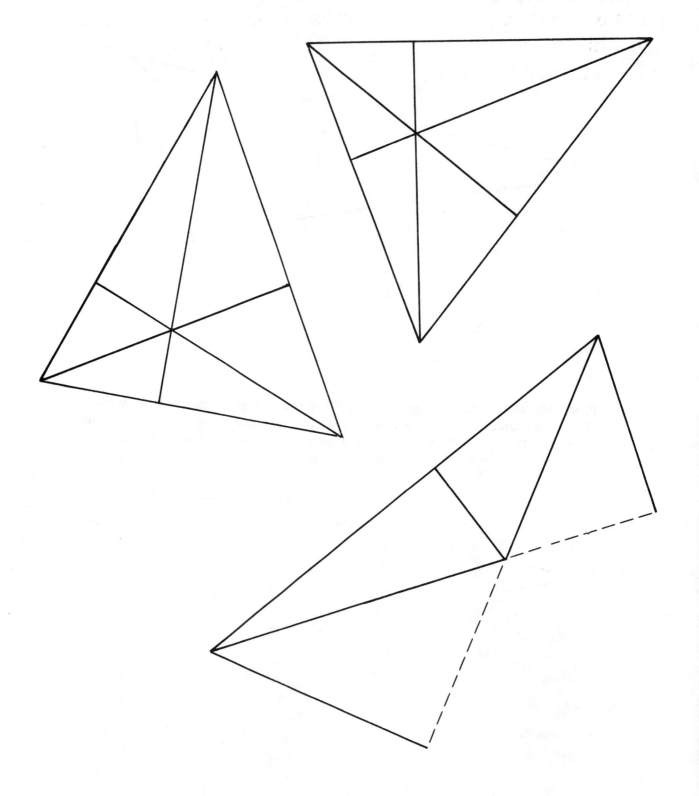

An altitude of a triangle is a segment which has as one end-point a vertex of a triangle, which has as the other endpoint a point on the side opposite this vertex (sometimes extended), and which is perpendicular to that side. Use an index card to find all three altitudes of the triangles pictured below.

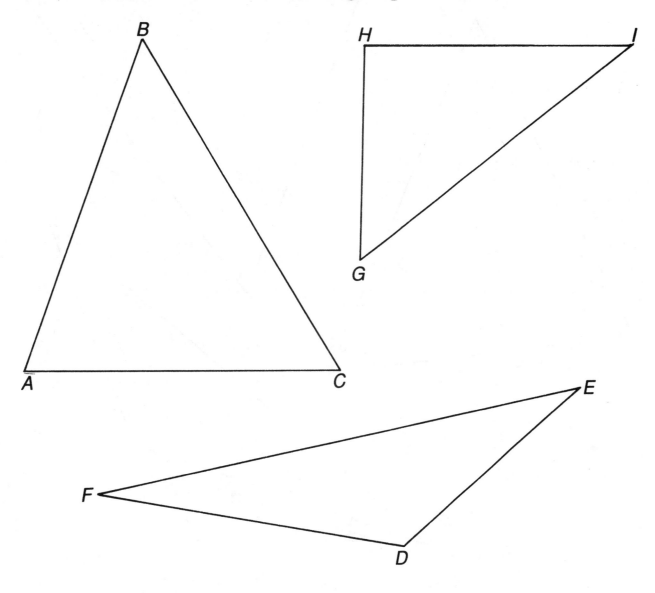

*Visualized Geometry*

# WORKSHEET 2-4-1
## Altitudes of a Triangle

An altitude of a triangle is a segment which has as one endpoint a vertex of a triangle, which has as the other endpoint a point on the side opposite this vertex (sometimes extended), and which is perpendicular to that side. Use an index card to find all three altitudes of the triangles pictured below.

**Lesson 2-5**
# Perpendicular Bisectors of the Sides of a Triangle

## *Materials Needed:*

One copy of each of the following pages for each student: pages 83 and 84.

One copy of page 83 for yourself.

One transparency of page 82.

One pair of scissors and one index card for each student.

## *Directions for the Teacher:*

Prior to class cut out △*ABC* (page 83). As your students watch, fold your copy of △*ABC* so that vertex *A* matches vertex *B*. Open the triangle and trace along the fold line. Argue that this segment is a perpendicular bisector of $\overline{AB}$ since the angles formed are right angles and the point on $\overline{AB}$ which is also on the fold line, is the midpoint of $\overline{AB}$. Distribute Worksheet 2-5-1 (page 83). Have the students cut out △*ABC* and then have them use the folding method to find the perpendicular bisector of each side. Help individual students when necessary.

**Correct Answer for Worksheet 2-5-1:**

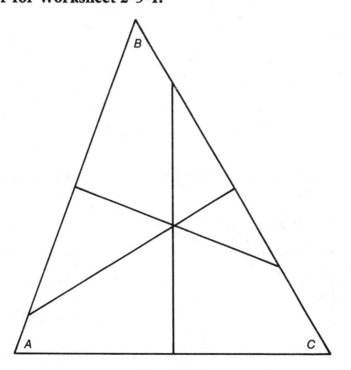

Ask the students to describe the relationship among the perpendicular bisectors of the sides of a triangle. (The three perpendicular bisectors meet in a point.)

Next, place the transparency on the overhead projector and direct their attention to the directions given there. Find the midpoint of the vertical side and draw in a perpendicular bisector. Next, go to another side, find the midpoint, and draw in a perpendicular bisector either by inspection or by using an index card (to make a right angle). Proceed in a similar manner to the third side.

**Correct Answer for Transparency 2-5-1:**

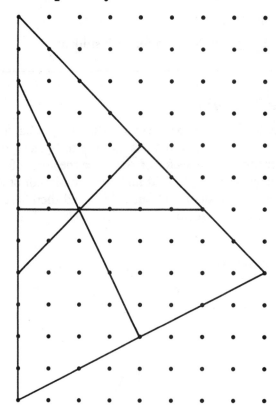

Distribute Worksheet 2-5-2 (page 84) and an index card to each student. Provide individual assistance as needed.

**Correct Answer for Worksheet 2-5-2:**

1. 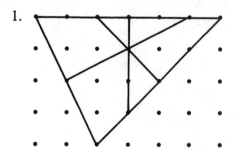    2.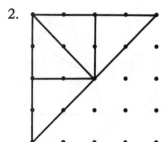

3.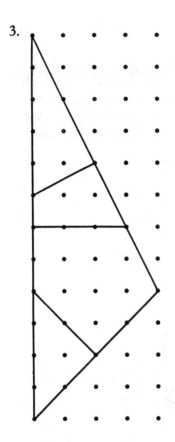

4.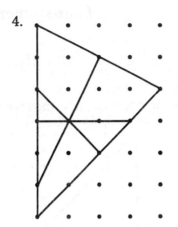

5.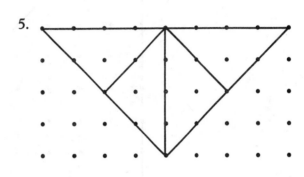

*Note:* The generalization made earlier that the three perpendicular bisectors meet in a point is not quite supported by problem 3 above. However, if the perpendicular bisectors are extended the generalization is supported.

Draw the perpendicular bisectors of the sides of the triangle pictured below.

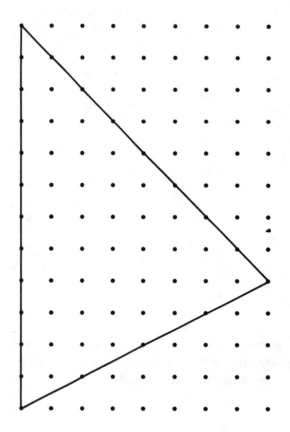

 *Visualized Geometry*

# WORKSHEET 2-5-1
## Perpendicular Bisectors of the Sides of a Triangle

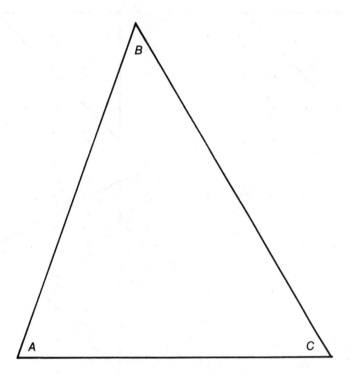

# WORKSHEET 2-5-2
## Perpendicular Bisectors of the Sides of a Triangle

Draw the perpendicular bisectors of the sides of the triangles pictured below.

1.
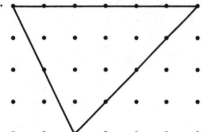

2.
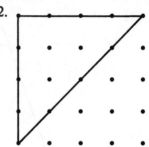

3.
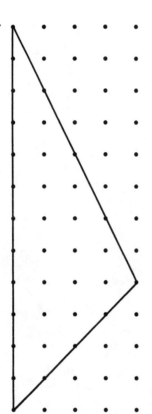

4.
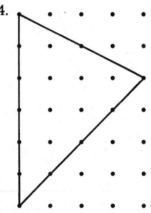

5.
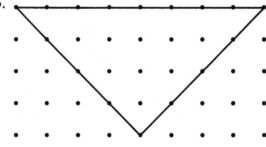

         *Visualized Geometry*

## Lesson 2–6
# Congruent Angles in Isosceles and Equilateral Triangles

## *Materials Needed:*

One transparency of each of the following pages: pages 86 and 87.

One blank transparency and an overhead projector pen.

## *Directions for the Teacher:*

This lesson is designed to convince your students that

a. in an isosceles triangle, the angles opposite congruent sides are congruent and

b. in an equilateral triangle, all three angles are congruent to each other.

Begin the class by reviewing the definitions of isosceles and equilateral triangles. Place the first transparency on the overhead projector but cover up the generalization at the bottom of that page. Direct the students' attention to $\triangle ABC$. Point out that $\triangle ABC$ is an isosceles triangle ($\overline{AB} \cong \overline{AC}$). Mention that in $\triangle ABC$, $\angle A$ is opposite $\overline{BC}$, $\angle B$ is opposite $\overline{AC}$ and $\angle C$ is opposite $\overline{AB}$. Place a blank transparency on top of the one on your overhead projector. Trace $\triangle ABC$ and the letters $A$, $B$, and $C$. Pick up the second transparency, turn it over and place it back on the projector so that point $A$ matches point $A$ on the original, point $B$ on the copy matches point $C$ on the original, and point $C$ on the copy matches point $B$ on the original. Emphasize that this shows that $\overline{AB} \cong \overline{AC}$ but also the angles match so $\angle B \cong \angle C$.

Now go on to $\triangle DEF$. This is also an isosceles triangle. Proceed as you did with $\triangle ABC$. This time you should conclude that $\overline{DE} \cong \overline{DF}$ and $\angle E \cong \angle F$. Finally proceed in a similar way with $\triangle GHI$ and conclude that $\overline{GH} \cong \overline{GI}$ and $\angle H \cong \angle I$. Mention that in each case you had an isosceles triangle and in each case the angles opposite congruent sides were congruent. Uncover the generalization which is at the bottom of the page.

Place the second transparency on your projector but cover up the generalization at the bottom of the page. Put a blank transparency on top of the one on your projector. Trace $\triangle ABC$ (including the letters). Turn the blank transparency so that point $A$ matches point $B$ on the original, point $B$ on the copy matches point $C$ on the original, and point $C$ on the copy matches point $A$ on the original. Turn the blank transparency again so that point $A$ on the copy matches point $C$ on the original, point $B$ on the copy matches point $A$ on the original, and point $C$ on the copy matches point $B$ on the original. Mention this shows that $\overline{AB} \cong \overline{BC} \cong \overline{AC}$ which means that the original triangle was equilateral. Emphasize that you found that $\angle A \cong \angle B \cong \angle C$. Uncover the generalization at the bottom of the page and read it aloud.

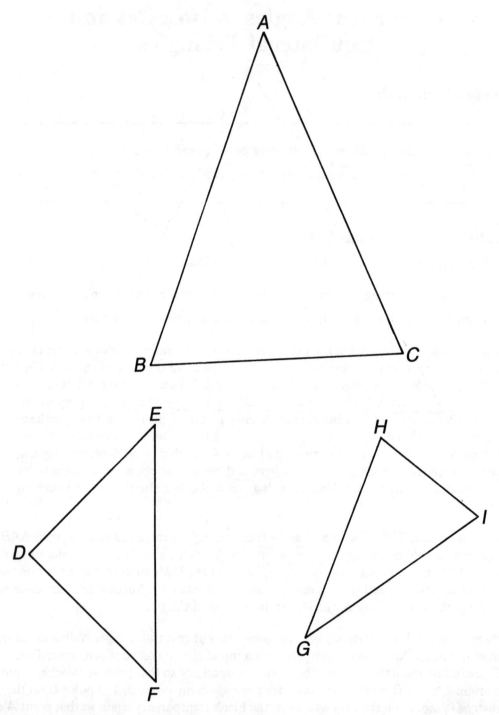

In an isosceles triangle, the angles opposite the congruent sides are congruent.

*Visualized Geometry*

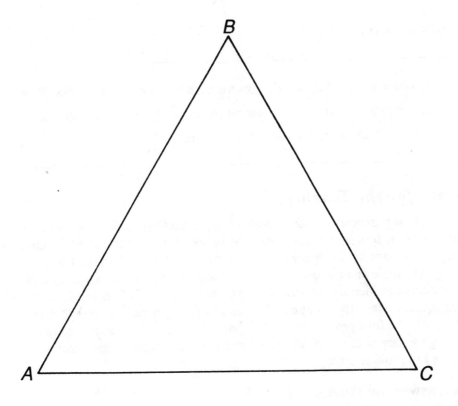

In an equilateral triangle, all three angles are congruent to each
other.

     *Visualized Geometry*

## Lesson 2-7
# The Pythagorean Theorem

## *Materials Needed:*

One copy of each of the following pages for each student: pages 94, 95, 96, and 97.

One transparency of each of the following pages: pages 94, 95, 96, and 97.

A pair of scissors and an index card for each student.

## *Directions for the Teacher:*

Note that transparencies are to be made of worksheet pages that are also given to students. Distribute the four worksheet pages, the index cards, and the scissors. Direct the students' attention to page 94. Have them use an index card to check to see that the triangle pictured is a right triangle and the quadrilaterals which look like squares are squares. We have assumed students can identify squares. Indicate that they are to find relationships among these three squares. Have them cut out the two smallest squares and then cut the middle-sized square into the four pieces. When they have completed this, ask them to see if they can cover the large square with the small square and the four pieces of the middle-sized square. You may need to provide assistance.

### Correct Answer for Worksheet 2-7-1:

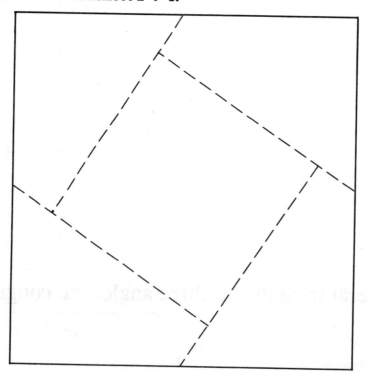

Now display the transparency of page 94. Label the parts as illustrated below.

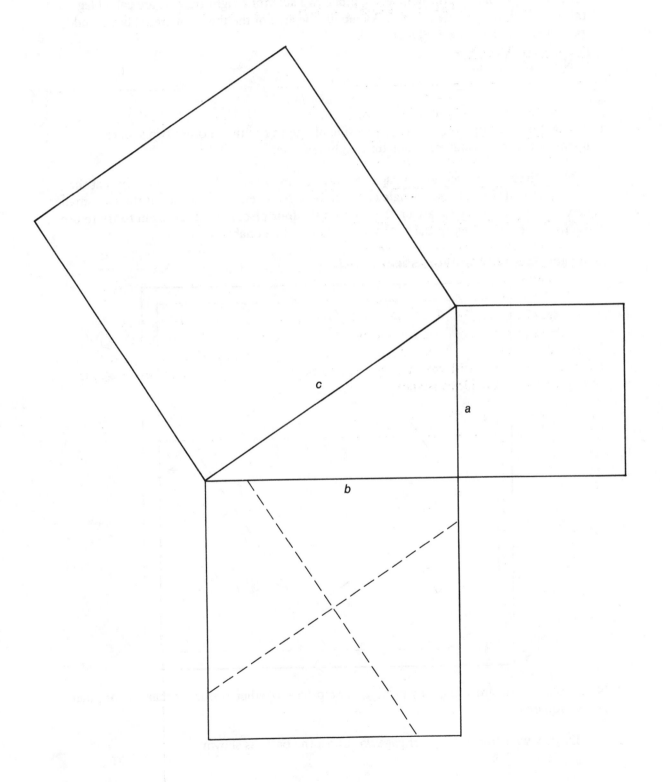

Point out that the longest side of the right triangle is called the hypotenuse and in this case its length is *c*. Similarly indicate that the other two sides of a right triangle are called legs and in this case their lengths are *a* and *b*. Ask about the area of the three squares. They should respond that these areas are $a^2$, $b^2$, and $c^2$.

Now indicate that

$$c^2 = a^2 + b^2$$

since you "covered up" the square with a side of length *c* with the other two squares. Emphasize that this condition holds for a right triangle.

Next direct their attention to page 95. Have them use an index card to verify that the triangle pictured is an obtuse triangle (Lesson 2–1). Now tell them to cut out the two smaller squares and then cut the square on the top into the four pieces. Next tell them to try to use those five pieces to cover up the big square. They will be unable to do this.

**Correct Answer for Worksheet 2–7–2:**

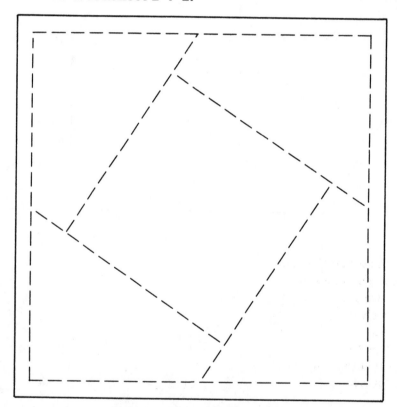

Notice that the square you get by putting these pieces together is smaller than the original largest square.

Display your transparency of page 95. Label the parts as shown.

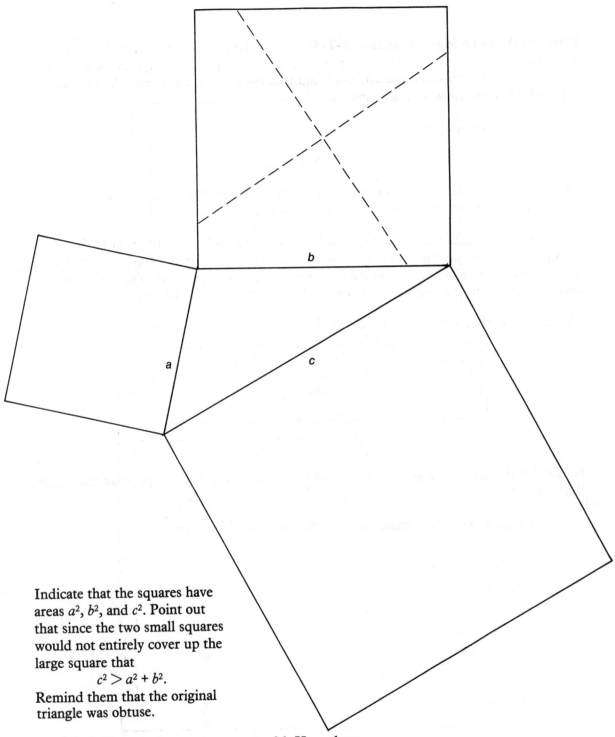

Indicate that the squares have areas $a^2$, $b^2$, and $c^2$. Point out that since the two small squares would not entirely cover up the large square that

$$c^2 > a^2 + b^2.$$

Remind them that the original triangle was obtuse.

Next direct their attention to page 96. Have them take an index card and check to see that the triangle pictured is actually an acute triangle (Lesson 2–1). Tell them to cut out the two smaller squares and to cut up the square as indicated by the dotted lines. Have them try to cover up the largest square with the smaller squares. It is impossible to do this.

**Correct Answer for Worksheet 2-7-3:**

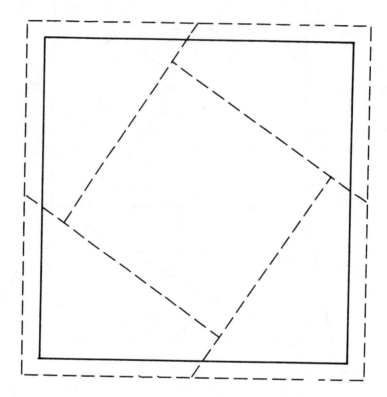

Notice that the square that you get by putting these pieces together is larger than the original largest square.

Now display your transparency of page 96. Label the sides as shown.

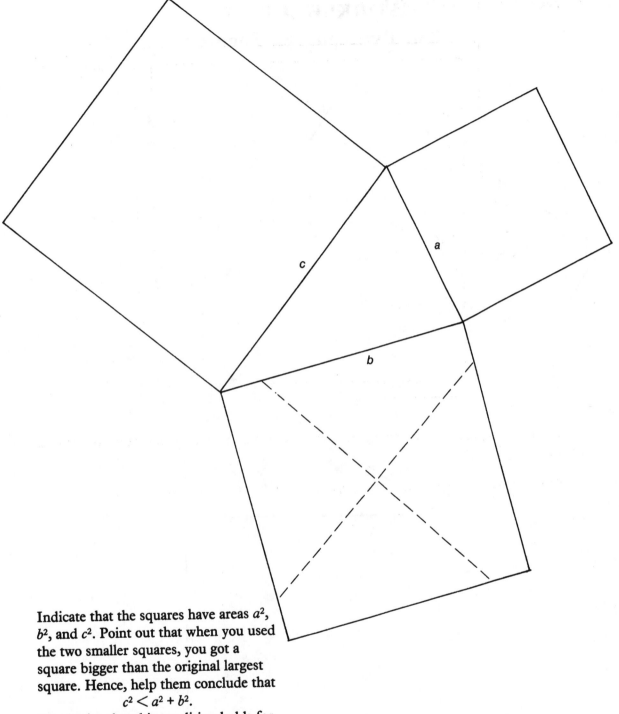

Indicate that the squares have areas $a^2$, $b^2$, and $c^2$. Point out that when you used the two smaller squares, you got a square bigger than the original largest square. Hence, help them conclude that
$$c^2 < a^2 + b^2.$$
Emphasize that this condition holds for an acute triangle.

Finally display your transparency of page 97. Go through each of the three generalizations carefully. Point out that these generalizations summarize how the squares of lengths of sides of triangles are related to each other depending on whether the triangle is right, acute, or obtuse. Emphasize that the first generalization is called the Pythagorean theorem.

Name: _____ Date: _____

# WORKSHEET 2-7-1
## The Pythagorean Theorem

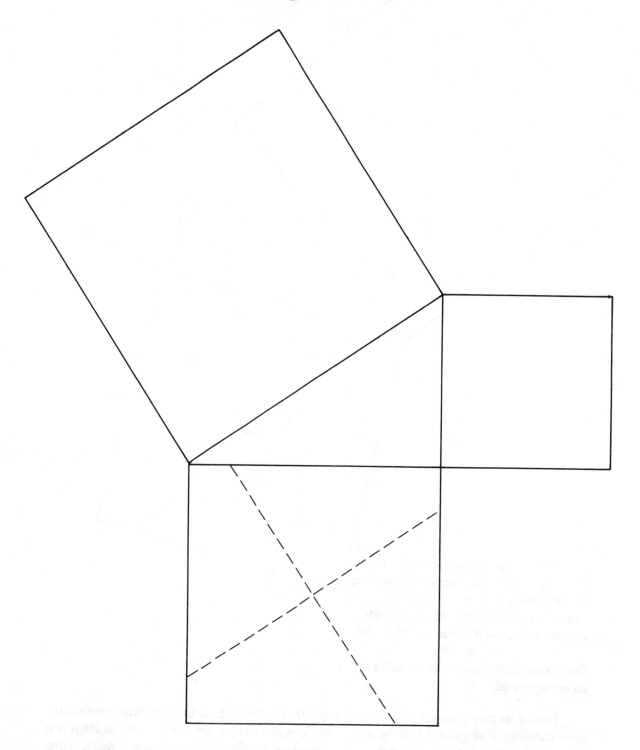

# WORKSHEET 2–7–2
## The Pythagorean Theorem

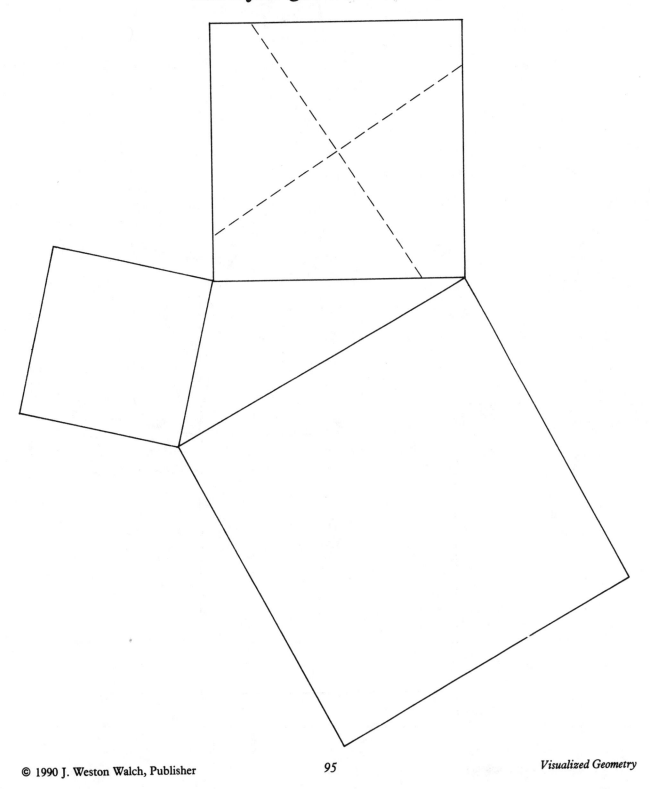

# WORKSHEET 2-7-3
## The Pythagorean Theorem

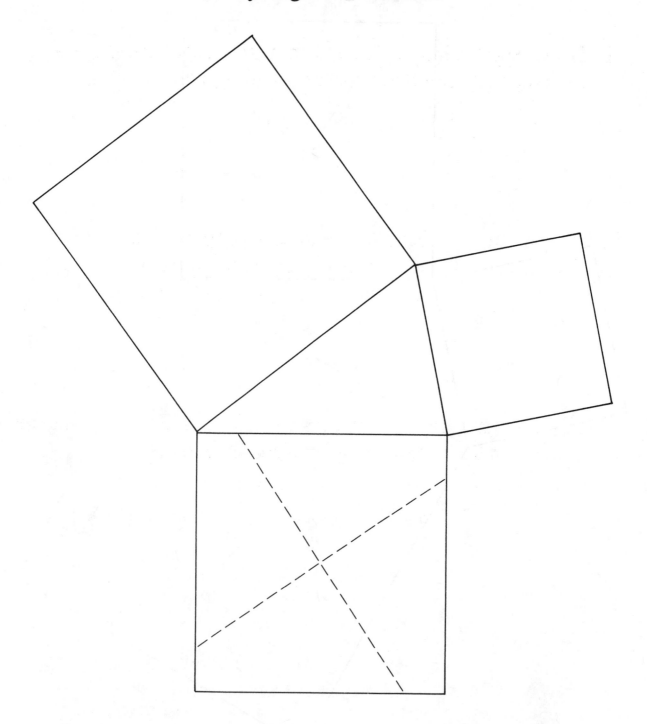

*Visualized Geometry*

# WORKSHEET 2-7-4
## The Pythagorean Theorem

I. If in a right triangle the length of the hypotenuse is $c$ and the length of the two legs are $a$ and $b$, then

$$c^2 = a^2 + b^2.$$

II. If in an obtuse triangle the longest side has length $c$ and the other two sides have lengths $a$ and $b$, then

$$c^2 > a^2 + b^2.$$

III. If in an acute triangle the longest side has length $c$ and the other two sides have lengths $a$ and $b$, then

$$c^2 < a^2 + b^2.$$

Lesson 2–8
# Application of the Pythagorean Theorem

## *Materials Needed:*

One copy of each of the following pages for each student: pages 100 and 101.

One copy of page 102 for each student who understands the square root notation.

One transparency of page 99.

## *Directions for the Teacher:*

Begin the lesson with a brief review of Lesson 2–7. (You may want to use your transparency of Worksheet 2–7–4.) Place Transparency 2–8–1 on the overhead projector. Emphasize that the triangle pictured is a right triangle and that you want to apply the Pythagorean theorem to this triangle. With the students' help, find values of $a$, $b$, $a^2$, $b^2$, and $c^2$. ($a = 5$, $b = 6$, $a^2 = 25$, $b^2 = 36$, and $c^2 = 61$).

Distribute the worksheets. Remember page 102 is appropriate only with those students who understand square root notation. Provide individual assistance as needed.

## Correct Answers for Worksheet 2–8–1:

1. $a = 1$
   $b = 3$
   $a^2 = 1$
   $b^2 = 9$
   $c^2 = 10$

2. $a = 2$
   $b = 2$
   $a^2 = 4$
   $b^2 = 4$
   $c^2 = 8$

3. $a^2 = 4$
   $b^2 = 9$
   $c^2 = 13$

4. $c^2 = 25$
   $c = 5$

5. $c^2 = 100$
   $c = 10$

6. $c^2 = 169$
   $c = 13$

7. $c^2 = 13$

8. $a^2 = 36$
   $c^2 = 100$
   $b^2 = 64$
   $b = 8$

9. $b^2 = 225$
   $c^2 = 289$
   $a^2 = 64$
   $a = 8$

10. $c = 5$

11. $c = \sqrt{20}$

12. $c = \sqrt{41}$

13. $c = \sqrt{58}$

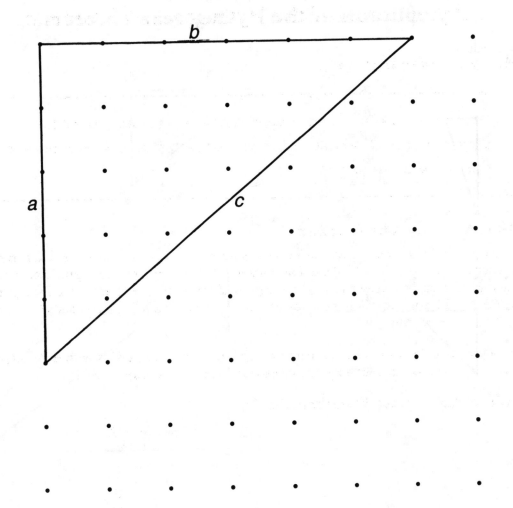

$a =$

$b =$

$a^2 =$

$b^2 =$

$c^2 =$

*Visualized Geometry*

# WORKSHEET 2-8-1
## Application of the Pythagorean Theorem

Find values.

**1.**

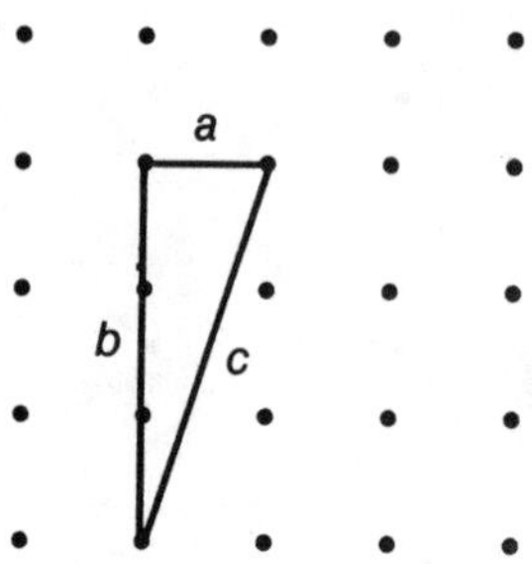

$a =$

$b =$

$a^2 =$

$b^2 =$

$c^2 =$

**4.**

$c^2 =$

$c =$

**2.**

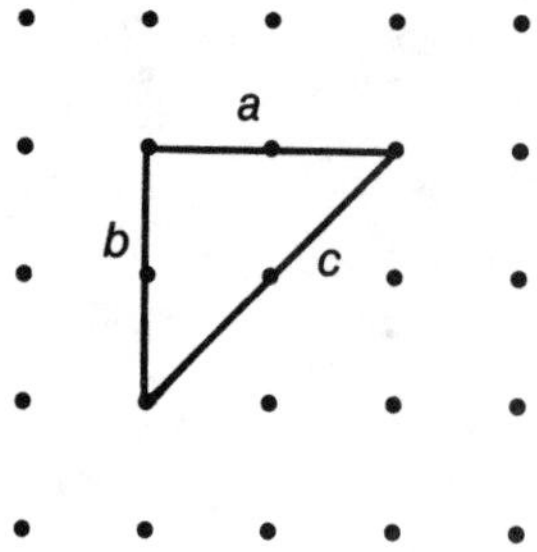

$a =$

$b =$

$a^2 =$

$b^2 =$

$c^2 =$

**5.**

$c^2 =$

$c =$

**3.**

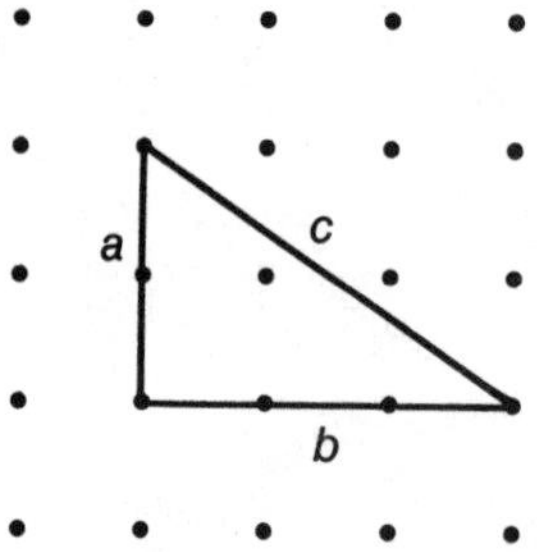

$a^2 =$

$b^2 =$

$c^2 =$

*(continued)*

*Visualized Geometry*

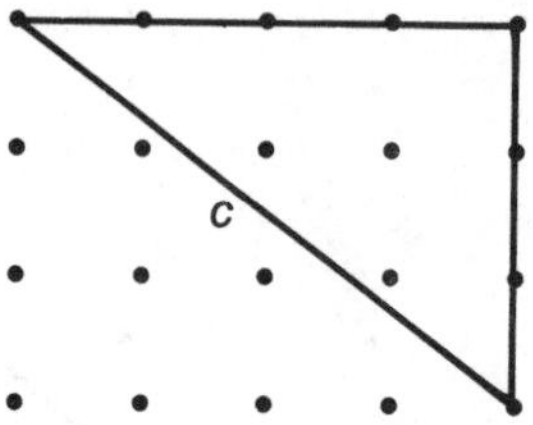

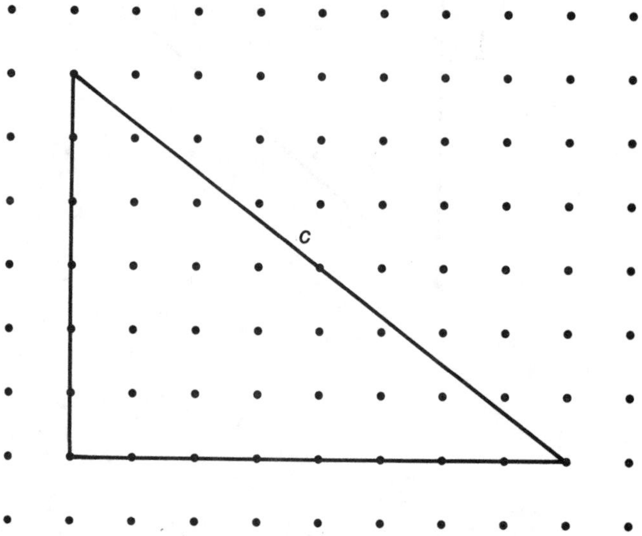

Name: _____  Date: _____

# WORKSHEET 2-8-1
## Application of the Pythagorean Theorem (*continued*)

6.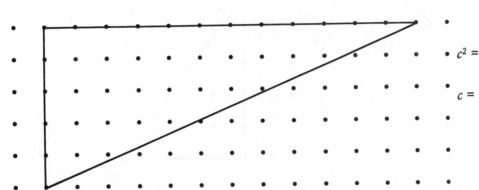

$c^2 =$

$c =$

7.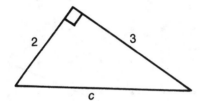

$c^2 =$

8.

$a^2 =$
$c^2 =$
$b^2 =$
$b =$

9.

$b^2 =$
$c^2 =$
$a^2 =$
$a =$

*(continued)*

*Visualized Geometry*

# WORKSHEET 2-8-1
## Application of the Pythagorean Theorem *(continued)*

10.

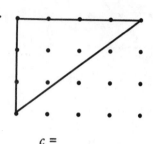

c =

12.

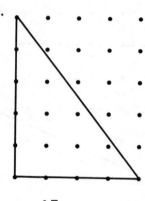

c =

11.

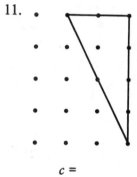

c =

13.

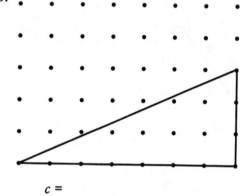

c =

*Visualized Geometry*

# Lesson 2-9
# The Triangle Inequality

## *Materials Needed:*

One copy of each of the following pages for each student: pages 104 and 105.

The narrow strips from the Appendix (pages 425, 427, 429, and 431).

*Note:* Save the strips because they will be needed in Lesson 3-5 and elsewhere.

A box of metal fasteners (about 30).

## *Directions for the Teacher:*

Prior to class cut out and punch holes in the strips from the Appendix pages. Separate the strips into nine sets with each set containing two strips labeled "a", one strip labeled "b", one strip labeled "c", and one strip labeled "d." Break your class into eight small groups and give each group one set of strips and three fasteners. Then

a. have your students make a triangle by fastening two "a" pieces together with one "b" piece, and ask them what kind of triangle is formed (isosceles);

b. have your students make a triangle with one "a" piece, one "b" piece, and one "c" piece, and ask them what kind of a triangle is formed (scalene); and

c. have your students (try to) make a triangle with one "a" piece, one "b" piece, and one "d" piece.

Point out that it is impossible to make a triangle when one side—"d"—is longer than the sum of the lengths of the other sides. Lead the students to the following generalization.

**The length of any side of a triangle is less than the sum of the lengths of the other two sides.**

Distribute the worksheets and provide individual assistance as needed. Students may need to review Lesson 2-7 in order to decide whether the triangles are right triangles, obtuse triangles, or acute triangles.

## Correct Answers for Worksheet 2-9-1:

1. no

2. yes, right, scalene

3. yes, obtuse, scalene

4. no

5. yes, acute, isosceles

6. yes, acute, isosceles, equilateral

# WORKSHEET 2-9-1
## The Triangle Inequality

1.

Can you make a triangle with sides the same
length as the three segments pictured?
_____ If so, what kind of a triangle
would it be (circle all correct answers)? Right,
Obtuse, Acute, Equilateral, Isosceles, Scalene

3.

Can you make a triangle with sides the same
length as the three segments pictured?
_____ If so, what kind of a triangle
would it be (circle all correct answers)? Right,
Obtuse, Acute, Equilateral, Isosceles, Scalene

2.

Can you make a triangle with sides the same
length as the three segments pictured?
_____ If so, what kind of a triangle
would it be (circle all correct answers)? Right,
Obtuse, Acute, Equilateral, Isosceles, Scalene

4.

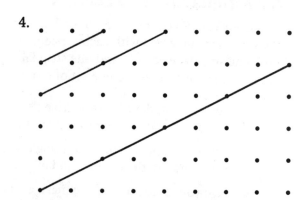

Can you make a triangle with sides the same
length as the three segments pictured?
_____ If so, what kind of a triangle
would it be (circle all correct answers)? Right,
Obtuse, Acute, Equilateral, Isosceles, Scalene

*(continued)*

# WORKSHEET 2-9-1
## The Triangle Inequality (continued)

5.

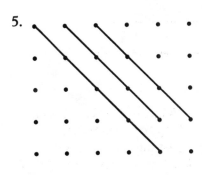

Can you make a triangle with sides the same length as the three segments pictured? _____ If so, what kind of a triangle would it be (circle all correct answers)? Right, Obtuse, Acute, Equilateral, Isosceles, Scalene

6.

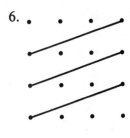

Can you make a triangle with sides the same length as the three segments pictured? _____ If so, what kind of a triangle would it be (circle all correct answers)? Right, Obtuse, Acute, Equilateral, Isosceles, Scalene

# CHAPTER 3

# Quadrilaterals

## Comments and Suggestions

This chapter illustrates the application of the van Hiele model better than any other chapter. In the case of parallelograms, rectangles, and squares, it is assumed that students are at the first van Hiele level. With this assumption the students are led through a series of lessons which require them to investigate the properties of these quadrilaterals. These lessons lead the students to the second level. In the case of parallelograms, students investigate three minimal-condition situations and finally arrive at the definition. This is followed by a lesson intended to motivate the definition of a rectangle (a parallelogram with at least one right angle). Finally, a square is defined to be a rectangle with at least one pair of adjacent congruent sides. Students who successfully complete these lessons will be at the third level concerning these concepts.

The rhombus and the trapezoid are handled in a comparable manner. In Lesson 3-10, students are required to apply all they have learned about quadrilaterals, finally using dot paper to draw quadrilaterals with particular properties. In Lesson 3-11, students learn to draw altitudes for parallelograms and trapezoids. The authors consider these activities prerequisites for later lessons concerning the development of area formulas for these quadrilaterals.

In the entire chapter, the authors were careful to present examples of rectangles and squares which did not have vertical and horizontal sides and parallelograms and trapezoids which did not have horizontal sides.

## Lesson 3–1
# Properties of Quadrilaterals

## *Materials Needed:*

One copy of page 110 for each student.

One transparency of page 109.

## *Directions for the Teacher:*

Place the transparency on the overhead projector. Briefly review the definition of the word "quadrilateral" (Lesson 1–9). Tell the students that in this lesson they will be investigating properties of quadrilaterals and indicate that they will do this by answering 10 questions. Proceed through these questions for problem I rather carefully. Concerning questions 8, 9, and 10, diagonals will need to be drawn. If the students do not know what a diagonal is, then briefly discuss this term. Concerning question 10, you may need to review what it means for two segments to bisect each other. (Proceed in a similar way with problem II.)

### Correct Answers for Transparency 3–1–1:

| I. | | | | II. | | | |
|---|---|---|---|---|---|---|---|
| 1. | yes | 6. | no | 1. | yes | 6. | no |
| 2. | no | 7. | no | 2. | yes | 7. | yes |
| 3. | no | 8. | no | 3. | yes | 8. | yes |
| 4. | no | 9. | no | 4. | yes | 9. | no |
| 5. | yes | 10. | no | 5. | no | 10. | yes |

Distribute the worksheet. Provide individual assistance as needed.

### Correct Answers for Worksheet 3–1–1:

| I. | | | | II. | | | |
|---|---|---|---|---|---|---|---|
| 1. | no | 6. | no | 1. | yes | 6. | yes |
| 2. | no | 7. | yes | 2. | yes | 7. | yes |
| 3. | yes | 8. | no | 3. | yes | 8. | yes |
| 4. | yes | 9. | no | 4. | yes | 9. | yes |
| 5. | no | 10. | yes | 5. | yes | 10. | yes |

# Transparency 3-1-1

## I.

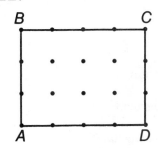

1. Is at least one angle a right angle?
2. Are all four angles right angles?
3. Are both pairs of opposite angles congruent?
4. Are both pairs of opposite sides congruent?
5. Is at least one pair of adjacent sides congruent?
6. Are all four sides congruent?
7. Are both pairs of opposite sides parallel?
8. Are the diagonals congruent?
9. Are the diagonals perpendicular?
10. Do the diagonals bisect each other?

## II.

1. Is at least one angle a right angle?
2. Are all four angles right angles?
3. Are both pairs of opposite angles congruent?
4. Are both pairs of opposite sides congruent?
5. Is at least one pair of adjacent sides congruent?
6. Are all four sides congruent?
7. Are both pairs of opposite sides parallel?
8. Are the diagonals congruent?
9. Are the diagonals perpendicular?
10. Do the diagonals bisect each other?

*Visualized Geometry*

# WORSHEET 3-1-1
## Properties of Quadrilaterals

**I.**

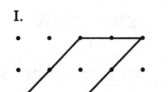

1. Is at least one angle a right angle?

2. Are all four angles right angles?

3. Are both pairs of opposite angles congruent?

4. Are both pairs of opposite sides congruent?

5. Is at least one pair of adjacent sides congruent?

6. Are all four sides congruent?

7. Are both pairs of opposite sides parallel?

8. Are the diagonals congruent?

9. Are the diagonals perpendicular?

10. Do the diagonals bisect each other?

**II.**

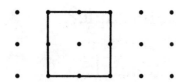

1. Is at least one angle a right angle?

2. Are all four angles right angles?

3. Are both pairs of opposite angles congruent?

4. Are both pairs of opposite sides congruent?

5. Is at least one pair of adjacent sides congruent?

6. Are all four sides congruent?

7. Are both pairs of opposite sides parallel?

8. Are the diagonals congruent?

9. Are the diagonals perpendicular?

10. Do the diagonals bisect each other?

# Lesson 3–2
# Properties of Parallelograms and Rectangles

## *Materials Needed:*

One copy of each of the following pages for each student: pages 115 and 116.

One transparency of each of the following pages: pages 113, 114, and 115.

## *Directions for the Teacher:*

Note that in addition to the regularly labeled transparency pages, you will need a transparency of a student worksheet page (page 115). This lesson is written for students who are at the first van Hiele level (visual) concerning parallelograms and rectangles (see the Introduction). This means they can identify these figures but are not aware of the properties of the figures.

Place the first transparency (page 113) on the overhead projector. Direct students' attention to the parallelograms. If a student suggests that any of these quadrilaterals is not actually a parallelogram, argue to the contrary. Mention that these quadrilaterals have the appropriate shape. Do not define the word "parallelogram." Students at van Hiele level 1 are not ready for the definition yet. Proceed to the quadrilaterals which are not parallelograms. If there is disagreement, merely indicate that these quadrilaterals do not have the appropriate shape.

Place the second transparency (page 114) on your projector. Proceed to the rectangles. A few students may argue that the quadrilaterals in the top row, middle position, and in the top row, right position, are not rectangles. If that happens, emphasize that the sides of rectangles do not have to be vertical and horizontal. Emphasize that these figures all have the appropriate shape to be rectangles and those at the bottom of the page do not have the appropriate shape.

Place the third transparency (Worksheet 3–2–1, page 115) on your overhead projector. Also, distribute the worksheets. With your students' help, complete that part of the table concerning parallelogram I in problem A. Direct the students to complete that table and also problem B on page 116.

## Correct Answers for Worksheet 3-2-1:

A.

| Property | Parallelogram I | Parallelogram II |
|---|---|---|
| 1. Is at least one angle a right angle? | No | No |
| 2. Are all four angles right angles? | No | No |
| 3. Are both pairs of opposite angles congruent? | Yes | Yes |
| 4. Are both pairs of opposite sides congruent? | Yes | Yes |
| 5. Is at least one pair of adjacent sides congruent? | No | No |
| 6. Are all four sides congruent? | No | No |
| 7. Are both pairs of opposite sides parallel? | Yes | Yes |
| 8. Are the diagonals congruent? | No | No |
| 9. Are the diagonals perpendicular? | No | No |
| 10. Do the diagonals bisect each other? | Yes | Yes |

B.

| Property | Rectangle I | Rectangle II |
|---|---|---|
| 1. Is at least one angle a right angle? | Yes | Yes |
| 2. Are all four angles right angles? | Yes | Yes |
| 3. Are both pairs of opposite angles congruent? | Yes | Yes |
| 4. Are both pairs of opposite sides congruent? | Yes | Yes |
| 5. Is at least one pair of adjacent sides congruent? | No | No |
| 6. Are all four sides congruent? | No | No |
| 7. Are both pairs of opposite sides parallel? | Yes | Yes |
| 8. Are the diagonals congruent? | Yes | Yes |
| 9. Are the diagonals perpendicular? | No | No |
| 10. Do the diagonals bisect each other? | Yes | Yes |

The following quadrilaterals are parallelograms.

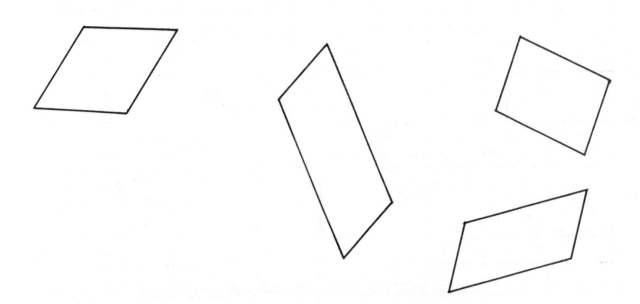

The following quadrilaterals are not parallelograms.

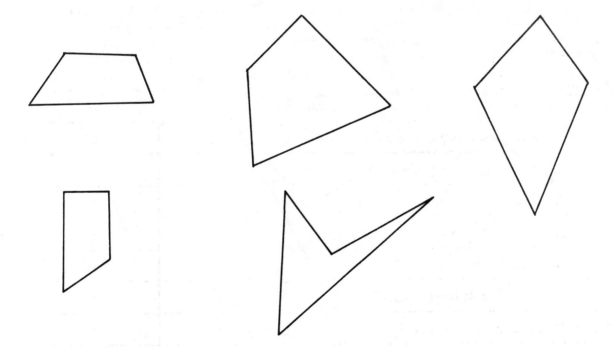

 *Visualized Geometry*

# The following quadrilaterals are rectangles.

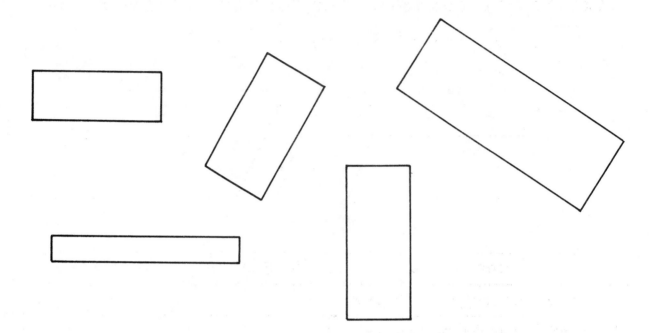

# The following quadrilaterals are not rectangles.

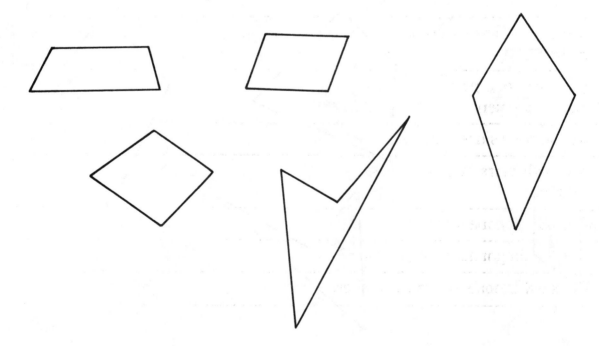

Name: _____  Date: _____

# WORKSHEET 3-2-1
## Properties of Parallelograms and Rectangles

A. Complete the table concerning the parallelograms below.

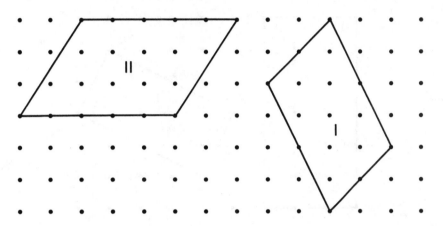

| Property | Parallelogram I | Parallelogram II |
|---|---|---|
| 1. Is at least one angle a right angle? | | |
| 2. Are all four angles right angles? | | |
| 3. Are both pairs of opposite angles congruent? | | |
| 4. Are both pairs of opposite sides congruent? | | |
| 5. Is at least one pair of adjacent sides congruent? | | |
| 6. Are all four sides congruent? | | |
| 7. Are both pairs of opposite sides parallel? | | |
| 8. Are the diagonals congruent? | | |
| 9. Are the diagonals perpendicular? | | |
| 10. Do the diagonals bisect each other? | | |

*(continued)*

   *Visualized Geometry*

Name: _____   Date: _____

B. Complete the table concerning the rectangles below.

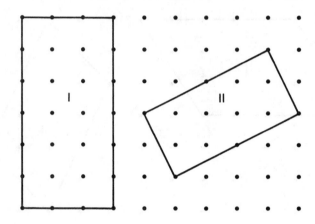

| Property | Rectangle I | Rectangle II |
|---|---|---|
| 1. Is at least one angle a right angle? | | |
| 2. Are all four angles right angles? | | |
| 3. Are both pairs of opposite angles congruent? | | |
| 4. Are both pairs of opposite sides congruent? | | |
| 5. Is at least one pair of adjacent sides congruent? | | |
| 6. Are all four sides congruent? | | |
| 7. Are both pairs of opposite sides parallel? | | |
| 8. Are the diagonals congruent? | | |
| 9. Are the diagonals perpendicular? | | |
| 10. Do the diagonals bisect each other? | | |

*Visualized Geometry*

## Lesson 3-3
# Comparing Properties of Parallelograms, Rectangles, and Squares

## *Materials Needed:*

One copy of each of the following pages for each student: pages 120 and 121.

One transparency of each of the following pages: pages 119, 120, and 121.

## *Directions for the Teacher:*

Note that transparencies are to be made of a regular transparency page and also two student worksheet pages. This lesson is written for students who are at the first van Hiele level concerning squares. Place the first transparency (page 119) on the overhead projector. Indicate that the figures at the top of the page are squares because they have the appropriate shape. Place the second transparency (page 120) on the overhead projector and distribute the worksheets. Complete the table for problem A.

Place the third transparency (page 121) on the projector. Proceed to problem B. With the students' assistance, complete the table. The square column can be completed by merely copying the answers from problem A or by investigating the properties of the square pictured. The other columns can be completed by extracting the corresponding answers from Lesson 3-2 or by very quickly answering the questions concerning the rectangle and the parallelogram pictured.

### Correct Answers for Worksheet 3-3-1:

A. The answers are all yes.

B.

| Questions | Square | Rectangle | Parallelogram |
|---|---|---|---|
| 1. Is at least one angle a right angle? | Yes | Yes | No |
| 2. Are all four angles right angles? | Yes | Yes | No |
| 3. Are both pairs of opposite angles congruent? | Yes | Yes | Yes |
| 4. Are both pairs of opposite sides congruent? | Yes | Yes | Yes |
| 5. Is at least one pair of adjacent sides congruent? | Yes | No | No |
| 6. Are all four sides congruent? | Yes | No | No |
| 7. Are both pairs of opposite sides parallel? | Yes | Yes | Yes |
| 8. Are the diagonals congruent? | Yes | Yes | No |
| 9. Are the diagonals perpendicular? | Yes | No | No |
| 10. Do the diagonals bisect each other? | Yes | Yes | Yes |

Next, ask the students what they notice about the table. Here are some possible responses.

a. The answers for the questions concerning the square are all yes. The square has many properties.

b. The rectangle has fewer properties than the square but more properties than the parallelogram.

c. The parallelogram has the fewest properties.

d. Each property of the parallelogram is also a property of the rectangle.

e. Each property of the rectangle is also a property of the square.

f. Each property of the parallelogram is also a property of the square.

# These quadrilaterals are squares.

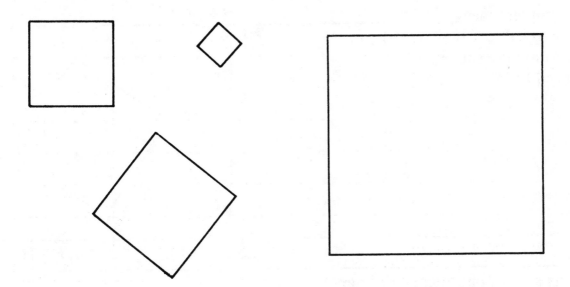

# These quadrilaterals are not squares.

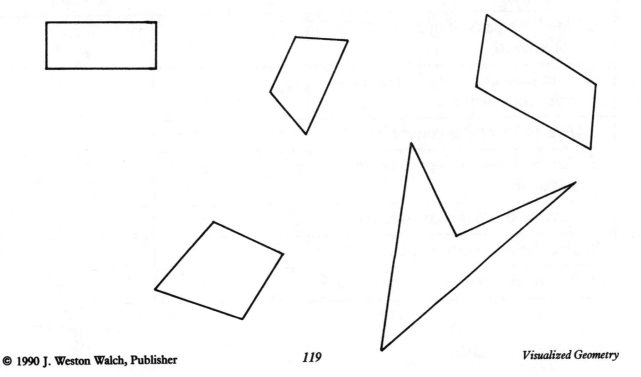

         *Visualized Geometry*

# WORKSHEET 3-3-1
## Comparing Properties of Parallelograms, Rectangles, and Squares

A. Complete the
following table
concerning the squares
pictured here.

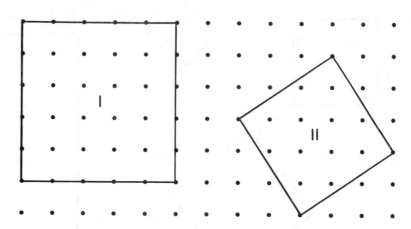

| Property | Square I | Square II |
|---|---|---|
| 1. Is at least one angle a right angle? | | |
| 2. Are all four angles right angles? | | |
| 3. Are both pairs of opposite angles congruent? | | |
| 4. Are both pairs of opposite sides congruent? | | |
| 5. Is at least one pair of adjacent sides congruent? | | |
| 6. Are all four sides congruent? | | |
| 7. Are both pairs of opposite sides parallel? | | |
| 8. Are the diagonals congruent? | | |
| 9. Are the diagonals perpendicular? | | |
| 10. Do the diagonals bisect each other? | | |

*(continued)*

# WORSHEET 3-3-1
## Comparing Properties of Parallelograms, Rectangles, and Squares *(continued)*

B. Complete the table below concerning the properties of squares, rectangles, and parallelograms.

Square          Rectangle          Parallelogram

| Questions | Square | Rectangle | Parallelogram |
|---|---|---|---|
| 1. Is at least one angle a right angle? | | | |
| 2. Are all four angles right angles? | | | |
| 3. Are both pairs of opposite angles congruent? | | | |
| 4. Are both pairs of opposite sides congruent? | | | |
| 5. Is at least one pair of adjacent sides congruent? | | | |
| 6. Are all four sides congruent? | | | |
| 7. Are both pairs of opposite sides parallel? | | | |
| 8. Are the diagonals congruent? | | | |
| 9. Are the diagonals perpendicular? | | | |
| 10. Do the diagonals bisect each other? | | | |

# Lesson 3–4
# Diagonal Properties of Parallelograms, Rectangles, and Squares

## *Materials Needed:*

One copy of page 125 for each student.

One transparency of each of the following pages: pages 123 and 124.

## *Directions for the Teacher:*

You may wish to begin this lesson with a review of Lesson 1–8. Put the first transparency on the overhead projector. With the students' help, draw the quadrilaterals and answer the questions.

**Correct Answers for Transparency 3–4–1:**

| | | | | |
|---|---|---|---|---|
| a. yes | d. no | | a. no | d. no |
| b. no | e. no | | b. yes | e. no |
| c. no | f. no | | c. no | f. no |

Distribute the worksheet. Provide individual assistance as needed. When each student has completed the worksheet (this may be the next day if this is a homework assignment), put the second transparency on your overhead projector, but cover up the generalizations which are at the bottom of the page. This is a completed version of the worksheet. Discuss the results. Emphasize that problem 1 suggests that when the diagonals of a quadrilateral bisect each other the quadrilateral is a parallelogram, problem 2 suggests that when the diagonals of a quadrilateral bisect each other and are congruent, the quadrilateral is a rectangle, and problem 3 suggests that when the diagonals of a quadrilateral are congruent and are perpendicular bisectors of each other, the figure is a square. Uncover the generalizations at the bottom of the page and go through these generalizations. These generalizations are, of course, just the generalizations that were made from the worksheet.

**Transparency 3-4-1**

In each situation the diagonals for a quadrilateral are drawn.
Draw the quadrilateral and answer the related questions.

1.

a. Are the diagonals congruent?
b. Are the diagonals perpendicular?
c. Do the diagonals bisect each other?
d. Is the figure a square?
e. Is the figure a rectangle?
f. Is the figure a parallelogram?

2.

a. Are the diagonals congruent?
b. Are the diagonals perpendicular?
c. Do the diagonals bisect each other?
d. Is the figure a square?
e. Is the figure a rectangle?
f. Is the figure a parallelogram?

1.

| | |
|---|---|
| a. Are the diagonals congruent? | **No** |
| b. Are the diagonals perpendicular? | **No** |
| c. Do the diagonals bisect each other? | **Yes** |
| d. Is the figure a square? | **No** |
| e. Is the figure a rectangle? | **No** |
| f. Is the figure a parallelogram? | **Yes** |

2.

| | |
|---|---|
| a. Are the diagonals congruent? | **Yes** |
| b. Are the diagonals perpendicular? | **No** |
| c. Do the diagonals bisect each other? | **Yes** |
| d. Is the figure a square? | **No** |
| e. Is the figure a rectangle? | **Yes** |

3.

| | |
|---|---|
| a. Are the diagonals congruent? | **Yes** |
| b. Are the diagonals perpendicular? | **Yes** |
| c. Do the diagonals bisect each other? | **Yes** |
| d. Is the figure a square? | **Yes** |

**When the diagonals of a quadrilateral bisect each other, the quadrilateral is a parallelogram.**

**When the diagonals of a quadrilateral are congruent and bisect each other, the quadrilateral is a rectangle.**

**When the diagonals of a quadrilateral are perpendicular, congruent, and bisect each other, the quadrilateral is a square.**

# WORSHEET 3-4-1
## Diagonal Properties of Parallelograms, Rectangles, and Squares

In each situation the diagonals for a quadrilateral are drawn. Draw the quadrilateral and answer the related questions.

1.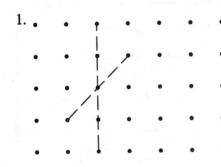

   a. Are the diagonals congruent?
   b. Are the diagonals perpendicular?
   c. Do the diagonals bisect each other?
   d. Is the figure a square?
   e. Is the figure a rectangle?
   f. Is the figure a parallelogram?

2.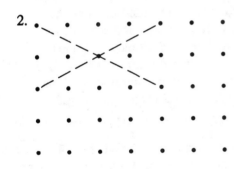

   a. Are the diagonals congruent?
   b. Are the diagonals perpendicular?
   c. Do the diagonals bisect each other?
   d. Is the figure a square?
   e. Is the figure a rectangle?

3.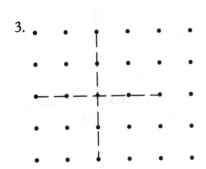

   a. Are the diagonals congruent?
   b. Are the diagonals perpendicular?
   c. Do the diagonals bisect each other?
   d. Is the figure a square?

*Visualized Geometry*

## Lesson 3-5
# The Parallelogram: Minimal Conditions and the Definition

## *Materials Needed:*

One transparency of each of the following pages: pages 128, 129, and 130.

The strips that were originally in the Appendix on pages 425, 427, 429, and 431. (They were used in Lesson 2-9.)

Thirty-six fasteners.

## *Directions for the Teacher:*

Place the first transparency on the overhead projector. Remind the students that you had previously decided (in Lessons 3-2 and 3-3) that parallelograms had the properties indicated with "yes" on the transparency. Indicate that if each time you wanted to show that a given quadrilateral was a parallelogram, you had to verify all four "yes" conditions, it would be quite a difficult job. Suggest that it would be nice to have some "minimal conditions." Tell them this means a list with as few properties as possible. Remind them that they already found that property 10, by itself, was enough to guarantee that a quadrilateral would be a parallelogram. Now ask the students if they think property 4 by itself is enough to establish that a quadrilateral is a parallelogram. (It is.)

Divide your class into eight groups. Provide each group with two strips labeled "a," two strips labeled "b," and four fasteners, and keep one set of those materials for yourself. Direct the students to make a quadrilateral so that the two pieces labeled "a" are opposite sides and the two pieces labeled "b" are opposite sides. Demonstrate this with your pieces. Show that the quadrilateral is not rigid but that no matter how it is shaped (as long as the figure is a quadrilateral) the figure is a parallelogram. Conclude that property 4 by itself is enough to establish that a quadrilateral is a parallelogram.

Now ask the students whether they think property 7 by itself is enough. (It is.) Place the second transparency on the overhead projector. Draw a quadrilateral (problem 1) so that the opposite sides are parallel. Here is one possibility.

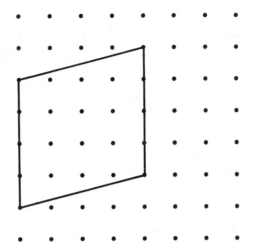

Of course this quadrilateral is a parallelogram.

Proceed to problem 2. Again draw a quadrilateral with opposite sides parallel. Again the figure is a parallelogram. Conclude that property 7 by itself is enough to establish that a quadrilateral is a parallelogram.

Place the third transparency on the overhead projector. Go through each statement. Point out that the last generalization is called the definition of a parallelogram.

The sum of the measures of the four angles of any convex quadrilateral is 360° (Lesson 5-1) which means that this is a required condition for any parallelogram. Then, if property 3 (both pairs of opposite angles congruent) *also* holds for a given convex quadrilateral, that quadrilateral is a parallelogram. This is a fact that is a little difficult to establish so it is recommended that property 3 not be investigated in the same way that properties 4 and 7 were investigated.

## Properties of a parallelogram

1. Is at least one angle a right angle?

No

2. Are all four angles right angles?

No

3. Are both pairs of opposite angles congruent?

Yes

4. Are both pairs of opposite sides congruent?

Yes

5. Is at least one pair of adjacent sides congruent?

No

6. Are all four sides congruent?

No

7. Are both pairs of opposite sides parallel?

Yes

8. Are the diagonals congruent?

No

9. Are the diagonals perpendicular?

No

10. Do the diagonals bisect each other?

Yes

1. Draw a quadrilateral which has the property that both pairs of opposite sides are parallel.

. . . . . . . .
. . . . . . . .
. . . . . . . .
. . . . . . . .
. . . . . . . .
. . . . . . . .
. . . . . . . .
. . . . . . . .

Is this quadrilateral a parallelogram? _____

2. Draw another quadrilateral which has the property that both pairs of opposite sides are parallel.

. . . . . . . .
. . . . . . . .
. . . . . . . .
. . . . . . . .
. . . . . . . .
. . . . . . . .
. . . . . . . .
. . . . . . . .

Is this quadrilateral a parallelogram? _____

         *Visualized Geometry*

**A quadrilateral with diagonals that bisect each other is a parallelogram.**

**A quadrilateral in which both pairs of opposite sides are congruent is a parallelogram.**

**A quadrilateral in which both pairs of opposite sides are parallel is a parallelogram.**

*Visualized Geometry*

## Lesson 3–6
# The Definition of a Rectangle and a Square

## *Materials Needed:*

One transparency of each of the following pages: pages 133, 134, and 135.

The strips that were originally in the Appendix on pages 425, 427, 429, and 431.

Thirty-six fasteners and nine index cards.

## *Directions for the Teacher:*

Place the first transparency on the overhead projector. Cover up the Definition of a Rectangle portion of the transparency. Remind the students that they had previously decided (in Lessons 3–2 and 3–3) that rectangles had the properties indicated with "yes" on the transparency. Indicate that if each time you wanted to show that a particular quadrilateral was a rectangle, you had to verify all the seven "yes" conditions, it would be quite a difficult job. Suggest that it would be nice to have a shorter list. Remind them that properties 8 and 10 together are enough to guarantee that a given quadrilateral is a rectangle.

Divide your class into eight groups and give each group two strips labeled "a," two strips labeled "b," four fasteners, and one index card. Keep one set of these materials for yourself. Have your students form a quadrilateral with the four strips, using two "a" strips as opposite sides and two "b" strips as opposite sides. Also make this quadrilateral yourself. Remind the students that a quadrilateral formed this way (Lesson 3–5) is a parallelogram. Now take your index card and make one of the angles of the quadrilateral match an index card angle. Have the students do the same thing. Ask the students what kind of a quadrilateral they have (a rectangle). Next, uncover the bottom portion of the transparency and discuss the definition in light of the demonstration you just gave.

Place the second transparency on the overhead projector. Proceed through the four problems.

## Correct Answers for Transparency 3–6–2:

1a. yes
 b. no
 c. $\overline{AB}$ is shorter than $\overline{BC}$.

2a. yes
 b. no
 c. $\overline{EF}$ is shorter than $\overline{FG}$.

3a. yes
 b. yes
 c. They are the same length.

4a. yes
 b. no
 c. $\overline{MN}$ is longer than $\overline{NO}$.

Some students may argue that the quadrilateral in problem 3 is not a rectangle. If that happens, argue that the quadrilateral actually is a rectangle because it is certainly a parallelogram with a right angle.

Next, place the third transparency on the overhead projector. Proceed carefully through the first definition given there. That definition was motivated by the results of the investigation of the quadrilaterals on the second transparency. Then proceed through the last two definitions.

## Properties of a Rectangle

| | |
|---|---|
| 1. Is at least one angle a right angle? | Yes |
| 2. Are all four angles right angles? | Yes |
| 3. Are both pairs of opposite angles congruent? | Yes |
| 4. Are both pairs of opposite sides congruent? | Yes |
| 5. Is at least one pair of adjacent sides congruent? | No |
| 6. Are all four sides congruent? | No |
| 7. Are both pairs of opposite sides parallel? | Yes |
| 8. Are the diagonals congruent? | Yes |
| 9. Are the diagonals perpendicular? | No |
| 10. Do the diagonals bisect each other? | Yes |

## Definition of a Rectangle

**A rectangle is a parallelogram with at least one right angle.**

**Transparency 3-6-2**

1.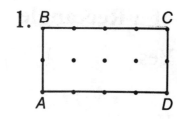
   a. Is quadrilateral *ABCD* a rectangle?
   b. Is quadrilateral *ABCD* a square?
   c. How do the lengths of $\overline{AB}$ and $\overline{BC}$ compare?

2.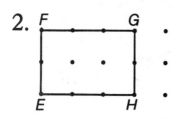
   a. Is quadrilateral *EFGH* a rectangle?
   b. Is quadrilateral *EFGH* a square?
   c. How do the lengths of $\overline{EF}$ and $\overline{FG}$ compare?

3.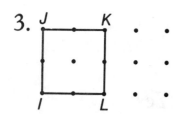
   a. Is quadrilateral *IJKL* a rectangle?
   b. Is quadrilateral *IJKL* a square?
   c. How do the lengths of $\overline{IJ}$ and $\overline{JK}$ compare?

4.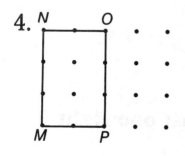
   a. Is quadrilateral *MNOP* a rectangle?
   b. Is quadrilateral *MNOP* a square?
   c. How do the lengths of $\overline{MN}$ and $\overline{NO}$ compare?

A square is a rectangle with at least one pair of adjacent sides which are congruent.

A rectangle is a parallelogram with at least one right angle.

A parallelogram is a quadrilateral with two pairs of parallel sides.

*Visualized Geometry*

## Lesson 3-7
# Identifying Squares, Rectangles, and Parallelograms

### Materials Needed:

One copy of each of the following pages for each student: pages 137, 138, 139, and 140.

### Directions for the Teacher:

Distribute the student worksheet. Go through the definitions on the first page. This is a review of the definitions given in Lesson 3-6. Have the students complete the worksheets. Provide individual assistance as needed.

### Correct Answers for Worksheet 3-7-2:

| 1a. no | 2a. yes | 3a. yes | 4a. yes | 5a. yes |
|--------|---------|---------|---------|---------|
| b. no | b. yes | b. no | b. yes | b. yes |
| c. no | c. no | c. no | c. no | c. yes |

6a.

e.

g.

b. not possible

c.

f.

d. not possible

(For problems 6a, c, e, f, and g, several correct figures are possible and only one possible correct answer is given.)

# WORKSHEET 3-7-1
## Identifying Squares, Rectangles, and Parallelograms

**A square is a rectangle with at least one pair of adjacent sides which are congruent.**

**A rectangle is a parallelogram with at least one right angle.**

**A parallelogram is a quadrilateral with two pairs of parallel sides.**

# WORKSHEET 3-7-2
## Identifying Squares, Rectangles, and Parallelograms

1.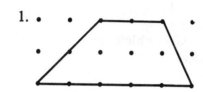

a. Is the quadrilateral a parallelogram?
b. Is the quadrilateral a rectangle?
c. Is the quadrilateral a square?

2.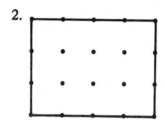

a. Is the quadrilateral a parallelogram?
b. Is the quadrilateral a rectangle?
c. Is the quadrilateral a square?

3.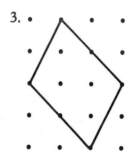

a. Is the quadrilateral a parallelogram?
b. Is the quadrilateral a rectangle?
c. Is the quadrilateral a square?

4.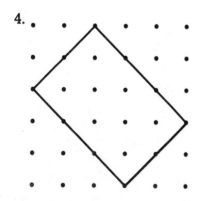

a. Is the quadrilateral a parallelogram?
b. Is the quadrilateral a rectangle?
c. Is the quadrilateral a square?

(continued)

*Visualized Geometry*

# WORKSHEET 3-7-2
## Identifying Squares, Rectangles, and Parallelograms *(continued)*

5.

a. Is the quadrilateral a parallelogram?
b. Is the quadrilateral a rectangle?
c. Is the quadrilateral a square?

6. If possible, draw a picture of a quadrilateral which is

a. a rectangle but not a square.

c. a parallelogram but not a rectangle.

b. a square but not a rectangle.

d. a rectangle but not a parallelogram.

*(continued)*

# WORKSHEET 3-7-2
## Identifying Squares, Rectangles, and Parallelograms *(continued)*

e. both a rectangle and a parallelogram.

    • • • • •

    • • • • •

    • • • • •

    • • • • •

    • • • • •

f. both a rectangle and a square.

    • • • • •

    • • • • •

    • • • • •

    • • • • •

    • • • • •

g. a parallelogram, a rectangle, and a square.

    • • • • •

    • • • • •

    • • • • •

    • • • • •

    • • • • •

*Visualized Geometry*

## Lesson 3-8
# The Rhombus

## *Materials Needed:*

One copy of page 144 for each student.

One transparency of page 143.

Four strips labeled "a" from the Appendix (pages 425, 427, 429, and 431) and four fasteners.

## *Directions for the Teacher:*

This lesson is written for the students who are not familiar with the word "rhombus." (They are not even at the first van Hiele level concerning rhombus.) Put the transparency on the overhead projector. Have the students examine each rhombus and also each quadrilateral which is not a rhombus. Help them to discover properties of a rhombus. Here are some possibilities.

a. All four sides are congruent.

b. Both pairs of opposite sides are parallel.

c. Opposite angles are congruent.

d. The diagonals are perpendicular.

e. The diagonals bisect each other.

Indicate that each rhombus is a parallelogram (because of property b above). Write the following definition on the transparency.

**A rhombus is a parallelogram with at least one pair of adjacent sides which are congruent.**

Next, take the four strips labeled "a" from Lesson 2-9 and fasten these four pieces together. Illustrate that the resulting "figure" is not rigid, but no matter how you change the shape, the figure is a rhombus. Now, take an index card and make one of the angles of the rhombus match an index card angle. Ask what kind of a figure you have (square). Point out that a square could be defined as a rhombus with at least one right angle.

Distribute the worksheet. Provide individual assistance as needed.

## Correct Answers for Worksheet 3-8-1:

1. Each of the quadrilaterals in parts b, c, e, and f is a rhombus.

2a.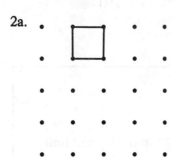

b.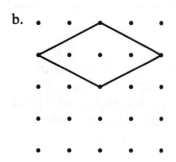

c. not possible

(For problems 2a and b, several correct figures are possible and only one correct answer is given.)

# Each of the quadrilaterals pictured below is a rhombus.

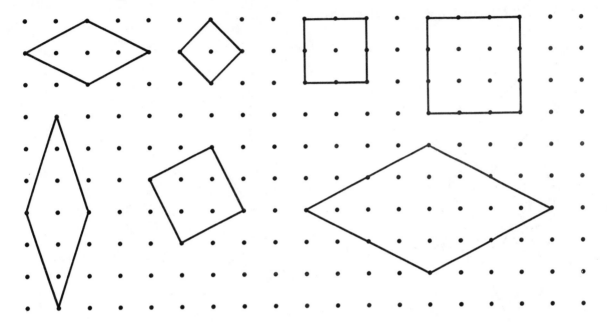

# None of the quadrilaterals pictured below is a rhombus.

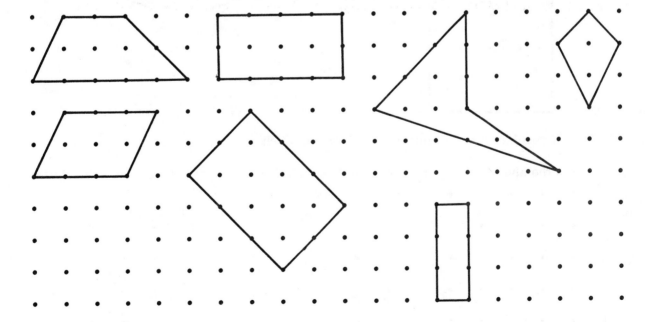

*Visualized Geometry*

Name: _____ Date: _____

# WORKSHEET 3-8-1
## The Rhombus

1. Write "R" in each quadrilateral which is a rhombus.

a.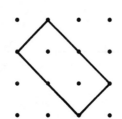

b.

c.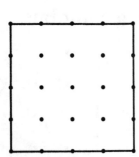

d.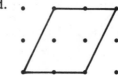

e.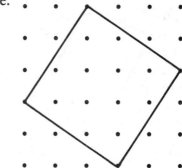

f.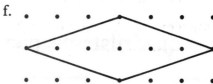

2. If possible, draw a picture of a quadrilateral which is

a. a rhombus.  b. a rhombus but not a square.  c. a square but not a rhombus.

## Lesson 3-9
# The Trapezoid

## *Materials Needed:*

One copy of page 147 for each student.

One transparency of page 146.

## *Directions for the Teacher:*

Place the transparency on the overhead projector. This lesson is written for students who do not know anything about trapezoids. (They are not even at the first van Hiele level concerning trapezoids). Have the students examine quadrilaterals that are trapezoids and those that are not trapezoids. They should see (possibly with your help) that the only significant property that trapezoids have is that they all have exactly one pair of parallel sides. Then state the following definition.

**A trapezoid is a quadrilateral with exactly one pair of parallel sides.**

Distribute the worksheet. Provide individual assistance as needed.

## Correct Answers for Worksheet 3-9-1:

1. Each of the quadrilaterals in parts a, d, and e is a trapezoid.

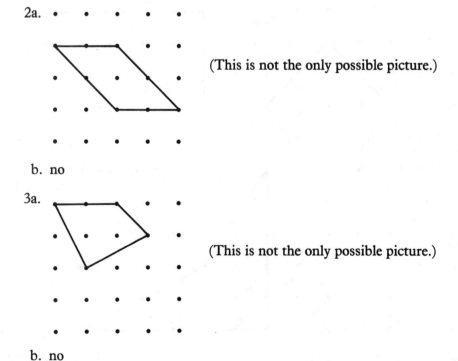

2a.

(This is not the only possible picture.)

b. no

3a.

(This is not the only possible picture.)

b. no

# The following quadrilaterals are trapezoids.

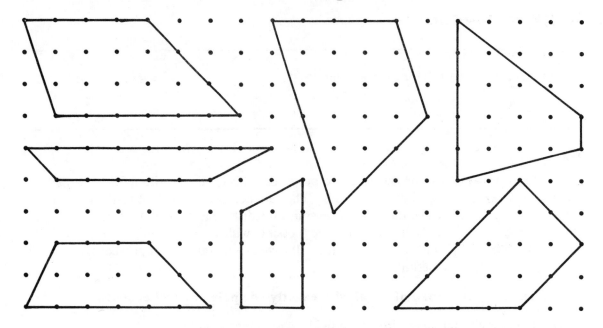

# The following quadrilaterals are not trapezoids.

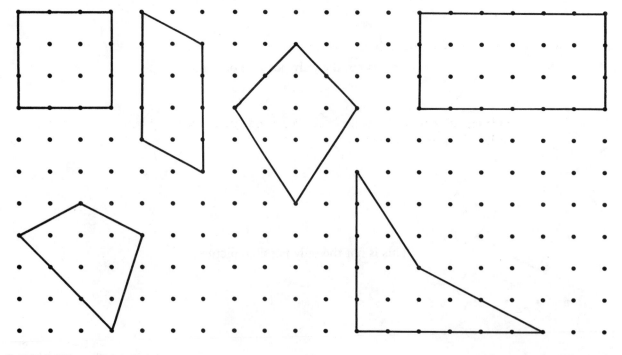

Name: _____     Date: _____

# WORKSHEET 3-9-1
## The Trapezoid

1. Write "T" in each trapezoid.

a.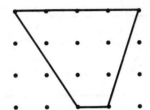

b.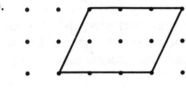

c.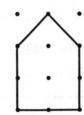

d.

e.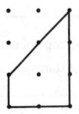

f.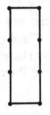

2a. Draw a quadrilateral which has two pairs of parallel sides.

b. Is this quadrilateral a trapezoid?

3a. Draw a quadrilateral which has zero pairs of parallel sides. (No two sides are parallel.)

b. Is this quadrilateral a trapezoid?

*Visualized Geometry*

# Lesson 3–10
# Identifying Quadrilaterals

## *Materials Needed:*

One copy of each of the following pages for each student: pages 149, 150, and 151.
One transparency of page 149.

## *Directions for the Teacher:*

Notice that you are to make a transparency of one of the worksheet pages that the students receive. Place the transparency on the overhead projector and go through the definitions carefully. Distribute the student worksheet pages and have the students complete the two worksheets. Provide individual assistance as needed.

### Correct Answers for Worksheet 3–10–2:

| | | | | | |
|---|---|---|---|---|---|
| 1a. no | 2a. yes | 3a. no | 4a. no | 5a. no | 6a. no |
| b. yes | b. no | b. yes | b. yes | b. yes | b. no |
| c. yes | c. no | c. no | c. yes | c. no | c. no |
| d. no | d. no | d. no | d. yes | d. no | d. no |
| e. no | e. no | e. yes | e. yes | e. no | e. no |

7. (For parts a, c, d, and e, a variety of pictures are possible and only one is given.)

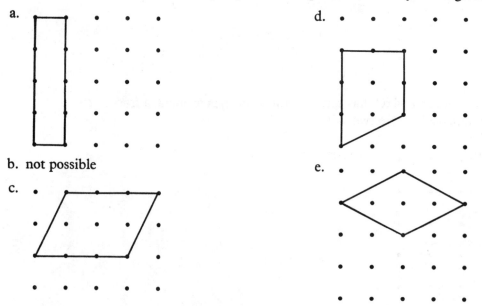

a.

b. not possible

c.

d.

e.

f. not possible

Name: _____ Date: _____

# WORKSHEET 3-10-1
## Identifying Quadrilaterals

## Definitions of Quadrilaterals

A *trapezoid* is a quadrilateral with exactly one pair of parallel sides.

A *parallelogram* is a quadrilateral with two pairs of parallel sides.

A *rectangle* is a parallelogram with at least one right angle.

A *square* is a rectangle with at least one pair of adjacent congruent sides.

A *rhombus* is a parallelogram with at least one pair of adjacent congruent sides.

# WORSHEET 3-10-2
## Identifying Quadrilaterals

1.
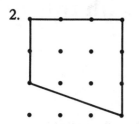

a.  Is the quadrilateral a trapezoid?      _____

b.  Is the quadrilateral a parallelogram?    _____

c.  Is the quadrilateral a rectangle?      _____

d.  Is the quadrilateral a square?       _____

e.  Is the quadrilateral a rhombus?      _____

2.
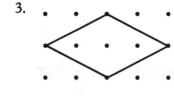

a.  Is the quadrilateral a trapezoid?      _____

b.  Is the quadrilateral a parallelogram?    _____

c.  Is the quadrilateral a rectangle?      _____

d.  Is the quadrilateral a square?       _____

e.  Is the quadrilateral a rhombus?      _____

3.
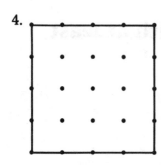

a.  Is the quadrilateral a trapezoid?      _____

b.  Is the quadrilateral a parallelogram?    _____

c.  Is the quadrilateral a rectangle?      _____

d.  Is the quadrilateral a square?       _____

e.  Is the quadrilateral a rhombus?      _____

4.

a.  Is the quadrilateral a trapezoid?      _____

b.  Is the quadrilateral a parallelogram?    _____

c.  Is the quadrilateral a rectangle?      _____

d.  Is the quadrilateral a square?       _____

e.  Is the quadrilateral a rhombus?      _____

*(continued)*

          *Visualized Geometry*

# WORKSHEET 3-10-2
## Identifying Quadrilaterals (*continued*)

5.

a. Is the quadrilateral a trapezoid?  _____
b. Is the quadrilateral a parallelogram?  _____
c. Is the quadrilateral a rectangle?  _____
d. Is the quadrilateral a square?  _____
e. Is the quadrilateral a rhombus?  _____

6.

a. Is the quadrilateral a trapezoid?  _____
b. Is the quadrilateral a parallelogram?  _____
c. Is the quadrilateral a rectangle?  _____
d. Is the quadrilateral a square?  _____
e. Is the quadrilateral a rhombus?  _____

7. If possible, draw a picture of a quadrilateral which is

a. a rectangle but not a square.

c. a parallelogram but not a rectangle.

e. a rhombus but not a square.

b. a square but not a rectangle.

d. a trapezoid.

f. a square but not a rhombus.

## Lesson 3-11
# Drawing Altitudes of Parallelograms and Trapezoids

## *Materials Needed:*

One copy of each of the following pages for each student: pages 158 and 159.

One transparency of each of the following pages: pages 156 and 157.

One index card for each student and one for yourself.

## *Directions for the Teacher:*

Place the first transparency on the overhead projector. Discuss the definition of altitude given there. Proceed to parallelogram *ABCD*. Identify $\overline{AD}$ as the base. Point out that this is an arbitrary choice on your part. Mention that it is common, although not required, for an altitude to be drawn from a vertex to the base. Take your index card and place it on parallelogram *ABCD* as shown.

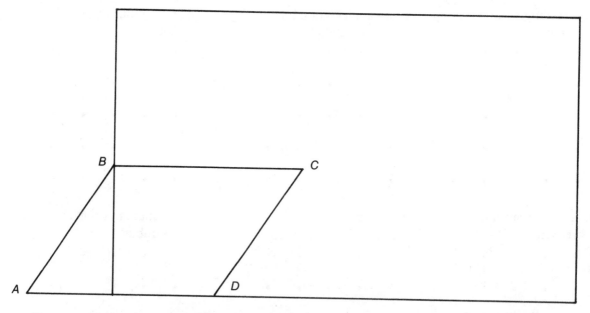

Draw a segment from *B* to $\overline{AD}$ along the edge of the index card. Point out that since the angles of an index card are all right angles, this segment is perpendicular to $\overline{AD}$ which means that it is an altitude to $\overline{AD}$. Proceed to parallelogram *EFGH*. Classify $\overline{EF}$ as the base. Use the index card to draw an altitude from *G* to $\overline{EF}$. For parallelogram *IJKL* classify $\overline{KL}$ as the base and use the index card to draw an altitude from *J* to $\overline{KL}$.

Proceed to the three parallelograms given on dot paper. Point out that for those parallelograms you do not need to use the index cards. For parallelogram *MNOP* classify $\overline{MP}$ as the base and draw an altitude from *N* to $\overline{MP}$, for quadrilateral *QRST* classify $\overline{ST}$ as the base and draw an altitude from *Q* to $\overline{ST}$ and finally classify $\overline{UX}$ as the base for quadrilateral *UVWX* and draw an altitude from *V* to $\overline{UX}$.

Place the second transparency on the overhead projector. Discuss the definition of an altitude of a trapezoid. Point out that it is common, though not required, to draw an altitude through a vertex. Take the index card and place it on trapezoid *ABCD* as shown below.

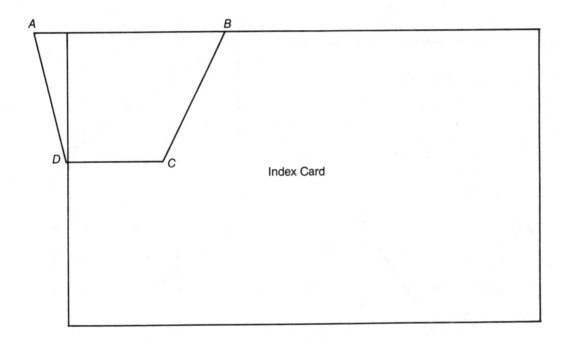

Draw a segment from *D* to $\overline{AB}$ along the side of the index card. Point out that this is an altitude. Proceed in a similar way with trapezoids *EFGH* and *IJKL* being careful to use parallel sides as bases. Go on to the other three trapezoids. Mention that in these three cases an index card is not needed. Specifically draw an altitude from *N* to $\overline{MP}$, from *S* to $\overline{RQ}$ and from *X* to $\overline{UV}$.

Distribute the worksheets. Provide individual assistance as needed.

## Possible Correct Answers for Worksheet 3-11-1:

1.

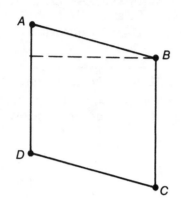

$\overline{AD}$ is the base

4.

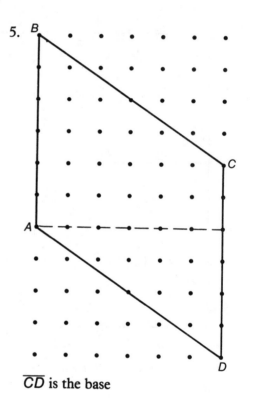

$\overline{AD}$ is the base

2.

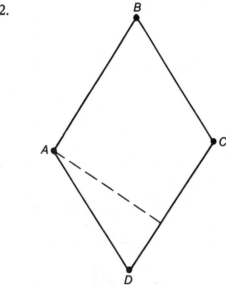

$\overline{CD}$ is the base

5.

$\overline{CD}$ is the base

3.

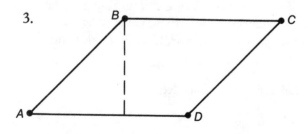

$\overline{AD}$ is the base

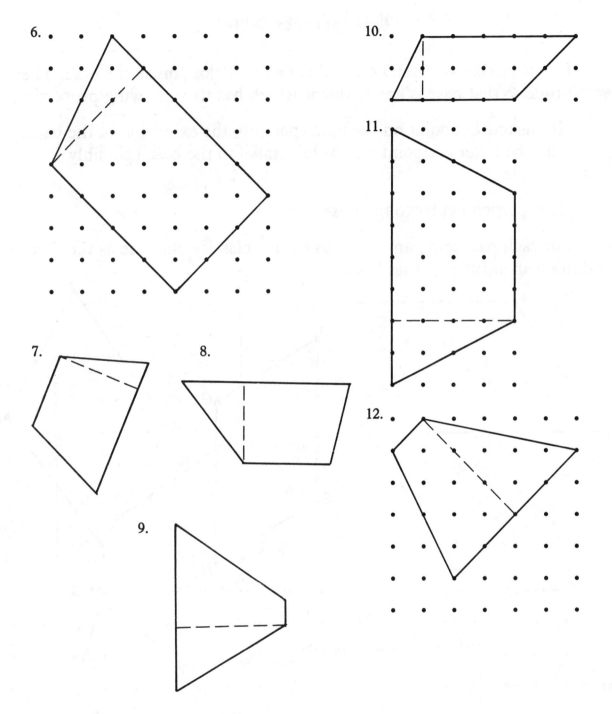

6.   7.   8.   9.   10.   11.   12.

(There are several correct answers for each figure.)

# Transparency 3–11–1

It is common to classify one side of a parallelogram as the base. Then an altitude to that base is any segment which has the following properties.

a. It has one endpoint on the base (possibly the extension of the base) and the other endpoint on a side parallel to the base (possibly extended).

b. It is perpendicular to the base.

For each parallelogram pictured below, classify one side as the base and draw an altitude to that base.

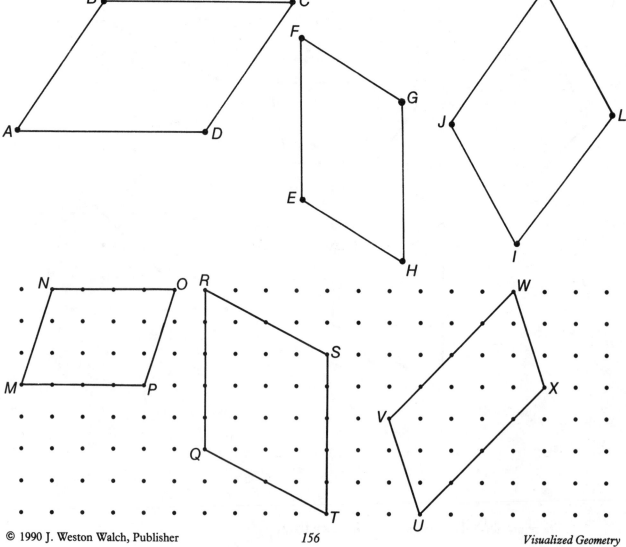

It is common to classify the two parallel sides of a trapezoid as the bases. Then an altitude is any segment with the following properties.

a. It has endpoints on the bases.

b. It is perpendicular to the bases.

For each trapezoid pictured below, draw in an altitude.

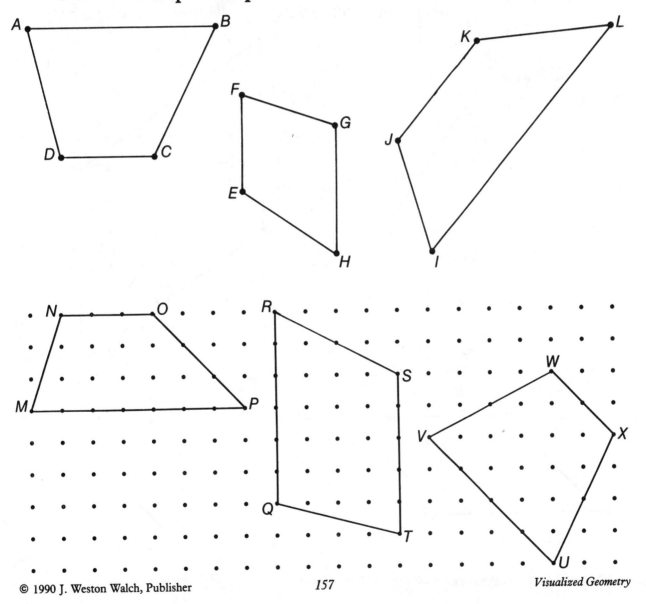

# WORKSHEET 3-11-1
## Drawing Altitudes of Parallelograms and Trapezoids

For each parallelogram below, a base has been selected. Draw an altitude to that base. Use an index card for problems 1–3.

1.

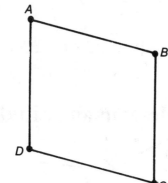

$\overline{AD}$ is the base

2.

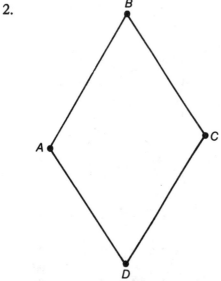

$\overline{CD}$ is the base

3.

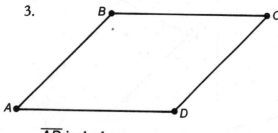

$\overline{AD}$ is the base

4.

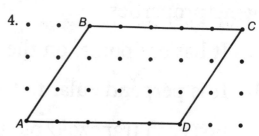

$\overline{AD}$ is the base

5.

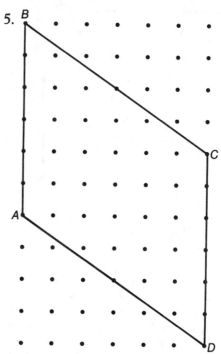

$\overline{CD}$ is the base

(continued)

# WORSHEET 3–11–1
## Drawing Altitudes of Parallelograms
## and Trapezoids *(continued)*

Using an index card, draw an altitude for each trapezoid.

6.

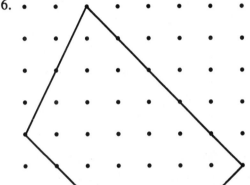

10.

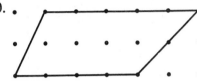

11.

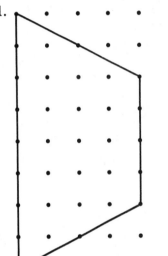

7.

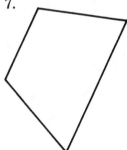

8.

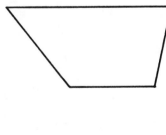

12.

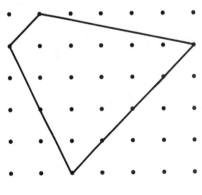

9.

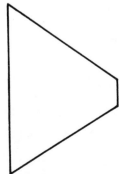

*Visualized Geometry*

# CHAPTER 4

# Measurement

## Comments and Suggestions

In the opinion of the authors, measurement is generally taught very poorly. Students often learn and apply formulas without understanding why they work and what the related concepts mean. For instance, students often confuse area and perimeter and do not realize, for example, that area best describes the size of a garden.

It should be noted that there are two lessons concerning the area of parallelograms, two lessons concerning the area of triangles, and two lessons concerning the area of trapezoids. In each case, the first lesson is written to motivate the formula. Then the formula is developed, stated, and applied in the second lesson. Those two lessons should be taught on different days. Students are often anxious to use formulas before they understand them and these pairs of lessons are designed to "force" the student to understand, but only if the lessons are taught on successive days.

The authors have noted that students have difficulty measuring angles. Lessons 4-3, 4-4, and 4-5 were written to alleviate this problem. In Lesson 4-4, the student actually constructs and uses a nonstandard protractor and this activity leads naturally to measuring with a standard protractor.

# Lesson 4-1
# Length of Dot Paper Segments

## *Materials Needed:*

One copy of page 166 for each student.

One copy of page 167 for each student who understands square root notation.

One transparency of page 165.

## *Directions for the Teacher:*

This lesson has two parts. The first part is quite simple. The second part requires an understanding of the Pythagorean theorem, the concept of square root, and the related symbology. If your students do not know about these things, you will probably want to do only the first part of the lesson.

Place the transparency on the overhead projector and draw the following picture on the transparency.

Point out that the distance between two adjacent vertical dots is the same as the distance between two adjacent horizontal dots. Indicate that the distance between two such dots is 1 unit. Argue that $\overline{AB}$ is 3 units long. Similarly, draw the following picture on the transparency.

Argue that $\overline{CD}$ is 4 units long. If you are only planning to do the first part of the lesson, pass out only the first worksheet at this time.

If you are going to do both parts of the lesson, draw the following picture on the transparency.

Then complete the triangle as shown below.

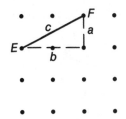

Point out that this is a right triangle and that is is appropriate to use the Pythagorean theorem. Then write

$c^2 = a^2 + b^2$
$c^2 = 1^2 + 2^2$
$c^2 = 1 + 4$
$c^2 = 5$
$c = \sqrt{5}$ or $\overline{EF}$ is $\sqrt{5}$ units long.

Draw the following picture and proceed as in the previous example to show *HI* is $\sqrt{13}$ units long.

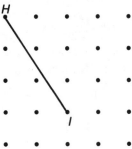

Now pass out both pages of the handout. Provide individual assistance to students as necessary.

## Correct Answers for Worksheet 4-1-1:

1. 2        2. 4        3. 4        4. 5        5. 7        6. 5

**Correct Answers for Worksheet 4-1-2:**

1. $\sqrt{8}$ or $2\sqrt{2}$

2. 5

3. $\sqrt{26}$

4. $\sqrt{34}$

(The answers for 5 and 6 may vary but here are two possibilities.)

5.

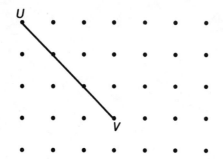

6.

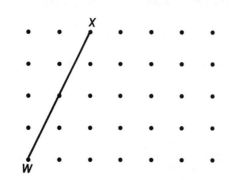

165

# WORKSHEET 4-1-1
## Length of Dot Paper Segments

Find the length of the segments pictured.

1.

$\overline{AB}$ is _____ units long.

2.

$\overline{CD}$ is _____ units long.

3.

$\overline{EF}$ is _____ units long.

4.

$\overline{GH}$ is _____ units long.

5.

$\overline{IJ}$ is _____ units long.

6.

$\overline{KL}$ is _____ units long.

*Visualized Geometry*

Name: _____ Date: _____

# WORKSHEET 4-1-2
## Length of Dot Paper Segments

Use the Pythagorean theorem to find the length of the segments pictured.

1.

$\overline{MN}$ is _____ units long.

2.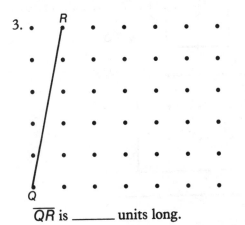

$\overline{OP}$ is _____ units long.

3.

$\overline{QR}$ is _____ units long.

4.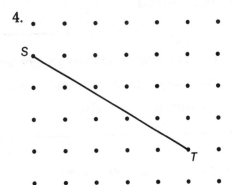

$\overline{ST}$ is _____ units long.

5. Draw a segment, $\overline{UV}$, that is $\sqrt{18}$ units long.

6. Draw a segment, $\overline{WX}$, that is $\sqrt{20}$ units long.

*Visualized Geometry*

## Lesson 4-2
# Perimeter

## *Materials Needed:*

One copy of each of the following pages for each student: pages 171 and 172.

One copy of page 173 for each student who understands square root notation.

One transparency of page 170.

## *Directions for the Teacher:*

Place the transparency on the overhead projector. Briefly review the concept of perimeter and with the students' help, find the perimeter of the three figures there (12, 10, and 16).

For those students who know about square root notation, distribute Worksheet 4-1-1 (pages 171–172) and Worksheet 4-1-2 (page 173). For less prepared students, pass out only the first worksheet. Provide individual assistance as needed.

## Correct Answers for Worksheet 4-2-1:

1. 12

2. 10

3. 16

4. 12

(There are a variety of possible correct answers for problems 5–8. Here are some possibilities.)

5.

6.

7.

8.

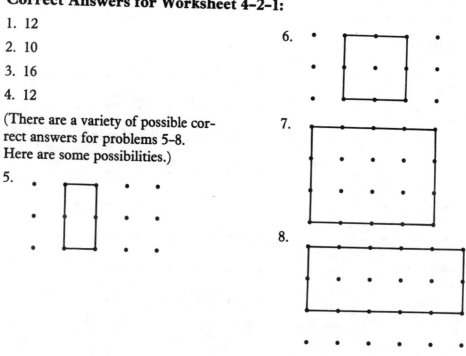

## Correct Answers for Worksheet 4-2-2:

1. $6\sqrt{5}$ or $2\sqrt{5} + 2\sqrt{20}$
2. $10\sqrt{2}$ or $2\sqrt{8} + 2\sqrt{18}$
3. $6 + 2\sqrt{5}$
4. $\sqrt{2} + \sqrt{13} + \sqrt{17}$

Here are possible answers for problems 5 and 6.

5.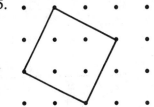

6.

(Problems 5 and 6 are very difficult.)

Find the perimeter.

1.

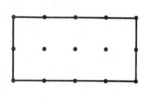

The perimeter is _____ units.

2.

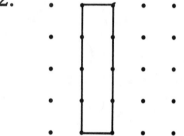

The perimeter is _____ units.

3.

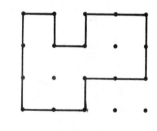

The perimeter is _____ units.

Name: _____  Date: _____

# WORKSHEET 4-2-1
## Perimeter

Find the perimeter of the figures pictured.

1.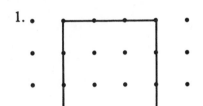

The perimeter is _____ units.

2.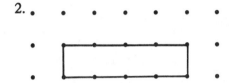

The perimeter is _____ units.

3.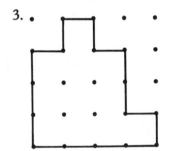

The perimeter is _____ units.

4.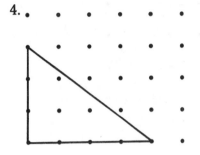

The perimeter is _____ units.

Draw a picture of a rectangle with the given perimeter.

5. Perimeter of 6 units

   •   •   •   •   •

   •   •   •   •   •

   •   •   •   •   •

6. Perimeter of 8 units

   •   •   •   •   •

   •   •   •   •   •

   •   •   •   •   •

*(continued)*

*Visualized Geometry*

# WORKSHEET 4-2-1
## Perimeter *(continued)*

7. Perimeter of 14 units

    •   •   •   •   •   •

    •   •   •   •   •   •

    •   •   •   •   •   •

    •   •   •   •   •   •

8. Perimeter of 14 units
   (Not congruent to your rectangle of problem 7.)

    •   •   •   •   •   •

    •   •   •   •   •   •

    •   •   •   •   •   •

    •   •   •   •   •   •

*Visualized Geometry*

## WORKSHEET 4-2-2
## Perimeter

Find the perimeter of the figures pictured.

1.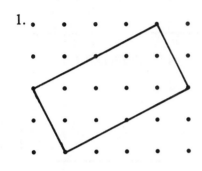

The perimeter is _____ units.

2.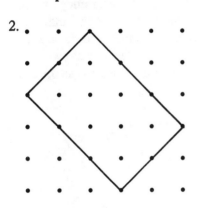

The perimeter is _____ units.

3.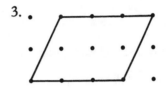

The perimeter is _____ units.

4.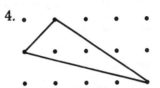

The perimeter is _____ units.

Draw a picture of a figure with the given conditions.

5. A square with perimeter $4\sqrt{5}$ units.

6. A triangle with perimeter $\sqrt{5} + \sqrt{10} + \sqrt{13}$ units.

# Lesson 4–3
# Measuring Angles with a Wedge

## Materials Needed:

One copy of each of the following pages for each student: **pages 177, 178, and 179.**

One copy of page 177 for yourself.

Several pairs of scissors.

One transparency of page 176.

## Directions for the Teacher:

Prior to class, cut out the wedge-shaped section labeled $x$. Place the transparency on the overhead projector and place piece $x$ on the transparency. Tell the students that the angle formed by the sides of this piece has measure 1 unit. Indicate we want to measure the angle on the transparency, in terms of the section labeled $x$. Place the piece labeled $x$ as shown below and outline it. Then move the piece up, outline it again, and repeat the process once more.

### Correct Answer for Transparency 4-3-1:

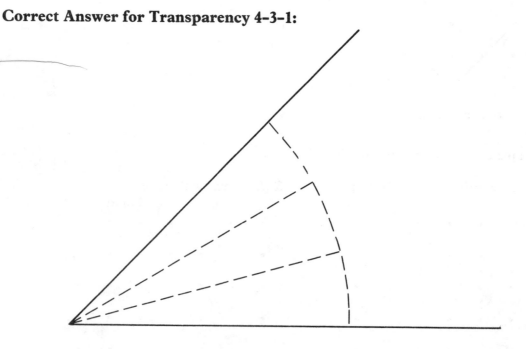

This diagram shows that the angle pictured on the transparency has measure 3 units.

Have the students cut out their wedge-shaped piece and use it to measure the angles pictured on the worksheets. They should keep the wedge-shaped piece and also the semicircle for the next lesson.

**Correct Answers for Worksheet 4-3-2:**

1. 2
2. 4
3. 3
4. 5
5. 7
6. 6

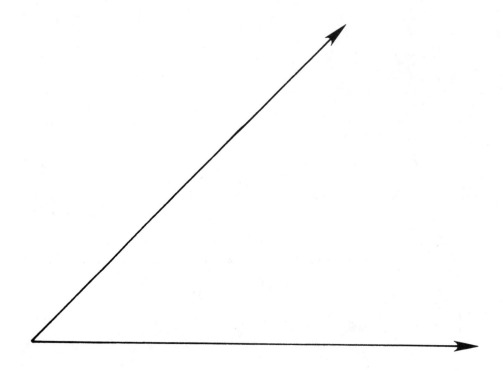

# WORKSHEET 4-3-1
## Measuring Angles with a Wedge

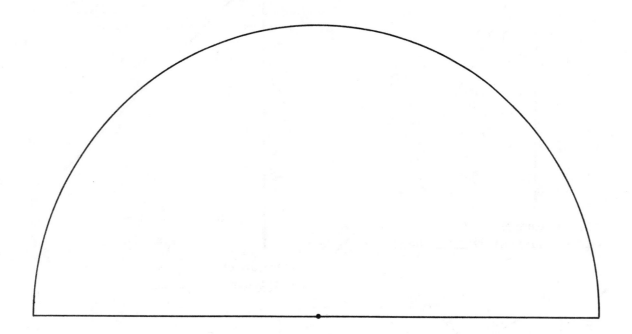

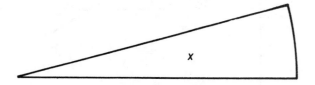

# WORKSHEET 4-3-2
## Measuring Angles with a Wedge

1.
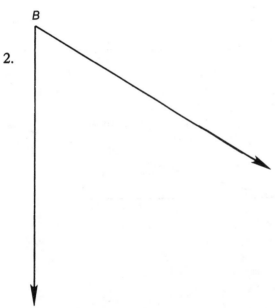

The measure of
∠A is approximately _____ units.

2.
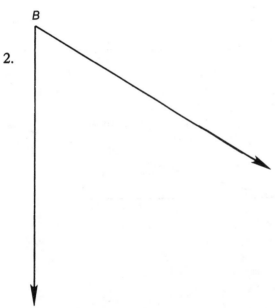

The measure of
∠B is approximately _____ units.

3.
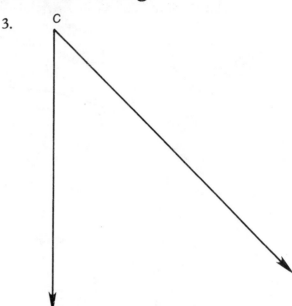

The measure of
∠C is approximately _____ units.

4.
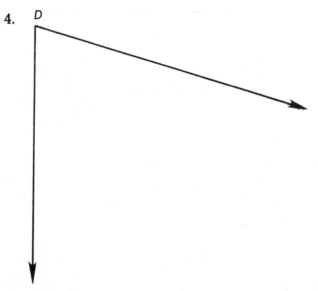

The measure of
∠D is approximately _____ units.

*(continued)*

         *Visualized Geometry*

# WORKSHEET 4-3-2
## Measuring Angles with a Wedge *(continued)*

5.                                              6.

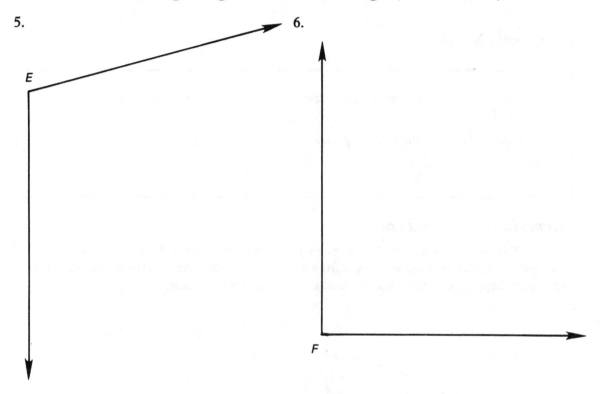

The measure of
∠*E* is approximately _____ units.

The measure of
∠*F* is approximately _____ units.

**Lesson 4–4**

# Making and Using a Nonstandard Protractor

## *Materials Needed:*

> Each student will need the wedge-shaped piece and the semicircle from Lesson 4–3 (page 177).
>
> One copy of each of the following pages for each student: pages 182 and 183.
>
> Several pairs of scissors.

## *Directions for the Teacher:*

In this lesson the students will be making their own protractor. Have them take the wedge-shaped piece and the semicircle from Lesson 4–3. Place the wedge-shaped piece on the semicircle and put a mark on the circumference as shown below.

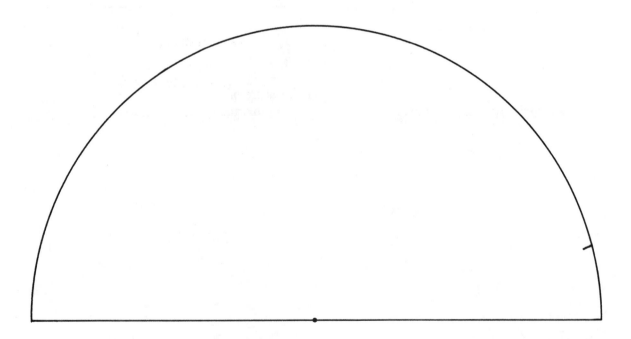

Pick up the piece and move it over, keeping the point at the center of the semicircle. Put another mark on the semicircle and continue around the semicircle. Then write numerals by the marks on the semicircle. The "protractor" should look like the following.

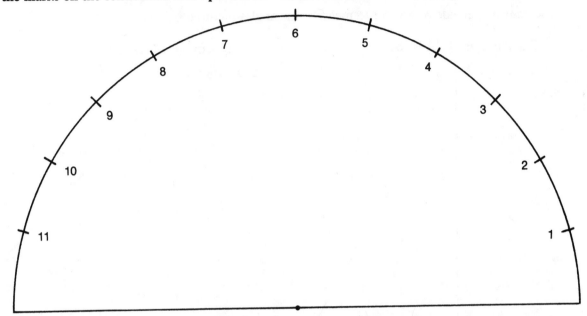

Have your students construct their protractors in a similar way. Pass out the worksheets and tell your students to use this protractor to measure the angles pictured.

## Correct Answers for Worksheet 4-4-1:

1. 2          2. 4          3. 3          4. 8

5a.                                                    b.

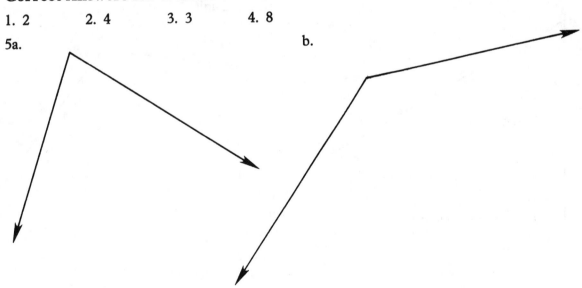

# WORKSHEET 4-4-1
## Making and Using a Nonstandard Protractor

Use your homemade protractor to measure the angles pictured below.

1. The measure of ∠A is about

_____ units.

3. The measure of ∠C is about

_____ units.

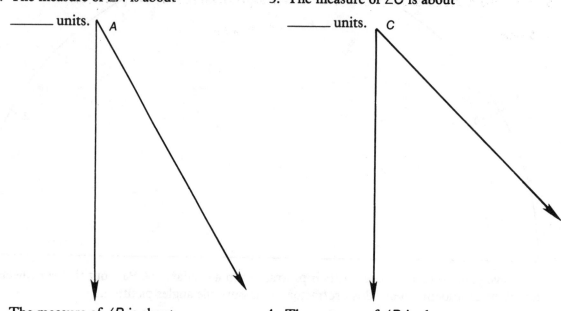

2. The measure of ∠B is about

_____ units.

4. The measure of ∠D is about

_____ units.

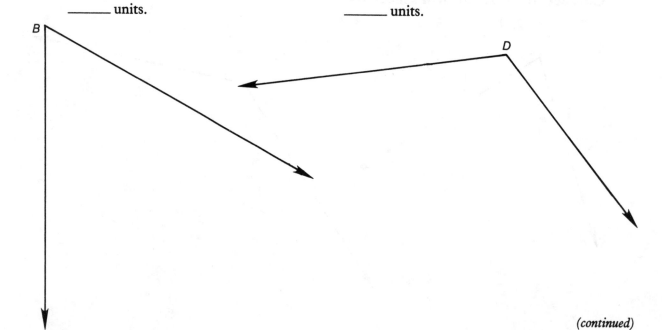

*(continued)*

# WORKSHEET 4–4–1
## Making and Using a Nonstandard Protractor
### *(continued)*

5. Use your homemade protractor to construct angles with the following measures.

a. 5 units

b. 9 units

## Lesson 4-5
# Using a Standard Protractor

### *Materials Needed:*

One copy of each of the following pages for each student: pages 185 and 186.

One standard protractor for each student.

### *Directions for the Teacher:*

Distribute the worksheets. Talk briefly about a standard protractor. Compare it to the homemade one students used in Lesson 4-4. Have them use their standard protractor to measure the angles. Answers may vary slightly.

### Probable Correct Answers for Worksheet 4-5-1:

1. 30°        2. 60°        3. 45°        4. 120°

5a.                                                                b.

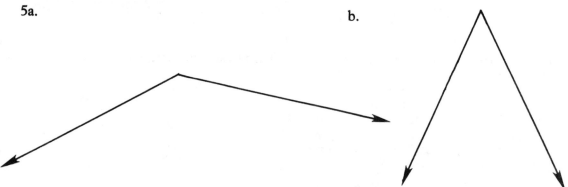

Name: _____   Date: _____

# WORKSHEET 4-5-1
## Using a Standard Protractor

Use a standard protractor to complete the following worksheet.

1. The measure of ∠A is about _____ .

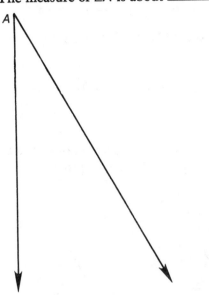

3. The measure of ∠C is about _____ .

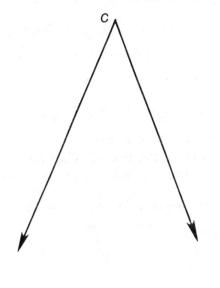

2. The measure of ∠B is about _____ .

4. The measure of ∠D is about _____ .

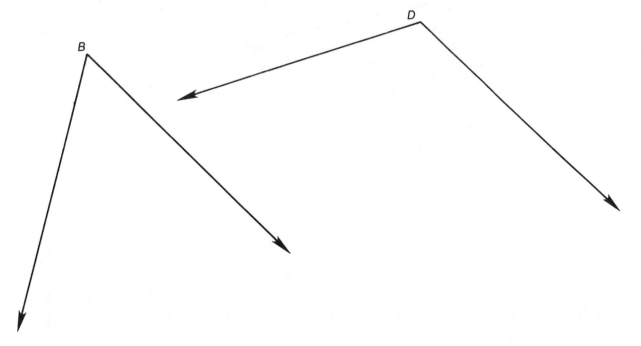

*(continued)*

*Visualized Geometry*

# WORKSHEET 4-5-1
## Using a Standard Protractor (continued)

5. Use a standard protractor to construct angles with the following measures.

    a. 140°                                        b. 50°

## Lesson 4-6
# General Concepts of Area

## *Materials Needed:*

One copy of page 189 for each student.

One transparency of page 188.

## *Directions for the Teacher:*

Place the transparency on the overhead projector. Direct the students' attention to problem 1. Indicate that area refers to the number of specified squares it takes to cover up a given region. Draw in dotted lines as shown and count as shown

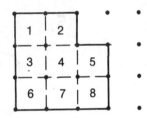

and write 8 in the blank. Do problems 2 (answer 9 square units) and 3 (answer 10 square units) in a similar way. Put dotted lines in for problem 4 as shown.

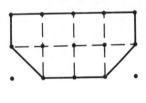

Point out that the area is 7 square units (from 6 complete squares and two half squares). Put dotted lines in for problem 5. Then with students' help, estimate the area (about 7 or 8 square units).

Distribute the worksheet. Provide individual assistance as needed. Students may find problem 6 a little hard.

## Correct Answers for Worksheet 4-6-1:

| | | |
|---|---|---|
| 1. 8 | 4. 7 | 7. About 11 or 12 |
| 2. 7 | 5. 8 | |
| 3. 10 | 6. 6 | |

Find the area.

1.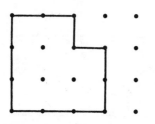

The area is _____
square units.

2.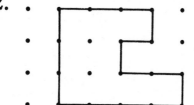

The area is _____
square units.

3.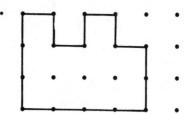

The area is _____
square units.

4.

The area is _____
square units.

Estimate the area.

5.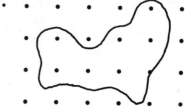

The area is approximately
_____ square units.

     *Visualized Geometry*

Name: _____  Date: _____

# WORKSHEET 4-6-1
## General Concepts of Area

Find the area.

1.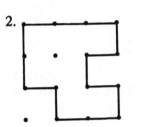

The area is _____
square units.

2.

The area is _____
square units.

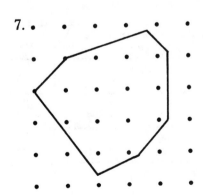

3.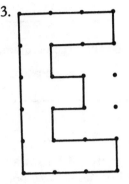

The area is _____
square units.

4.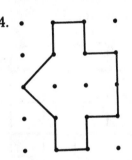

The area is _____
square units.

5.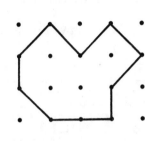

The area is _____
square units.

6.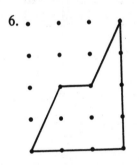

The area is _____
square units.

Estimate the area.

7.

The area is approximately _____ square units.

# Lesson 4-7
# Area of Squares and Rectangles

## *Materials Needed:*

One copy of each of the following pages for each student: pages 196 and 197.

One transparency of each of the following pages: pages 193, 194, and 195.

## *Directions for the Teacher:*

In this lesson area formulas will be developed for rectangles and squares. The students probably already "know" these formulas but perhaps do not understand them.

Place the first transparency on the overhead projector and direct the students' attention to problem 1. Place the third transparency (grid) on the first one so that the area of this rectangle can be found. A partial picture of this follows.

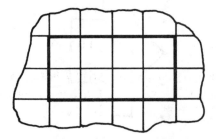

Ask how many small squares it takes to cover up the rectangle. They should, of course, say "eight." Emphasize that area usually refers to the number of small squares it takes to cover a given region. Proceed with problems 2, 3, and 4 in a similar way. Then direct students' attention to problem 5. Complete the area column. Then examine the other two columns. The grid may be needed for these figures. This table then should look like this:

|  | Length of one side | Length of another side (adjacent) | Area |
|---|---|---|---|
| Rectangle from problem 1 | 2 | 4 | 8 |
| Rectangle from problem 2 | 4 | 3 | 12 |
| Rectangle from problem 3 | 2 | 5 | 10 |
| Rectangle from problem 4 | 6 | 1 | 6 |
| Arbitrary rectangle |  |  |  |

Of course in the first line you might have 4 followed by 2 instead of what is there. The same thing might happen in the other rows. Now write *l* in the left column of the bottom row and *w* in the center column. Tell your students that it is common to call the length of one side of a rectangle its length and to denote it by "*l*" and to call the length of another side (adjacent) the width and to denote it by "*w*." Now ask them what should go in the third column. They should respond *lw*. Then write the formula

$$A = lw$$

on your transparency. Emphasize that this formula gives you the number of square units it takes to cover up the rectangle.

Next, place the second transparency on the overhead projector. Indicate that the quadrilateral pictured is a square. Tell them that it is common to use "*s*" to denote the length of each side of a square. Remind them that a square is a special kind of rectangle so the area formula for rectangles carries over to squares. Under the square, write

$$A = lw$$

and emphasize that this is the rectangle area formula. Tell them that in the case of a square, $l = s$ and $w = s$. Then write the formula

$$A = s^2$$

and emphasize that this is the area formula for a square.

Pass out a copy of worksheet pages 196 and 197 to each student. Emphasize that now it is appropriate to use area formulas. Assist students as is necessary. Question 10 is very difficult.

## Correct Answers for Worksheet 4-7-1:

1. 15
2. 16
3. 35
4. 49
5. 21
6. 36

(For problems 7–10 a variety of answers are possible. One correct answer is given in each case.)

7.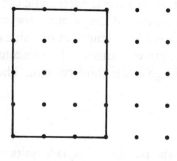

8.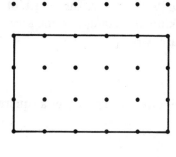

9.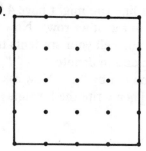

10.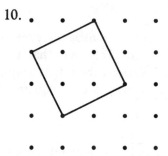

# Transparency 4-7-1

Find the area of the rectangles.

1.

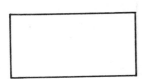

The area is _____ square units.

3.

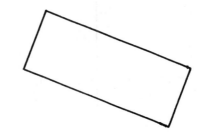

The area is _____ square units.

2.

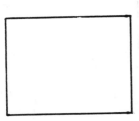

The area is _____ square units.

4.

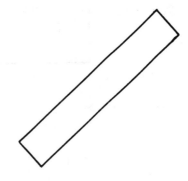

The area is _____ square units.

5. Complete the table below.

| | Length of one side | Length of another side (adjacent) | Area |
|---|---|---|---|
| Rectangle from problem 1 | | | |
| Rectangle from problem 2 | | | |
| Rectangle from problem 3 | | | |
| Rectangle from problem 4 | | | |
| Arbitrary rectangle | | | |

*Visualized Geometry*

# Transparency 4-7-3

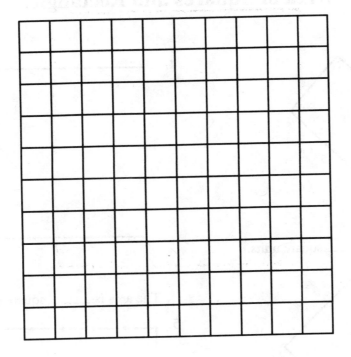

# WORKSHEET 4-7-1
## Area of Squares and Rectangles

Find the area.

1.

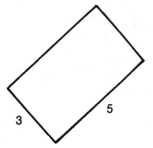

The area is _____ square units.

2.

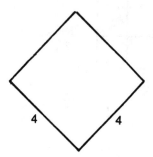

The area is _____ square units.

3.

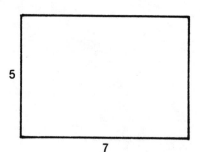

The area is _____ square units.

4.

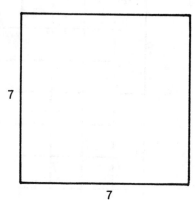

The area is _____ square units.

5.

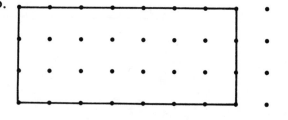

The area is _____ square units.

6.

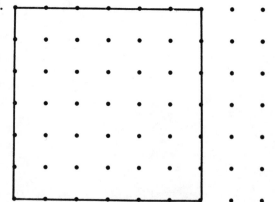

The area is _____ square units.

*(continued)*

*Visualized Geometry*

Name: _____    Date: _____

# WORKSHEET 4-7-1
## Area of Squares and Rectangles (*continued*)

7. Draw a picture of a rectangle with area 12 square units.

. . . . . .
. . . . . .
. . . . . .
. . . . . .
. . . . . .
. . . . . .

8. Draw a picture of a rectangle with area 15 square units.

. . . . . .
. . . . . .
. . . . . .
. . . . . .
. . . . . .
. . . . . .

9. Draw a picture of a rectangle with area 16 square units.

. . . . .
. . . . .
. . . . .
. . . . .
. . . . .

10. Draw a picture of a rectangle with area 5 square units.

. . . . .
. . . . .
. . . . .
. . . . .
. . . . .

*Visualized Geometry*

## Lesson 4–8
# Area and Perimeter of Rectangles

## *Materials Needed:*

One copy of page 200 for each student.

## *Directions for the Teacher:*

Distribute the worksheet. Provide individual assistance as needed. When the students complete the worksheet, point out that it is possible to have two rectangles with the same perimeter but different areas and two rectangles with the same area but different perimeters.

### Correct Answers for Worksheet 4–8–1:

1.

3.

2.

4.

5.

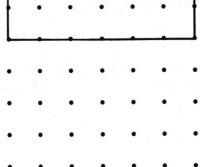

6.

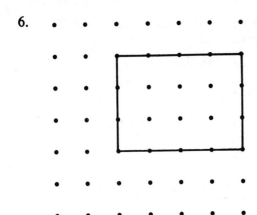

Name: _____   Date: _____

# WORKSHEET 4-8-1
## Area and Perimeter of Rectangles

Draw a rectangle with the given area and perimeter.

1. Perimeter of 12 units and area of 8 square units.

2. Perimeter of 12 units and area of 5 square units.

3. Perimeter of 10 units and area of 6 square units.

4. Perimeter of 10 units and area of 4 square units.

5. Perimeter of 16 units and area of 12 square units.

6. Perimeter of 14 units and area of 12 square units.

*Visualized Geometry*

# Lesson 4–9
# Area of Parallelograms I

## *Materials Needed:*

One copy of page 205 for each student.

One copy of page 203 for yourself.

One transparency of page 204 for each student.

## *Directions for the Teacher:*

You may want to review the topic of altitudes of parallelograms (Lesson 3–11) prior to teaching this lesson. The purpose of this lesson is to motivate the development of the area formula for parallelograms, so this lesson should be taught on one day and Lesson 4–10 should be taught on another day. Prior to class cut out the parallelogram from page 203. Begin class by showing the students the cut-out parallelogram. Ask them what kind of a figure it is. Tell them the concern is with finding a method of determining the areas of parallelograms. Indicate that $\overline{AB}$ has arbitrarily been called the base. Point out that $\overline{DE}$ is perpendicular to $\overline{AB}$ and that $\overline{DE}$ is called an altitude to that base. As the students watch, cut along $\overline{DE}$. Take the triangular piece and put it together with the other piece as shown below.

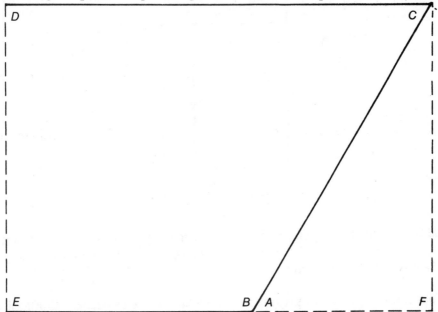

Ask them what kind of a figure this is. Then remind them they already know how to find the area of a rectangle.

Next place the transparency on the overhead projector. Direct their attention to parallelogram *ABCD*. Tell them to call $\overline{AB}$ the base. Draw in segment $\overline{DE}$ so that $\overline{DE}$ is perpendicular to $\overline{AB}$. Point out that $\overline{DE}$ is an altitude to $\overline{AB}$. Draw $\triangle CFB$ as shown below.

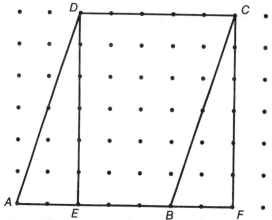

Mention that $\triangle ADE$ is congruent to $\triangle BCF$. Tell them to "mentally" cut off $\triangle ADE$ and place it on $\triangle BCF$. Point out that the "new" figure is a rectangle and its area is 30 square units (5 · 6). Argue that this rectangle has the same area as the original parallelogram. Conclude that the area of the original parallelogram is 30 square units.

Now direct their attention to parallelogram *GHIJ*. Tell them to call $\overline{JG}$ the base. Draw in $\overline{IK}$ (pictured below) and indicate this is an altitude to $\overline{JG}$. Also draw in $\triangle GHL$.

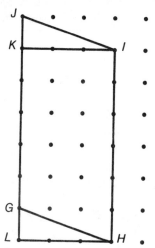

Argue that the area of rectangle *LHIK* is the same as the area of parallelogram *GHIJ*. Find the area of the rectangle (18 square units) and conclude that the area of the original parallelogram is also 18 square units.

Pass out the worksheet and provide individual assistance as needed. Emphasize that students are to find areas in a manner similar to the one used in class. **Do not allow them to use a formula.**

**Correct Answers for Worksheet 4–9–1:**

1. 21          2. 12          3. 30          4. 9          5. 12

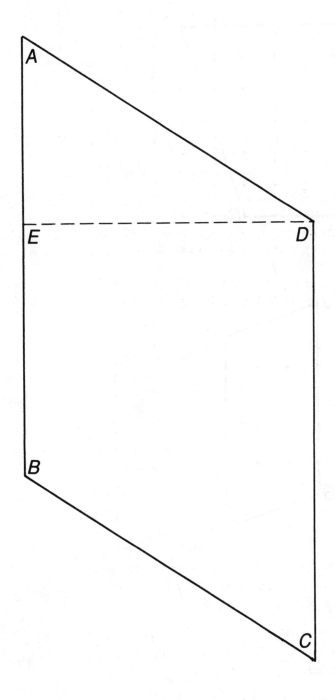

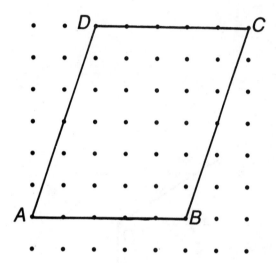

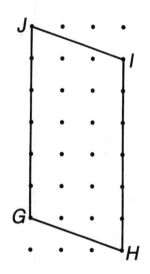

*Visualized Geometry*

# WORKSHEET 4-9-1
## Area of Parallelograms I

Find the area of each parallelogram using the method described in class.

1.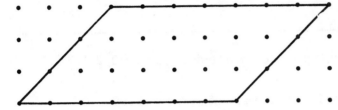

The area is _____ square units.

2.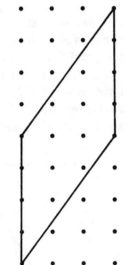

The area is _____ square units.

4.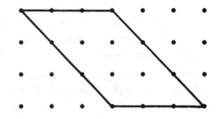

The area is _____ square units.

3.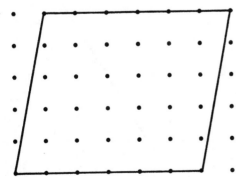

The area is _____ square units.

5.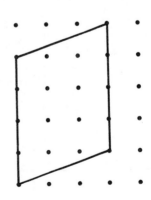

The area is _____ square units.

## Lesson 4–10
# Area of Parallelograms II

### *Materials Needed:*

One copy of each of the following pages for each student: pages 210, 211, 212, and 213.

One transparency of each of the following pages: pages 208 and 209

### *Directions for the Teacher:*

Place the first transparency on the overhead projector. Point out that quadrilateral *ABCD* is a parallelogram. Tell students you want to find a formula for the area of a parallelogram. Indicate that it is common to start by classifying one side as the base, and that in this case we choose $\overline{AB}$ as the base. Below the parallelogram write "*AB = b*" and tell them to let the length of the base be *b*. Draw a segment from *D* to the dot on $\overline{AB}$. Label that dot *E*, indicate that $\overline{DE}$ is perpendicular to $\overline{AB}$ and that $\overline{DE}$ is called an altitude. Below the parallelogram write "$\overline{DE} = h$." Next draw a segment from *C* to the dot directly beneath *C*. Label that dot *F* and draw $\overline{FB}$. Here is what the transparency should look like.

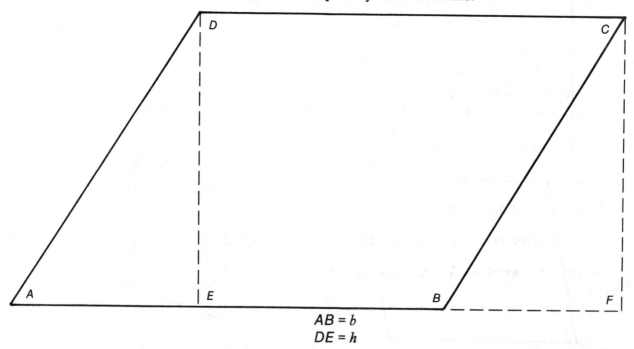

$$AB = b$$
$$DE = h$$

Now argue that $\triangle ADE$ is congruent to $\triangle BCF$ which means that quadrilateral $EFCD$ is a rectangle and parallelogram $ABCD$ has the same area as rectangle $EFCD$. Now write the following statements on your overhead projector and justify them as you go.

$$AB = EF$$
**The area of rectangle $EFCD$ is $EF \cdot DE$.**
**The area of rectangle $EFCD$ is $bh$.**
**The area of parallelogram $ABCD$ is $bh$.**

Finally write the following:
**The area formula for a parallelogram is**
$$A = bh$$

where $b$ is the length of a base and $h$ is the length of an altitude to that base. Mention that in this case, $A$ stands for the area and is not the name of a point.

Place the second transparency on the projector. In each case find the area of the parallelogram. For problem I write

$$A = bh$$
$$= 13 \cdot 8$$
$$= 104.$$

Then write 104 in the blank. In this case, emphasize that $b = 13$ and $h = 8$ and that the side of length 10 is not involved in the formula. For problem II write

$$A = bh$$
$$= 10 \cdot 12$$
$$= 120.$$

Then write 120 in the blank. For problem III, call the bottom side the base and show that its length is 4. Draw an altitude to that base and show that its length is 3. Then write

$$A = bh$$
$$= 4 \cdot 3$$
$$= 12.$$

Then write 12 in the blank.

Pass out the worksheets. Provide individual assistance as needed.

## Correct Answers for Worksheet 4–10–1:

1. 84
2. 100
3. 70
4. 196

5. 6
6. 12
7. 18
8. 4

There are several correct answers for problems 9–12.

# Transparency 4–10–1

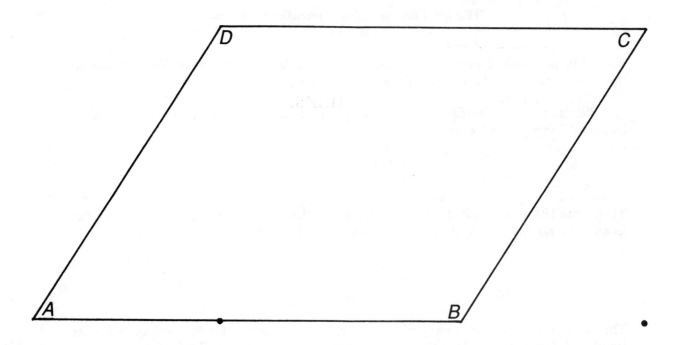

*Visualized Geometry*

# Find the area of the parallelograms pictured below.

I.

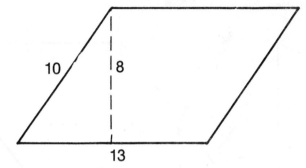

The area is _____ square units.

II.

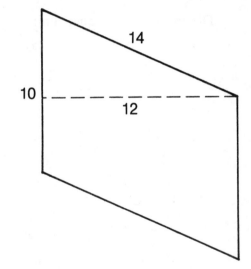

The area is _____ square units.

III.

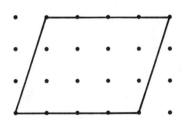

The area is _____ square units.

*Visualized Geometry*

# WORKSHEET 4-10-1
## Area of Parallelograms II

Find the area of the parallelograms pictured.

1.

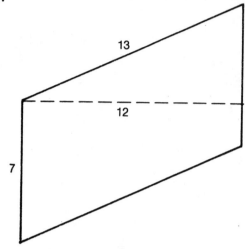

The area is _____ square units.

3.

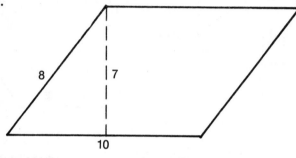

The area is _____ square units.

2.

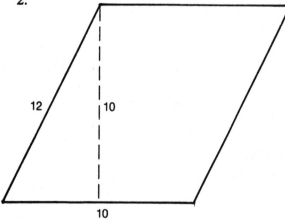

The area is _____ square units.

(continued)

# WORKSHEET 4-10-1
## Area of Parallelograms II *(continued)*

4.

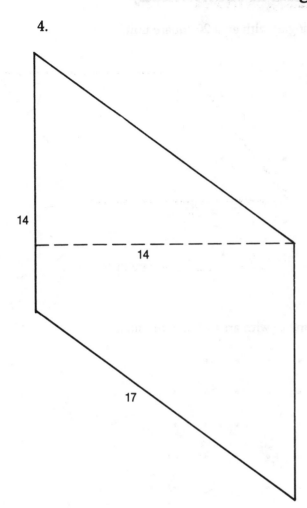

14

14

17

The area is _____ square units.

5.

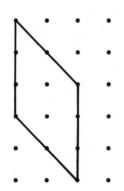

The area is
_____ square units.

6.

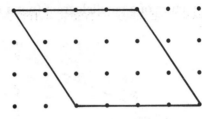

The area is _____ square units.

7.

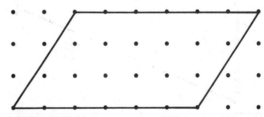

The area is _____ square units.

8.

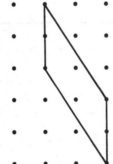

The area is _____ square units.

*(continued)*

*Visualized Geometry*

# WORKSHEET 4-10-1
## Area of Parallelograms II *(continued)*

9. Draw a picture of a parallelogram (not a rectangle) with area 20 square units.

10. Draw a picture of a parallelogram (not a rectangle) with area 24 square units.

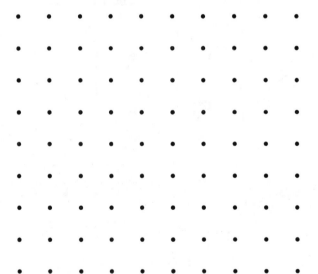

*(continued)*

             *Visualized Geometry*

Name: _____  Date: _____

# WORKSHEET 4-10-1
## Area of Parallelograms II (continued)

11.

Draw a picture of a parallelogram (not a rectangle) with area 40 square units.

12.

Draw a picture of a parallelogram (not a rectangle) with area 48 square units.

# Lesson 4-11
# Area of Triangles I

## *Materials Needed:*

One copy of page 220 for each student.

One copy of page 217 for yourself.

One transparency of each of the following pages: pages 218 and 219.

## *Directions for the Teacher:*

The purpose of this lesson is to motivate the area formula for triangles, so this lesson should be taught on one day and Lesson 4-12 should be taught on another day. Prior to class, cut out the two triangles on your copy of page 217. Begin class by showing these triangles to the students. Illustrate that the triangles are congruent by showing that one triangle will "match" (cover up) the other one. Then place the triangles together as shown below. (You may want to show this on an overhead projector if your class is large.)

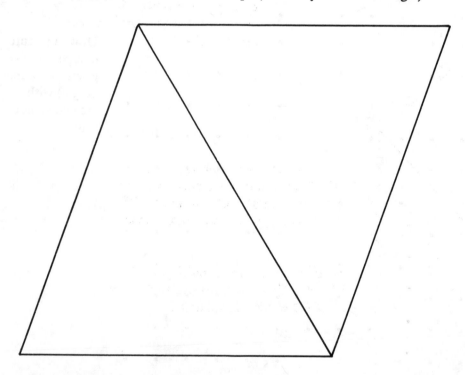

Ask the students what kind of figure is formed (parallelogram). Argue that you could find the area of one triangle by taking one half of the area of the parallelogram.

Put the first transparency on the overhead projector. Tell the students that you want to find the area of each triangle pictured but this will be done in a special way. Direct their attention to △*ABC*. Tell them that you want to draw a segment $\overline{BD}$ which

a. has *B* as one endpoint

b. is parallel to $\overline{AC}$ and

c. is congruent to $\overline{AC}$.

Draw such a segment in (to the right of point *B*), label the endpoint of this segment *D*, and draw segment $\overline{DC}$. The transparency should look as follows.

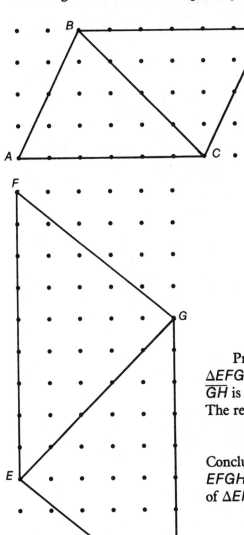

Now point out that quadrilateral *ABDC* is a parallelogram. Classify $\overline{AC}$ as the base of that parallelogram and draw an altitude from *B* to $\overline{AC}$. Point out that this segment is an altitude of both the parallelogram and the original triangle. With their help, find the area of this parallelogram (24 square units). Argue that △*ABC* and △*DCB* have the same area (they are congruent). Thus, conclude that the area of △*ABC* is one half of the parallelogram so its area is 12 square units.

Proceed in a similar way with △*EFG*. This time find a point *H* so that $\overline{GH}$ is congruent to and parallel to $\overline{FE}$. The resulting picture will look as follows.

Conclude the area of parallelogram *EFGH* is 45 square units and so the area of △*EFG* is 22 $\frac{1}{2}$ square units.

Place the second transparency on the overhead projector. With problem 3, the resulting figure includes a rectangle.

The area of the parallelogram (rectangle) is 8 square units so the area of the triangle is 4 square units.

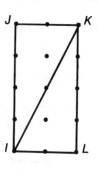

Proceed in a similar way with $\triangle MNO$. The area of the parallelogram is 8 square units and the area of $\triangle MNO$ is 4 square units.

Distribute the worksheets. Point out that students are to draw a segment parallel and congruent to one of the existing sides. When they do this appropriately they will get a parallelogram and it will be easy to get the area of the triangle from the area of the parallelogram. Provide individual assistance as needed.

## Correct Answers for Worksheet 4-11-1:

1a. 9        3a. 18        5a. 6

  b. $4\frac{1}{2}$       b. 9         b. 3

2a. 15       4a. 6

  b. $7\frac{1}{2}$       b. 3

# Lesson 4–11
## Teacher Copy Page

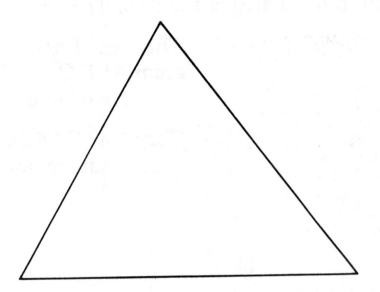

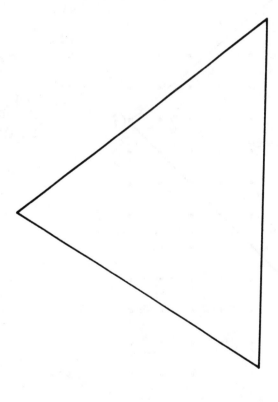

217

*Visualized Geometry*

Construct an appropriate parallelogram. Find the area of the parallelogram and then find the area of the triangle.

1.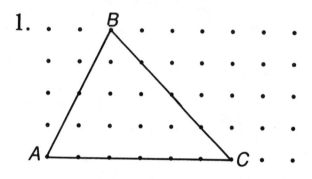

   a. The area of parallelogram *ABDC* is
     _____ square units.

   b. The area of △*ABC* is
     _____ square units.

2.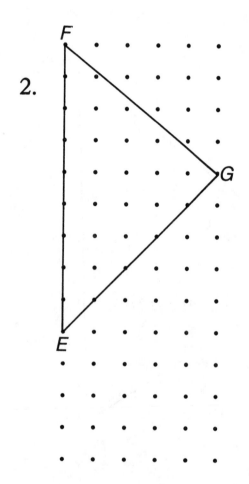

   a. The area of parallelogram *EFGH* is _____ square units.

   b. The area of △*EFG* is _____ square units.

*Visualized Geometry*

3.

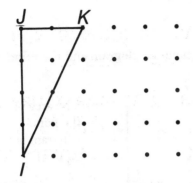

a. The area of parallelogram *IJKL* is _____ square units.

b. The area of △*IJK* is _____ square units.

4.

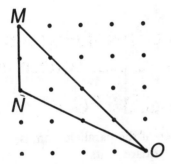

a. The area of parallelogram *MNOP* is _____ square units.

b. The area of △*MNO* is _____ square units.

*Visualized Geometry*

# WORKSHEET 4-11-1
## Area of Triangles I

Construct an appropriate parallelogram, find the area of the parallelogram and then find the area of the triangle.

1.

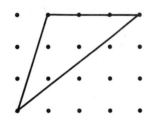

   a. The area of the parallelogram is _____ square units.

   b. The area of the triangle is _____ square units.

2.

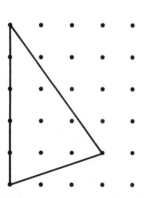

   a. The area of the parallelogram is _____ square units.

   b. The area of the triangle is _____ square units.

3.

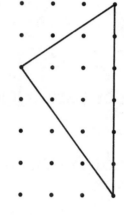

   a. The area of the parallelogram is _____ square units.

   b. The area of the triangle is _____ square units.

4.

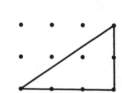

   a. The area of the parallelogram is _____ square units.

   b. The area of the triangle is _____ square units.

5.

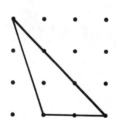

   a. The area of the parallelogram is _____ square units.

   b. The area of the triangle is _____ square units.

*Visualized Geometry*

# Lesson 4–12
# Area of Triangles II

## *Materials Needed:*

One copy of each of the following pages for each student: pages 227 and 228.

One transparency of each of the following pages: pages 225 and 226.

## *Directions for the Teacher:*

Briefly review the topic of altitudes of triangles (Lesson 2–4) and the area formula for parallelograms. Put the first transparency on the overhead projector. With an index card construct the altitude from $B$ to $\overline{AC}$ for $\triangle ABC$. Label the other endpoint of this altitude $D$. Draw in $\overline{BE}$ and $\overline{EC}$. The transparency should look as follows.

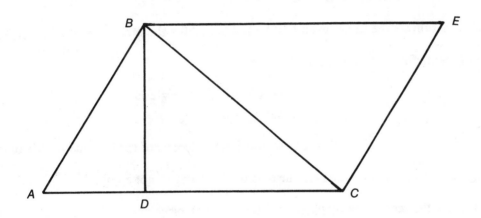

Tell the students that $\overline{BE}$ is parallel to and congruent to $\overline{AC}$. Point out that quadrilateral $ABEC$ is a parallelogram and that the area of $\triangle ABC$ is one half of the area of this parallelogram. Next write "$\overline{AC} = b$" and "$BD = h$." Emphasize that in terms of the parallelogram $\overline{AC}$ is a base and $\overline{BD}$ is an altitude to that base. Next write the following.

**The area of the parallelogram *ABEC* is *bh*.**

**The area of $\triangle ABC$ is $\frac{1}{2}$ *bh*.**

Proceed with $\triangle FGH$ in a similar way. Draw in altitude $\overline{GI}$ and draw segments $\overline{GJ}$ and $\overline{JH}$. The transparency should look as follows.

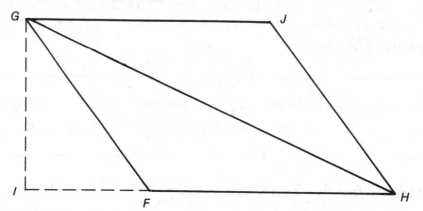

Write "$FI = b$" and "$GI = h$." Argue that quadrilateral $FGJH$ is a parallelogram and that the area of $\triangle FGH$ is one half of the area of the parallelogram. Then write

**The area of the parallelogram *FGJH* is *bh*.**
**The area of $\triangle$*FGH* is $\frac{1}{2}$ *bh*.**

Emphasize that this is the same result that was obtained for the other triangle.

Finally write the following on the transparency.

**The area formula for a triangle is**
$$A = \tfrac{1}{2}\,bh$$

where $b$ is the length of a side called a base and $h$ is the length of the altitude to that base.

Mention that in this case $A$ stands for the area of the triangle, not a point.

Now place the second transparency on the overhead projector. Indicate that to use the formula just developed, the following steps are to be executed.

a. Classify one side of the triangle as a base,
b. find the length of this base and call it $b$,
c. find an altitude to that base,
d. find the length of this altitude and call it $h$, and
e. apply the formula $A = \frac{1}{2} bh$.

Direct students' attention to the first problem. Classify $\overline{AC}$ as a base and $\overline{BD}$ as the altitude to that base. Note that $AC = 11$ and $BD = 8$. Write

$$A = \tfrac{1}{2} bh$$
$$= \tfrac{1}{2} \cdot 11 \cdot 8$$
$$= 44.$$

Write "44" in the blank. For problem 2, indicate that an altitude must be drawn.

Classify $\overline{EG}$ as a base. Draw in $\overline{FH}$ as shown below and indicate that this segment is the altitude to that base. With student help, conclude that $b = 2$, $h = 3$ and $A = \frac{1}{2} \cdot 2 \cdot 3 = 3$, and write "3" in the blank.

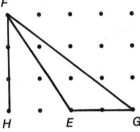

For problems 3, 4, and 5, a base must be determined. Then altitudes (shown below) should be drawn in before the area can be calculated.

3.

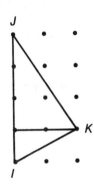

$A = \frac{1}{2} bh$

$= \frac{1}{2} \cdot 4 \cdot 2$

$= 4.$

The area of $\triangle IJK$ is <u>4</u> square units.

5.

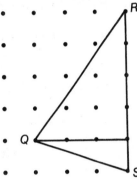

$A = \frac{1}{2} bh$

$= \frac{1}{2} \cdot 5 \cdot 3$

$= \frac{15}{2}.$

The area of $\triangle QRS$ is $7\frac{1}{2}$ square units.

4.

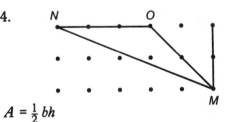

$A = \frac{1}{2} bh$

$= \frac{1}{2} \cdot 3 \cdot 2$

$= 3.$

The area of $\triangle MNO$ is <u>3</u> square units.

6. Identify $\overline{UW}$ as a base. Then the altitude to that base is $\overline{VU}$. In this case a side of the triangle is an altitude to another side of the triangle.

$A = \frac{1}{2} bh$

$= \frac{1}{2} \cdot 2 \cdot 3$

$= 3.$

The area of $\triangle UVW$ is <u>3</u> square units.

Distribute the worksheets. Provide individual assistance as needed.

**Correct Answers for Worksheet 4-12-1:**

1. $22 \frac{1}{2}$

2. $32 \frac{1}{2}$

3. 4

4. 6

5. 12

6. $7 \frac{1}{2}$

7. 6 (all parts)

There are several correct answers for problems 8–11.

# Transparency 4–12–1

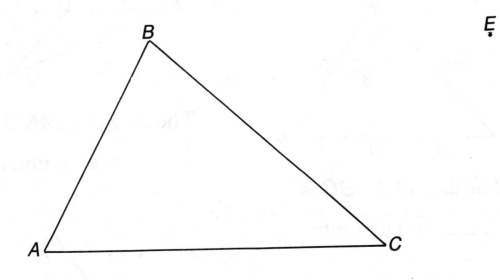

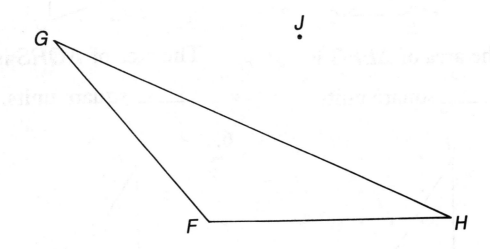

225

# Find the area of the triangle.

1.

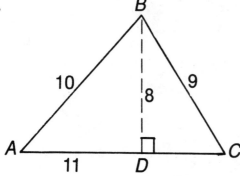

The area of △ABC is

_____ square units.

2.

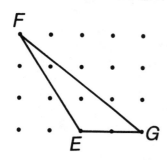

The area of △EFG is

_____ square units.

3.

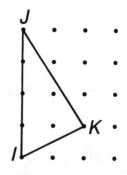

The area of △IJK is

_____ square units.

4.

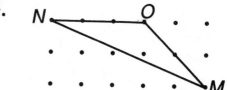

The area of △MNO is

_____ square units.

5.

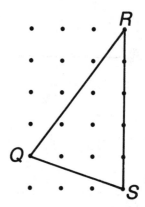

The area of △QRS is

_____ square units.

6.

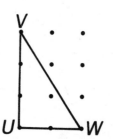

The area of △UVW is

_____ square units.

     *Visualized Geometry*

Name: _____  Date: _____

# WORKSHEET 4-12-1
## Area of Triangles II

Find the area.

1.

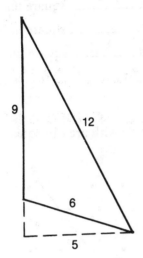

The area is _____ square units.

2.

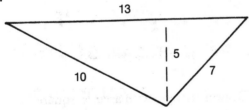

The area is _____ square units.

3.

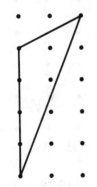

The area is _____ square units.

4.

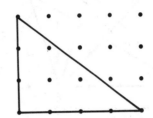

The area is _____ square units.

5.

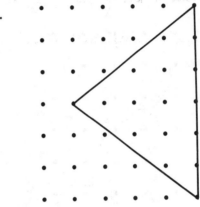

The area is _____ square units.

6.

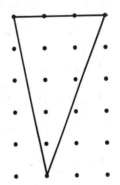

The area is _____ square units.

*(continued)*

*Visualized Geometry*

# WORKSHEET 4-12-1
## Area of Triangles II (continued)

7.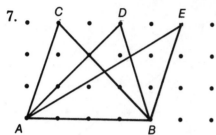

The area of $\triangle ABC$ is _____ square units.

The area of $\triangle ABD$ is _____ square units.

The area of $\triangle ABE$ is _____ square units.

8. Draw a triangle with area 5 square units.

10. Draw a triangle with area 10 square units.

9. Draw a triangle with area 6 square units.

11. Draw a triangle with area $\frac{15}{2}$ square units.

*Visualized Geometry*

## Lesson 4-13
# Area of Trapezoids I

## *Materials Needed:*

One copy of page 233 for each student.

One copy of page 231 for yourself.

One transparency of page 232.

## *Directions for the Teacher:*

Prior to class cut out the two trapezoids that are on page 231. Begin the class by placing the trapezoids on top of each other. Mention that this shows that the trapezoids are congruent. Place one trapezoid next to the other so they look like the following.

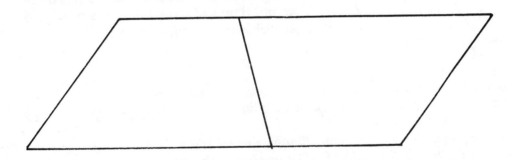

Mention that the large quadrilateral is a parallelogram.

Next, place the transparency on the overhead projector and direct your students' attention to problem 1. With their assistance, find the length of $\overline{AD}$ (6 units). Then find the point six units to the right of $C$ and label it $E$. Draw $\overline{CE}$ and mention that $\overline{CE} \cong \overline{AD}$. Find the length of $\overline{BC}$ (3 units); find the point three units to the right of $D$ and label it $F$. Draw segments $\overline{DF}$ and $\overline{EF}$. Mention that $\overline{DF} \cong \overline{BC}$. This is what the picture should look like.

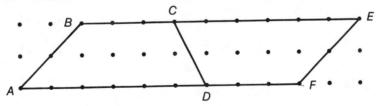

Now ask the students to examine trapezoid $ABCD$ and trapezoid $EFDC$. They should conclude that these trapezoids are congruent. If they cannot see that, use a blank transparency to trace trapezoid $ABCD$ and place it on top of trapezoid $EFDC$ so that corresponding parts match. Indicate that quadrilateral $ABEF$ is a parallelogram with area 18 square units (using the area formula for a parallelogram). Then argue that

$$\text{area trapezoid } ABCD = \tfrac{1}{2} \text{ (area parallelogram } ABEF)$$

$$= \tfrac{1}{2} \cdot 18$$

$$= 9.$$

Notice that as long as $E$ is on $\overrightarrow{BC}$ so $CE = AD$ and $F$ is on $\overrightarrow{AD}$ so that $DF = BC$, two things will happen:

- trapezoid $ABCD \cong$ trapezoid $EFDC$ and

- quadrilateral $ABEF$ is a parallelogram.

    Proceed with problem 2 as in problem 1. Find a point $E$ to the right of $C$ so that $\overline{CE} \cong \overline{AD}$, and a point $F$ to the right of $D$ so that $\overline{DF} \cong \overline{BC}$. Draw segments $\overline{CE}$, $\overline{EF}$, and $\overline{DF}$.

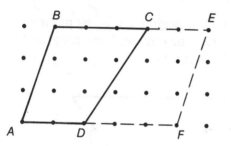

Argue that trapezoid $ABCD \cong EFDC$ and that quadrilateral $ABEF$ is a parallelogram. Calculate the area of this parallelogram (15 square units) and conclude that the area of the original trapezoid is one half of the area of the parallelogram ($7\frac{1}{2}$ square units).

    Proceed in a similar way with problem 3. This time point $E$ is selected below $C$ and point $F$ is selected below point $D$.

Calculate the area of the parallelogram (20 square units) and conclude that the area of trapezoid $ABCD$ is one half of the area of the parallelogram (10 square units).

    Distribute the student worksheets and provide individual assistance as needed.

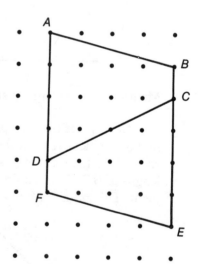

## Correct Answers for Worksheet 4–13–1:

| 1a. | 18 | 3a. | 21 | 5a. | 18 |
|---|---|---|---|---|---|
| b. | 9 | b. | $10\frac{1}{2}$ | b. | 9 |
| 2a. | 5 | | | | |
| b. | $2\frac{1}{2}$ | 4a. | 6 | | |
| | | b. | 3 | | |

# Lesson 4–13
## Teacher Copy Page

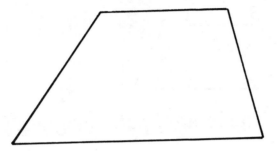

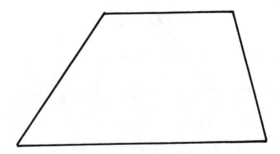

*Visualized Geometry*

Find the area of trapezoid *ABCD* by first constructing an appropriate parallelogram, then finding the area of that parallelogram, and finally using the area of the parallelogram to find the area of the trapezoid.

1.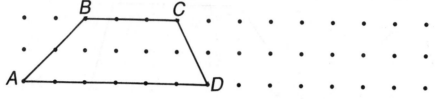

    a.  The area of the related parallelogram is _____ square units.

    b.  The area of trapezoid *ABCD* is _____ square units.

2.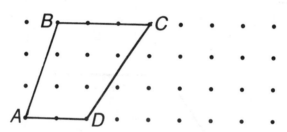

    a.  The area of the related parallelogram is _____ square units.

    b.  The area of trapezoid *ABCD* is _____ square units.

3.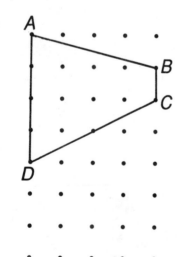

    a.  The area of the related parallelogram is _____ square units.

    b.  The area of trapezoid *ABCD* is _____ square units.

Name: _____ Date: _____

# WORKSHEET 4–13–1
## Area of Trapezoids I

Find the area of trapezoid *ABCD* by first constructing an appropriate parallelogram, then finding the area of that parallelogram, and finally using the area of the parallelogram to find the area of the trapezoid.

1.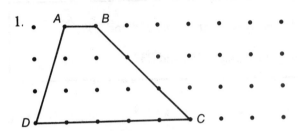

    a. The area of the related parallelogram is _____ square units.
    b. The area of trapezoid *ABCD* is _____ square units.

2.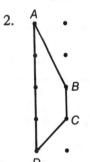

    a. The area of the related parallelogram is _____ square units.
    b. The area of trapezoid *ABCD* is _____ square units.

3.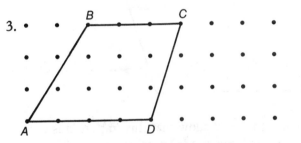

    a. The area of the related parallelogram is _____ square units.
    b. The area of trapezoid *ABCD* is _____ square units.

4.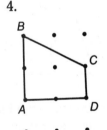

    a. The area of the related parallelogram is _____ square units.
    b. The area of trapezoid *ABCD* is _____ square units.

5.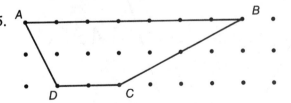

    a. The area of the related parallelogram is _____ square units.
    b. The area of trapezoid *ABCD* is _____ square units.

*Visualized Geometry*

# Lesson 4–14
# Area of Trapezoids II

## *Materials Needed:*

One copy of each of the following pages for each student: pages 238 and 239.

One transparency of each of the following pages: pages 236 and 237.

## *Directions for the Teacher:*

Place the first transparency on the overhead projector. Point out that the quadrilateral is a trapezoid. Note that an altitude is drawn (dotted) and its length is $h$. Also mention that it is common to call the two parallel sides bases, and to let their lengths be $b_1$ and $b_2$. Using the given dots (to the right) draw in segments as shown below.

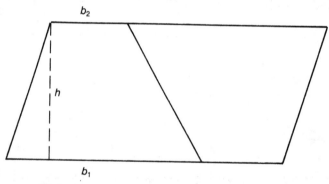

Trace one of these trapezoids on a blank transparency and show that this trapezoid is congruent to the other one (cover it up). Argue that the large quadrilateral is a parallelogram and further label it as follows.

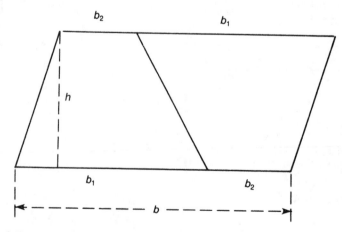

Then write the following on the transparency, justifying as you proceed.

**The area of the parallelogram is _bh_, but**
$$bh = (b_1 + b_2)\, h.$$

**The area of the trapezoid is $\frac{1}{2}(b_1 + b_2)\, h$, but**
$$\tfrac{1}{2}(b_1 + b_2)\, h = \tfrac{1}{2} h\,(b_1 + b_2).$$

**The area formula for a trapezoid is**
$$A = \tfrac{1}{2} h\,(b_1 + b_2).$$

Next, put the second transparency on the projector.

## Correct Answers for Transparency 4–14–2:

1. $b_1 = 12$, $b_2 = 5$, $h = 8$

   $A = \tfrac{1}{2} h\,(b_1 + b_2)$

   $\quad = \tfrac{1}{2} \cdot 8\,(12 + 5)$

   $\quad = 68.$

   The area is 68 square units.

2. $b_1 = 5$, $b_2 = 10$, $h = 4$

   $A = \tfrac{1}{2} \cdot 4\,(5 + 10)$

   $\quad = 30.$

   The area is 30 square units.

3. (Draw an altitude.)

   $b_1 = 8$, $b_2 = 5$, $h = 2$

   $A = \tfrac{1}{2} \cdot 2\,(8 + 5)$

   $\quad = 13.$

   The area is 13 square units.

4. (Draw an altitude.)

   $b_1 = 5$, $b_2 = 2$, $h = 3$

   $A = \tfrac{1}{2} \cdot 3\,(2 + 5)$

   $\quad = 10\tfrac{1}{2}.$

   The area is $10\tfrac{1}{2}$ square units.

Distribute the worksheet. Provide individual assistance as needed.

## Correct Answers for Worksheet 4–14–1:

1. 40
2. 38
3. 20
4. 12
5. 12
6. $37\tfrac{1}{2}$

There are several correct answers for problems 7 and 8.

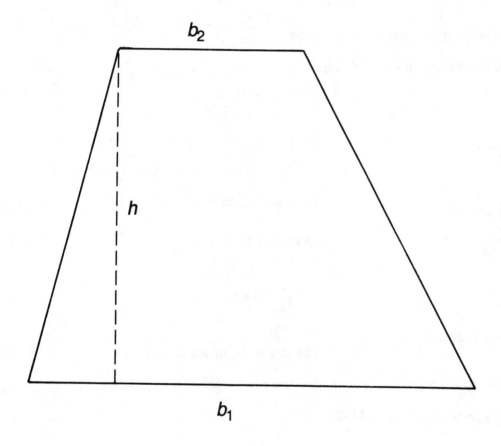

# Find the area.

1.

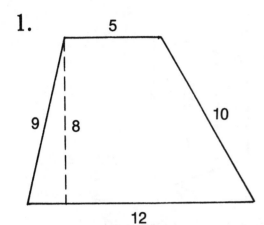

The area is _____ square units.

2.

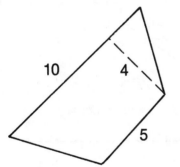

The area is _____ square units.

3.

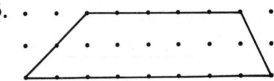

The area is _____ square units.

4.

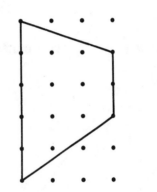

The area is _____ square units.

     *Visualized Geometry*

Name: _____ Date: _____

# WORKSHEET 4-14-1
## Area of Trapezoids II

Find the area using the formula developed earlier.

1.

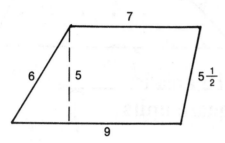

The area is _____ square units.

4.

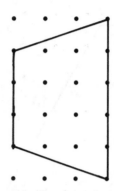

The area is _____ square units.

2.

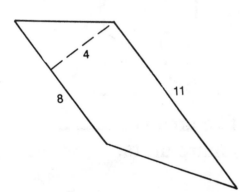

The area is _____ square units.

5.

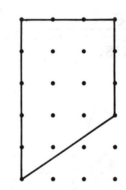

The area is _____ square units.

3.

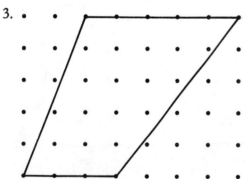

The area is _____ square units.

6.

The area is _____ square units.

(continued)

# WORKSHEET 4–14–1
## Area of Trapezoids II (continued)

7. Draw a picture of a trapezoid with area 15 square units.

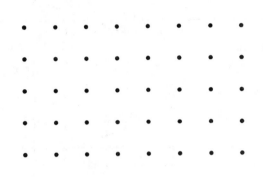

8. Draw a picture of a trapezoid with area 20 square units.

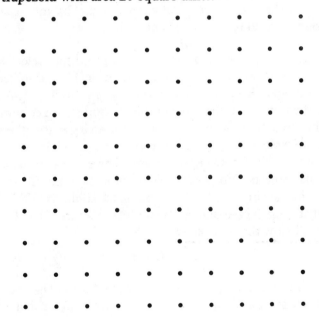

 *Visualized Geometry*

# Lesson 4-15
# Circumference of Circles

## *Materials Needed:*

One copy of page 245 for each student.

One transparency of each of the following pages: pages 242, 243, and 244.

One piece of string about five or six feet long.

One meterstick or yardstick and several circular objects.

## *Directions for the Teacher:*

Place the first transparency on the overhead projector. Mention that point $O$ is at the center of the circle, that $\overline{AB}$ is a diameter of the circle, and that it is common to call the length of a diameter $d$. Point out that $\overline{OD}$ is a radius and it is common to call the length of a radius $r$. Indicate that the circumference of a circle is the distance around the circle and the letter $C$ is commonly used to represent this quantity.

Place the second transparency on the overhead projector. Select one of the circular objects you brought to class. Wrap the string around the circular object. Mark the portion of the string which corresponds to the circumference of the circle. Measure that portion of the string and record the number in the table in the circumference column. Similarly, measure the diameter of the circle by placing a portion of the string across the circle (maximum length) or use the meterstick directly. Then record this number in the diameter column. Also record the name of the object in the appropriate column. In a similar manner, continue with several other circular objects. When the table is completed, ask the students to compare corresponding entries in the circumference and diameter columns. They should conclude (possibly with help) that in each case, the circumference is approximately three times as large as the diameter. Next, below the transparency write

$$C = \pi d.$$

Tell them that $\pi$ is a number which is a little greater than 3. Also tell them that two approximations of $\pi$ that are standardly used are $\frac{22}{7}$ and 3.14. Indicate that in this lesson and also in the next lesson, no approximation for $\pi$ will be used. Instead, answers will be given as a multiple of $\pi$. Finally, on the transparency write

$$C = 2\pi r.$$

Justify this by indicating that $d = 2r$.

Place the third transparency on the overhead projector. With student assistance find the circumference of the three circles pictured. Specifically, under the circle for problem 1 write

$$d = 7$$
$$C = \pi d$$
$$= \pi \cdot 7$$
$$= 7\pi.$$

Then write "$7\pi$" in the blank. Under the circle for problem 2 write

$$r = 5$$
$$C = 2\pi r$$
$$= 2\pi \cdot 5$$
$$= 10\pi.$$

Then write "$10\pi$" in the blank.

Problem 3 may be worked using the diameter or the radius. Then write

$$d = 4 \qquad\qquad r = 2$$
$$C = \pi d \qquad\qquad C = 2\pi r$$
$$\quad\text{or}$$
$$= \pi\,(4) \qquad\qquad = 2\pi(2)$$
$$= 4\pi. \qquad\qquad = 4\pi.$$

Finally, write "$4\pi$" in the blank.

Distribute the worksheet. Provide individual assistance as needed.

## Correct Answers for Worksheet 4–15–1:

1. $3\pi$

2. $5\pi$

3. $2\pi$

4. $6\pi$

5.

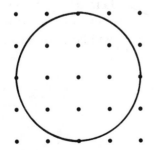

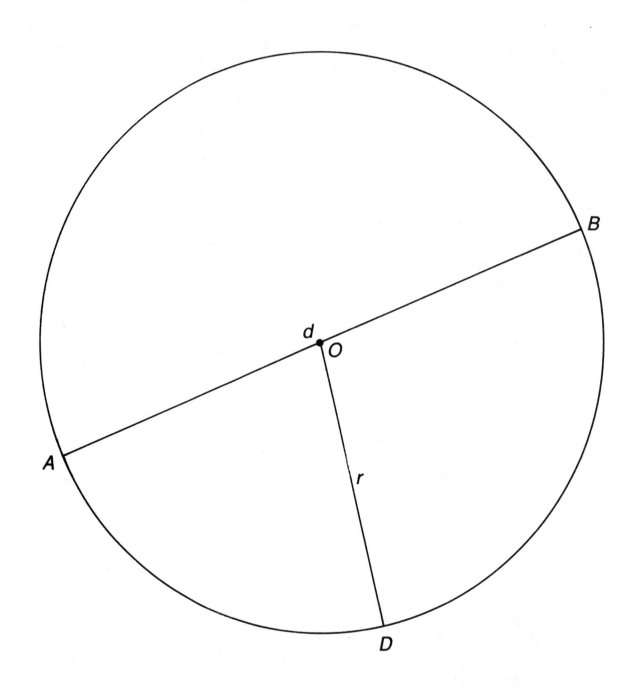

*Visualized Geometry*

| Name of object | Circumference | Diameter |
|---|---|---|
|  |  |  |
|  |  |  |
|  |  |  |
|  |  |  |
|  |  |  |
|  |  |  |
|  |  |  |

*Visualized Geometry*

# Find the circumference.

1.

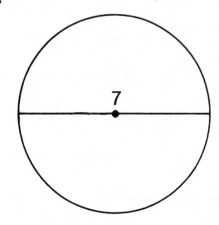

The circumference is
_____ units.

3.

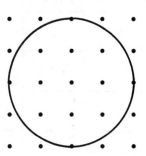

The circumference is
_____ units.

2.

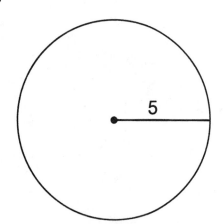

The circumference is
_____ units.

# WORKSHEET 4–15–1
## Circumference of Circles

1. Find the circumference.

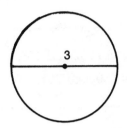

The circumference is _____ units.

2. Find the circumference.

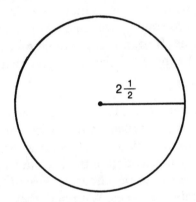

The circumference is _____ units.

3. Find the circumference.

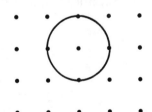

The circumference is _____ units.

4. Find the circumference.

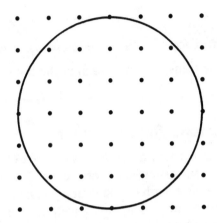

The circumference is _____ units.

5. Draw a rough sketch of a circle with circumference of $4\pi$ units.

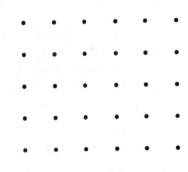

# Lesson 4–16
# Area of Circles

## *Materials Needed:*

One copy of each of the following pages for each student: pages 252 and 253.

One transparency of each of the following pages: pages 249, 250, and 251.

## *Directions for the Teacher:*

Place the first transparency on the overhead projector. Tell the students that in this lesson you want to develop a formula for finding the area of a circle. Point out that finding area means finding out how many unit squares it takes to cover up the circle. As a class activity, count the number of squares covered by the circle. Start with the squares that are entirely inside the circle. Number these squares (1, 2, 3, . . . ) as you count them. The other squares will need to be "paired up." A lively discussion could ensue. If so, this approximation by counting increases the need for an exact answer. Be very happy if the class can agree that it takes about 38 or 39 squares to cover up the circle.

Place the second transparency on the overhead projector. Direct the students' attention to the circle. Indicate that the little wedge-shaped pieces are all the same size (congruent) and if they were cut out they could put them together as shown below the circle. Ask them what this figure looks like (a parallelogram). Then direct their attention to the bottom "side" of this figure. Point out that the length of this "side" is one half of the circumference of the circle since the bottom "side" is made up of the even-numbered pieces. With help they should see that an altitude to this "side" is simply a radius of the circle. Then go through the argument at the bottom of the transparency.

Place the third transparency on the overhead projector. With student assistance, calculate the area of each circle. Do not make an approximation for $\pi$. Specifically under the circle for problem 1 write

$$r = 4$$
$$A = \pi r^2$$
$$= \pi \cdot 4^2$$
$$= 16\pi.$$

Then write "$16\pi$" in the blank.

Continue with problem 2 in a similar way ($36\pi$). For problem 3, draw in a diameter and write

$$d = 4$$
$$r = 2$$
$$A = \pi r^2$$
$$= \pi \cdot 2^2$$
$$= 4\pi.$$

Then write "$4\pi$" in the blank.

Place the first transparency on the projector again. With students' help conclude that $d = 7$, $r = 3\frac{1}{2}$ and

$$A = \pi r^2$$
$$= \pi \left(3\tfrac{1}{2}\right)^2$$
$$= \pi \left(\tfrac{7}{2}\right)^2$$
$$= \tfrac{49}{4}\,\pi$$
$$= 12\tfrac{1}{4}\,\pi.$$

Using 3.14 as an approximation for $\pi$, write

$$A \approx 12\tfrac{1}{4} \cdot (3.14)$$
$$\approx 38.5.$$

Compare this answer with the answer found by counting. Point out that 38.5 and also the answer found by counting are approximations but $\frac{49}{4}\,\pi$ is the actual area, not an approximation of the area.

Distribute the worksheets. Provide individual assistance as needed.

## Correct Answers for Worksheet 4–16–1:

1. $9\pi$
2. $25\pi$
3. $36\pi$
4. $\pi$
5. $9\pi$
6. $2\frac{1}{4}\,\pi$

7.
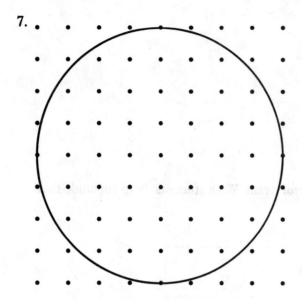

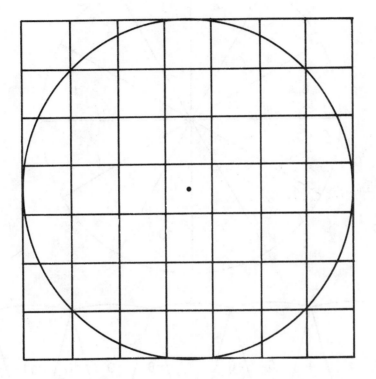

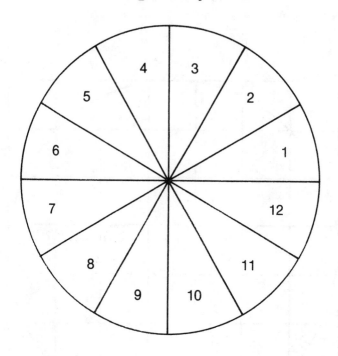

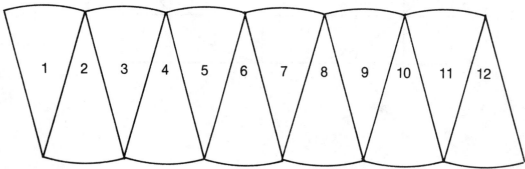

This figure approximates a parallelogram with $b = \frac{1}{2} C$ and $h = r$. Then

$$A = bh$$
$$= \left(\tfrac{1}{2} C\right) \cdot r$$
$$= \left(\tfrac{1}{2} \cdot 2\pi r\right) \cdot r$$
$$= \pi r^2.$$

     *Visualized Geometry*

# Find the area.

1.

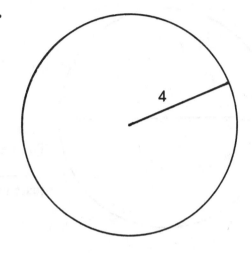

The area is _____ square units.

2.

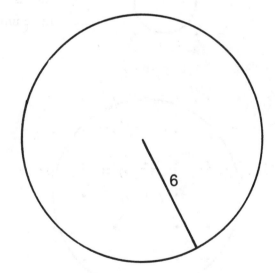

The area is _____ square units.

3.

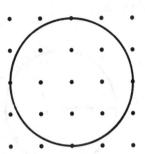

The area is _____ square units.

# WORKSHEET 4-16-1
## Area of Circles

Find the area.

1.

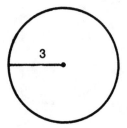

The area is _____ square units.

3.

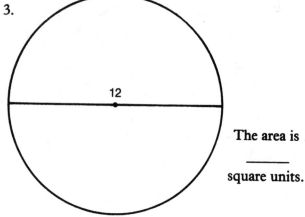

The area is
_____
square units.

2.

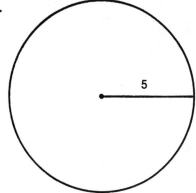

The area is _____ square units.

4.

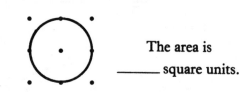

The area is
_____ square units.

5.

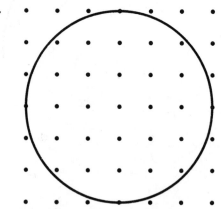

The area is _____ square units.

*(continued)*

*Visualized Geometry*

# WORKSHEET 4-16-1
## Area of Circles (continued)

6.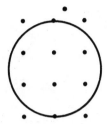

The area is _____ square units.

7. Draw a sketch of a circle with area $16\pi$ square units.

# Lesson 4–17
# More Area and Perimeter

## *Materials Needed:*

One copy of each of the following pages for each student: pages 257 and 258.

One transparency of page 256.

## *Directions for the Teacher:*

Place the transparency on the overhead projector. Direct the students' attention to problem 1. Point out that the "top" of the figure is a semicircle. With the students' help, find the perimeter $(8 + 6 + 8 + 3\pi = 22 + 3\pi)$. Draw in a diameter and find the area by separating the figure into a semicircle and a rectangle $(48 + 4\frac{1}{2}\,\pi)$.

Proceed to problem 2. Find the area by separating the figure into several smaller parts. One possibility is shown below.

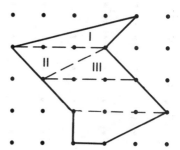

In this instance, the area of each of the three triangular parts is $1\frac{1}{2}$ square units, the area of the parallelogram is 3 square units and the area of the trapezoid is 2 square units, so the area of the original figure is $9\frac{1}{2}$ square units.

Next, find the area of this same figure by first drawing a larger rectangle "around" it as shown below.

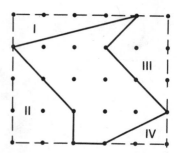

Next, calculate the area of regions I, II, III, and IV (2 square units, 4 square units, $3\frac{1}{2}$ square units, 1 square unit). Find the sum of those areas and subtract this sum from the area of the rectangle.

Proceed to problem 3. Point out that since the central angle is 90°, the length of the arc is $\frac{1}{4}$ the circumference of the "corresponding" circle. Thus, conclude that the length of the arc is $\frac{1}{4}(2\pi \cdot 6)$ units or $3\pi$ units and the perimeter is $(3\pi + 12)$ units. Similarly, point out that the area of the sector is $\frac{1}{4}$ the area of the "corresponding" circle or $9\pi$ square units.

Distribute the worksheets. Provide individual assistance as needed.

## Correct Answers for Worksheet 4–17–1

1a. The perimeter is $14 + 2\pi$ units.

 b. The area is $20 - 2\pi$ square units.

2a. The perimeter is $10 + 4\pi$ units.

 b. The area is 20 square units.

3a. The perimeter is $12\pi$ units.

 b. The area is $35 + \frac{49\pi}{4}$ square units.

4a. The area is 5 square units.

 b. The area is 7 square units.

 c. The area is $8\frac{1}{2}$ square units.

 d. The area is 9 square units.

5a. The perimeter is $18 + 6\pi$ units.

 b. The area is $27\pi$ square units.

6a. The perimeter is $16 + 12\pi$ units.

 b. The area is $48\pi$ square units.

1. Find the perimeter and find the area.

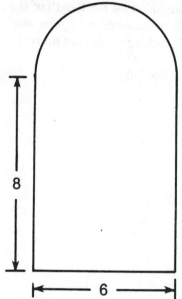

a. The perimeter is _____ units.

b. The area is _____ square units.

2. Find the area.

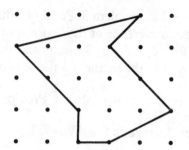

The area is _____ square units.

3.

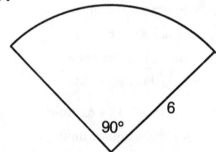

a. The perimeter is _____ units.

b. The area is _____ square units.

*Visualized Geometry*

# WORKSHEET 4-17-1
## More Area and Perimeter

1. Find the perimeter and the area.

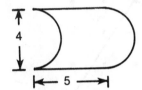

   a.  The perimeter is _____ units.

   b.  The area is _____ square units.

2. Find the perimeter and the area.

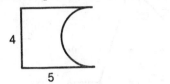

   a.  The perimeter is _____ units.

   b.  The area is _____ square units.

3. Find the perimeter and the area.

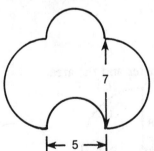

   a.  The perimeter is _____ units.

   b.  The area is _____ square units.

*(continued)*

              *Visualized Geometry*

# WORKSHEET 4-17-1
## More Area and Perimeter *(continued)*

4. Find the area.

a.

The area is _____ square units.

c.

The area is _____ square units.

b.

The area is _____ square units.

d.

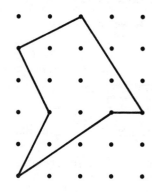

The area is _____ square units.

5. Find the perimeter and the area.

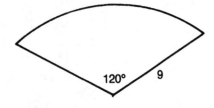

120°   9

a. The perimeter is _____ units.

b. The area is _____ square units.

6. Find the perimeter and the area.

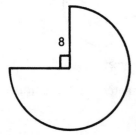

8

a. The perimeter is _____ units.

b. The area is _____ square units.

         *Visualized Geometry*

# CHAPTER 5

# Angles in Polygons and Circles

## Comments and Suggestions

In this chapter, students cut out a triangular region, "tear off" the angles, and put them together to see that the sum of the measures of those angles is 180°. A similar approach is taken for convex quadrilaterals. Then the sum of the measures of angles of more complicated figures is found by separating these figures into triangles. Next, measures of exterior angles are investigated. The last four lessons are concerned with angles involved with circles.

This chapter includes an intuitive introduction to most of the significant "angle theorems" and is particularly practical for those students who are enrolled in or who will later enroll in high school geometry.

## Lesson 5-1
# Sum of the Measures of Angles of a Triangle and of a Quadrilateral

## *Materials Needed:*

One blank sheet of paper for each student.

One ruler for each pair of students.

One pair of scissors for each student.

## *Directions for the Teacher:*

Begin the lesson by drawing the following kind of picture on the chalkboard or on a blank transparency.

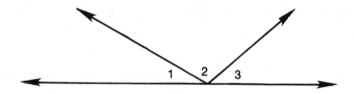

Ask the students about the sum of the measures of these three angles. They should respond that m∠1 + m∠2 + m∠3 = 180°. Next, draw the following picture.

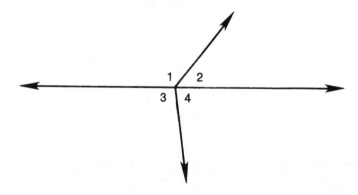

Now ask them about the sum of the measures of these four angles. They should respond m∠1 + m∠2 + m∠3 + m∠4 = 360°.

Have your students use a ruler to make a rather large triangle on a blank sheet of paper. Have them label the angles as shown below.

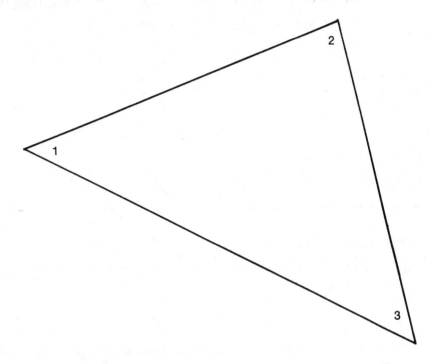

Have them cut out the triangle, tear off the corners, and put them together as shown.

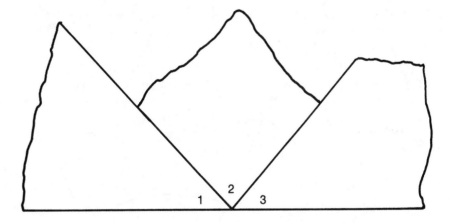

Now ask them about the sum of the measures of the angles of their triangle. They should conclude that the sum of the measures of the angles is 180°.

Next, have each student draw a large quadrilateral.

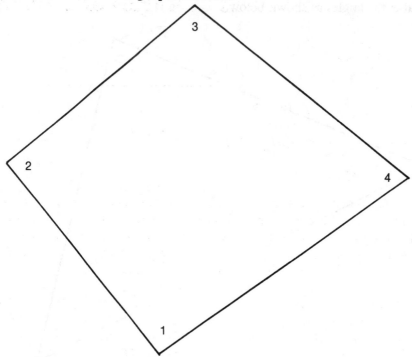

Have them cut out the quadrilateral, tear off the corners, and put them together as shown.

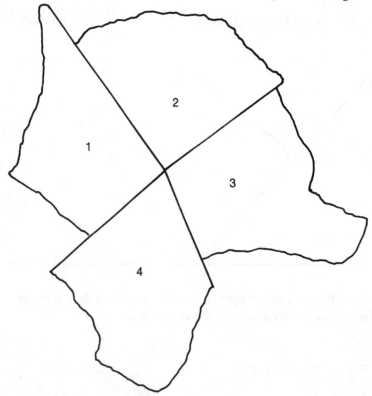

Now ask about the sum of the measures of the angles of their quadrilateral. They should conclude that the sum of the measures of the angles is 360°.

# Lesson 5-2
# Sum of the Measures of Angles of a Triangle

## *Materials Needed:*

One transparency of each of the following pages: pages 264 and 265.

## *Directions for the Teacher:*

Place the first transparency on the overhead projector. Direct the students' attention to the parallel lines. Remind them that in a previous lesson (Lesson 1-3) they found that when a transversal intersects two parallel lines, the alternate interior angles are congruent. Point out that in this case $\angle 1$ and $\angle 4$ are alternate interior angles and thus $\angle 1 \cong \angle 4$. Point out that $\angle 2$ and $\angle 3$ are also alternate interior angles which means that $\angle 2 \cong \angle 3$.

Next, place the second transparency on your projector. Cover up the information below the figure. Indicate that you want to find the sum of the measures of the angles of $\triangle ABC$ which means you want to find $m\angle 1 + m\angle 2 + m\angle 3$. Point out that $\overrightarrow{BD}$ is parallel to $\overrightarrow{AC}$. Tell your students that you want them to consider transversal $\overleftrightarrow{AB}$. Then $\angle 1$ and $\angle 4$ are alternate interior angles and $\angle 1 \cong \angle 4$. Next have them consider transversal $\overleftrightarrow{BC}$. In this case $\angle 2$ and $\angle 5$ are alternate interior angles. Next uncover line by line the information which is under the figure. Emphasize that now you have found another way to show that the sum of the measures of the angles of a triangle is 180°.

# Transparency 5–2–1

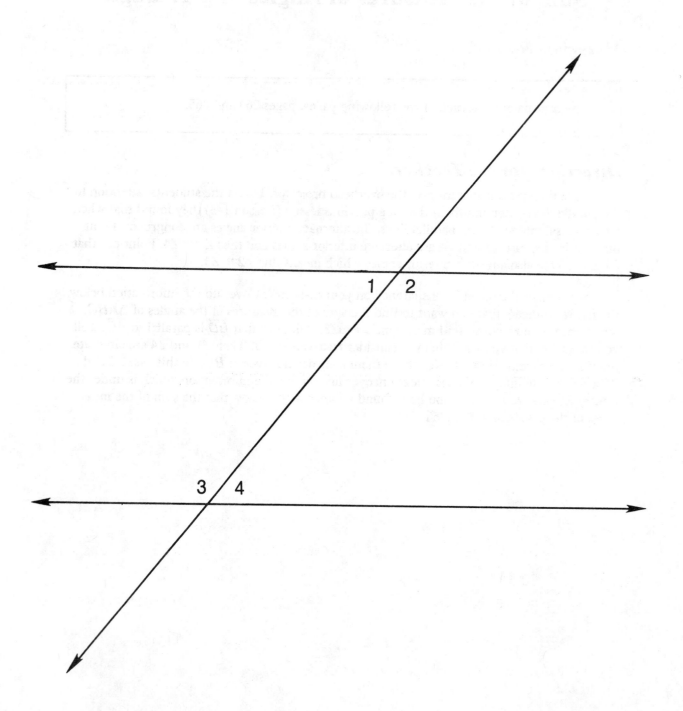

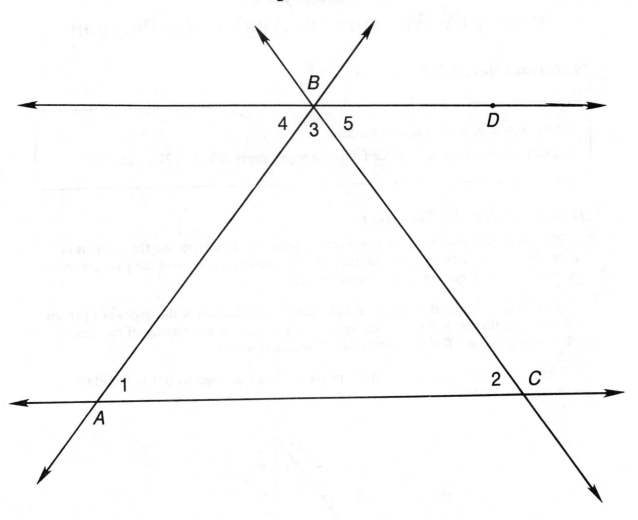

$$m\angle 1 \;=\; m\angle 4 \text{ (congruent angles)}$$
$$m\angle 2 \;=\; m\angle 5 \text{ (congruent angles)}$$
$$m\angle 4 + m\angle 5 + m\angle 3 \;=\; 180°$$
$$m\angle 1 + m\angle 2 + m\angle 3 \;=\; 180° \text{ (substituting } m\angle 1 \text{ for } m\angle 4 \text{ and}$$
$$m\angle 2 \text{ for } m\angle 5)$$

*Visualized Geometry*

## Lesson 5–3
# Sum of the Measures of Angles of a Polygon

### *Materials Needed:*

> One copy of page 273 for each student.
>
> One transparency of each of the following pages: pages 269, 270, 271, and 272.

### *Directions for the Teacher:*

Place the first transparency on the overhead projector. Briefly review the concepts of convex and concave (Lesson 1–10). Indicate why the figures at the top of the page are concave and those at the bottom of the page are convex.

Remind the students that they found the sum of the measures of the angles of a particular convex quadrilateral is 360° by cutting out the quadrilateral and tearing off the corners. In this lesson, they will find a different way of finding this sum.

Place the second transparency on the projector. Draw in diagonal *BD* and label the angles as shown below.

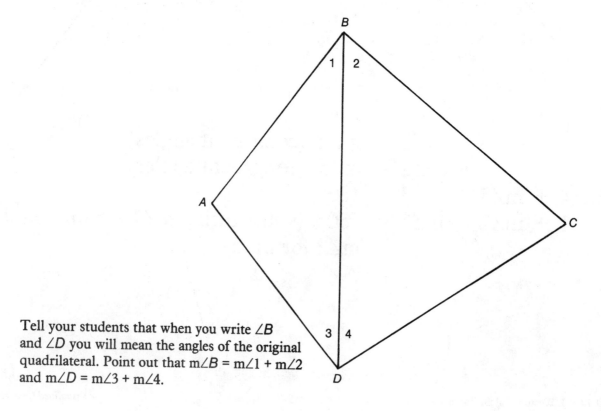

Tell your students that when you write ∠*B* and ∠*D* you will mean the angles of the original quadrilateral. Point out that m∠*B* = m∠1 + m∠2 and m∠*D* = m∠3 + m∠4.

Then go through the following argument. (Write the steps on the transparency.)

$$m\angle A + m\angle B + m\angle C + m\angle D = m\angle A + (m\angle 1 + m\angle 2) + m\angle C + (m\angle 3 + m\angle 4)$$
$$= (m\angle A + m\angle 3 + m\angle 1) + (m\angle C + m\angle 2 + m\angle 4)$$
$$= 180° + 180° \text{ (Three angles of a triangle)}$$
$$= 360°$$

Next put the third transparency on the projector. The purpose of this part of the lesson is to show that when the quadrilateral is concave, the sum of the measures of the angles is not 360°. Have the students estimate the measures of the angles of the quadrilateral and complete the table. Pay particular attention to $\angle C$ ($m\angle C$ is approximately 90°). Here is roughly what the table will look like.

| $m\angle A$ | 40° |
|---|---|
| $m\angle B$ | 20° |
| $m\angle C$ | 90° |
| $m\angle D$ | 30° |
| $m\angle A + m\angle B + m\angle C + m\angle D$ | 180° |

They should conclude that in this case the sum of the measures of the angles is about 180°. Emphasize that the sum of the measures is 360° only when the quadrilateral is convex.

Put the fourth transparency on the projector. Emphasize that the pentagon pictured is convex. Draw in diagonals $\overline{BD}$ and $\overline{BE}$. Ask about the sum of the measures of the angles of the pentagon. They should conclude that the sum is 180° + 180° + 180° or 540° because of the three triangles involved.

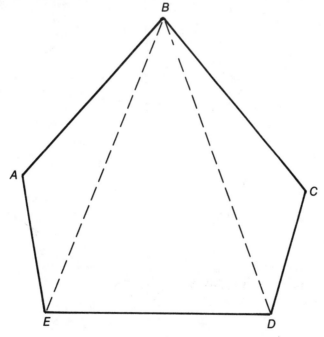

Distribute the worksheet. Provide individual assistance as needed. The students should draw in diagonals as was done in the case of the quadrilateral and the pentagon.

## Correct Answers for Worksheet 5–3–1:

1. 720°

2. 1080°

# Concave

# Convex

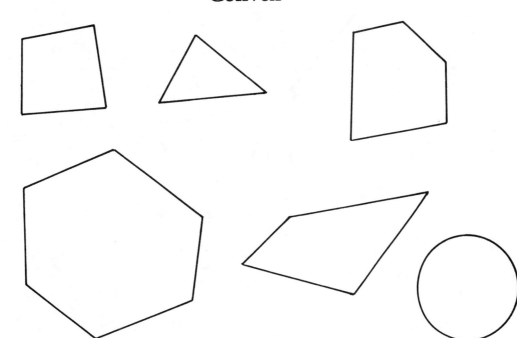

 *Visualized Geometry*

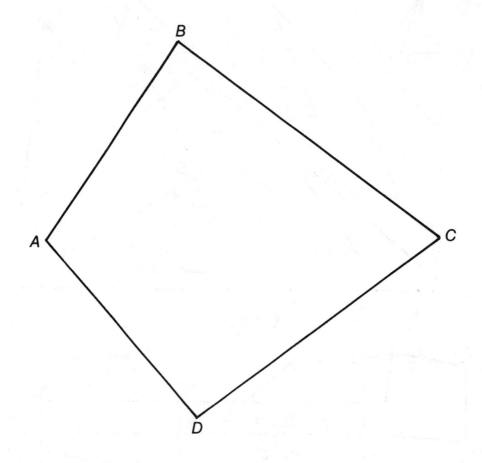

# Transparency 5-3-3

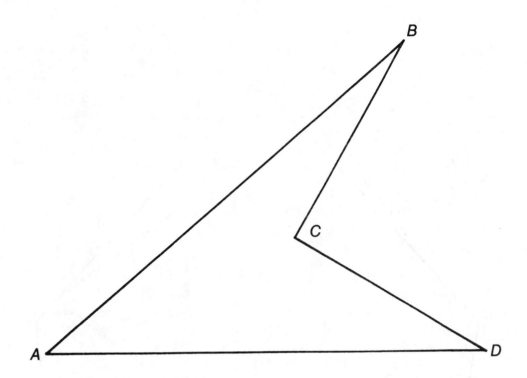

## Approximations

| | |
|---|---|
| m∠A | |
| m∠B | |
| m∠C | |
| m∠D | |
| m∠A + m∠B + m∠C + m∠D | |

*Visualized Geometry*

# Transparency 5-3-4

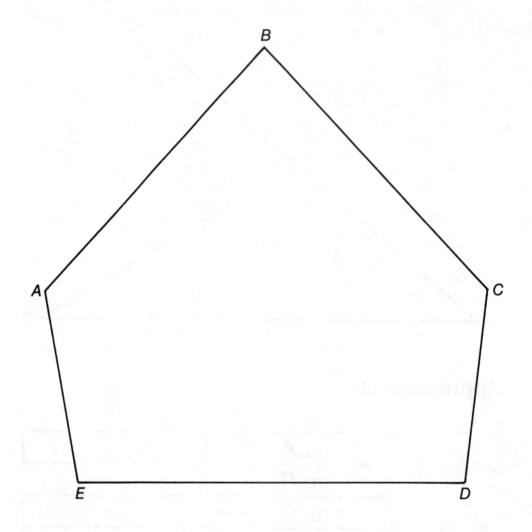

# WORKSHEET 5-3-1
## Sum of the Measures of Angles of a Polygon

Find the sum of the measures of the angles of the convex hexagon and the convex octagon pictured below.

1.

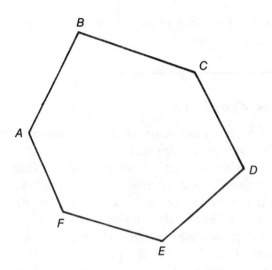

m∠A + m∠B + m∠C + m∠D + m∠E + m∠F =

2.

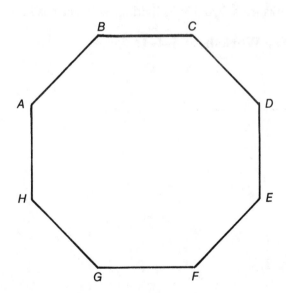

m∠A + m∠B + m∠C + m∠D + m∠E + m∠F + m∠G + m∠H =

## Lesson 5–4
# Finding Measures of Angles of Polygons

## *Materials Needed:*

One copy of each of the following pages for each student: pages 276 and 277.

One transparency of page 275.

## *Directions for the Teacher:*

Place the transparency on the projector. Direct the students' attention to problem 1. They should see (possibly with your help) that since $m\angle A + m\angle B + m\angle C = 180°$, $m\angle B = 28°$. Proceed to problem 2. Mention that $\angle A$ is a right angle. Then they should conclude that $m\angle C = 39°$. Go on to problem 3. Mention that the single mark across $\overline{AB}$ and the single mark across $\overline{CB}$ means that these two segments are congruent. Remind them that this means that the triangle is isosceles and in an earlier lesson (Lesson 2–6) they found that the angles opposite congruent sides in an isosceles triangle are congruent. From this they should conclude that $m\angle C = 73°$ and $m\angle B = 34°$. Finally, proceed to problem 4. They should conclude (possibly with your help) that $m\angle D = 90°$, since the sum of the measures of the angles of this quadrilateral is 360°.

Distribute the worksheets. Provide individual assistance as needed.

## Correct Answers for Worksheet 5–4–1:

1. 60°

2. 27°

3. 56°

4. 71°

5. 45°

6. 60°

7. 90°

8. 111°

9. 150°

# Find the measures of the angles listed.

**1.**

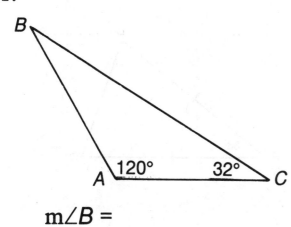

m∠B =

**2.**

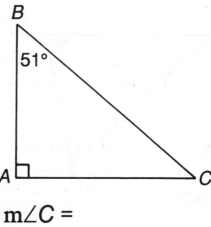

m∠C =

**3.**

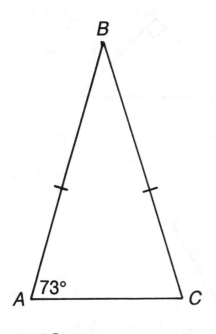

m∠C =
m∠B =

**4.**

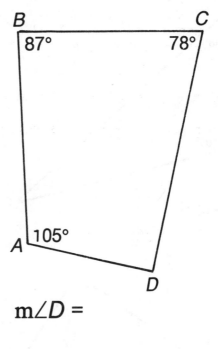

m∠D =

*Visualized Geometry*

# WORSHEET 5-4-1
## Finding Measures of Angles of Polygons

Find the measures of the angles.

1.

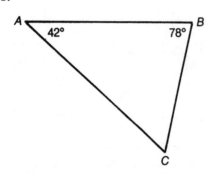

m∠C =

2.

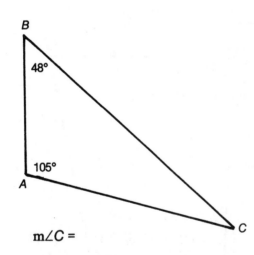

m∠C =

3.

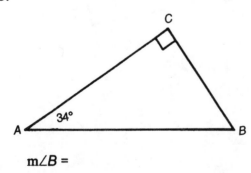

m∠B =

4.

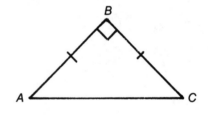

m∠C =

5.

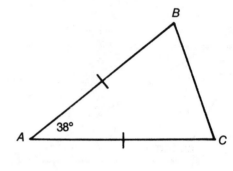

m∠A =

6.

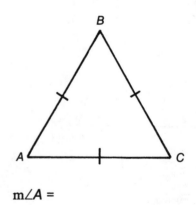

m∠A =

*(continued)*

   *Visualized Geometry*

# WORSHEET 5-4-1
## Finding Measures of Angles of Polygons (*continued*)

7.

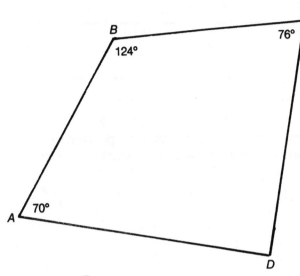

m∠D =

9.

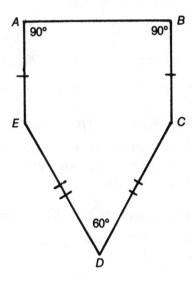

m∠C =

8.

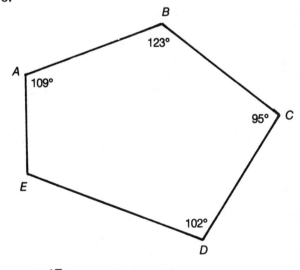

m∠E =

*Visualized Geometry*

## Lesson 5-5
# Measures of Angles in a Regular Polygon

### *Materials Needed:*

One copy of page 279 for each student.

### *Directions for the Teacher:*

Distribute the worksheet. Remind the students that a regular polygon is a polygon in which all the sides are congruent and all angles are congruent. Provide individual assistance as needed.

### Correct Answers for Worksheet 5-5-1:

1a. equilateral triangle

  b. 60°

2a. square

  b. 90°

3. 108°

4. 120°

5. 135°

# WORKSHEET 5-5-1
## Measures of Angles in a Regular Polygon

1a. What is the common name for a regular three-sided polygon?

  b. What is the measure of each angle of a regular three-sided polygon?

2a. What is the common name for a regular four-sided polygon?

  b. What is the measure of each angle of a regular four-sided polygon?

3. What is the measure of each angle of a regular pentagon? (Hint: What is the sum of the measures of the angles of any convex pentagon?)

4. What is the measure of each angle of a regular hexagon (six-sided polygon)?

5. What is the measure of each angle of a regular octagon (eight-sided polygon)?

         *Visualized Geometry*

# Lesson 5–6
# Measure of an Exterior Angle of a Triangle

## *Materials Needed:*

One copy of page 282 for each student.

One blank transparency, an overhead projector pen, and one ruler for each student.

## *Directions for the Teacher:*

Have each student use the ruler to draw a triangle (fairly large) on a piece of paper. Have them label the triangle as shown below. Then have them extend side $\overline{AB}$ as shown. Tell them that $\angle DBC$ is called an exterior angle of $\triangle ABC$.

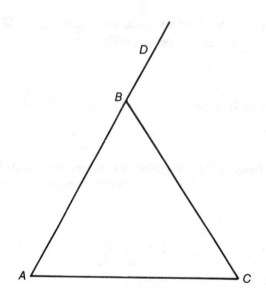

Now have the students copy $\angle A$ on their transparency. Next have them copy $\angle C$ on the transparency in such a way that this copy of $\angle C$ is adjacent to the copy of $\angle A$. Then they are to match the "large" angle formed on the transparency with the exterior angle at vertex $B$. Since there is a match, conclude that $m\angle A + m\angle C = m\angle DBC$. Ask the students if they think this will always happen.

Next indicate that you can illustrate this relationship in another way. Draw the following picture on the chalkboard or on a blank transparency.

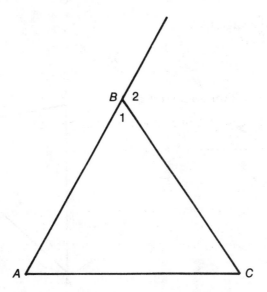

Proceed with the following argument.

$$m\angle 1 + m\angle 2 = 180°$$
$$m\angle 1 + m\angle A + m\angle C = 180°$$
$$m\angle 1 + m\angle 2 = m\angle 1 + m\angle A + m\angle C$$
$$m\angle 2 = m\angle A + m\angle C$$

Tell your students that $\angle 2$ is called an exterior angle of $\triangle ABC$. State the following theorem.

**In any triangle the sum of the measures of any two angles of the triangle is equal to the measure of the remote exterior angle.**

You may want to talk a little about "remote."

Distribute the worksheet. Provide individual assistance as needed.

## Correct Answers for Worksheet 5–6–1:

1. 105°

2. 102°

3. 79°

4. 80°

# WORKSHEET 5–6–1
## Measure of an Exterior Angle of a Triangle

Find the measures of the angles.

1.

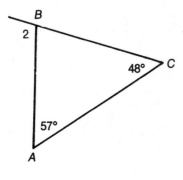

m∠2 =

2.

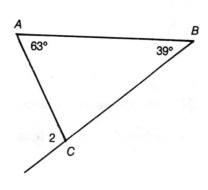

m∠2 =

3.

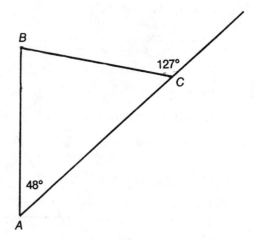

m∠B =

4.

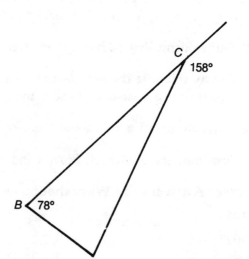

m∠A =

*Visualized Geometry*

## Lesson 5-7
# Sum of the Measures of the Exterior Angles of a Triangle

## *Materials Needed:*

One copy of page 285 for each student.

One transparency of page 285.

One blank transparency and one overhead projector pen for each student.

## *Directions for the Teacher:*

Note that you are to make a transparency of a worksheet page. Distribute the worksheet. Point out that $\angle 1$, $\angle 2$, and $\angle 3$ are exterior angles of the triangle and that you have one exterior angle at each vertex. Next have students

a. copy $\angle 1$ on a blank transparency,

b. copy $\angle 2$ so that the copy of $\angle 2$ is adjacent to $\angle 1$, and

c. copy $\angle 3$ so that it is adjacent to $\angle 2$.

When that is done correctly, the copy of $\angle 3$ is also adjacent to $\angle 1$. Here is a picture of what should happen.

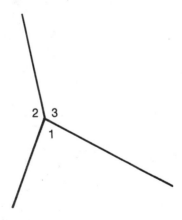

They should realize that $m\angle 1 + m\angle 2 + m\angle 3 = 360°$.

Next, place the transparency (page 285) on the overhead projector. Suggest that you could show that

$$m\angle 1 + m\angle 2 + m\angle 3 = 360°$$

without copying the angles on a blank transparency.

Give the following argument.

$$m\angle 4 + m\angle 5 + m\angle 6 = 180°$$
$$m\angle 1 + m\angle 4 = 180°$$
$$m\angle 2 + m\angle 5 = 180°$$
$$m\angle 3 + m\angle 6 = 180°$$
$$(m\angle 1 + m\angle 4) + (m\angle 2 + m\angle 5) + (m\angle 3 + m\angle 6) = 180° + 180° + 180°$$
$$(m\angle 1 + m\angle 2 + m\angle 3) + (m\angle 4 + m\angle 5 + m\angle 6) = 360° + 180°$$
$$(m\angle 1 + m\angle 2 + m\angle 3) + 180° = 360° + 180°$$
$$m\angle 1 + m\angle 2 + m\angle 3 = 360°$$

# WORKSHEET 5-7-1
## Sum of the Measures of the
## Exterior Angles of a Triangle

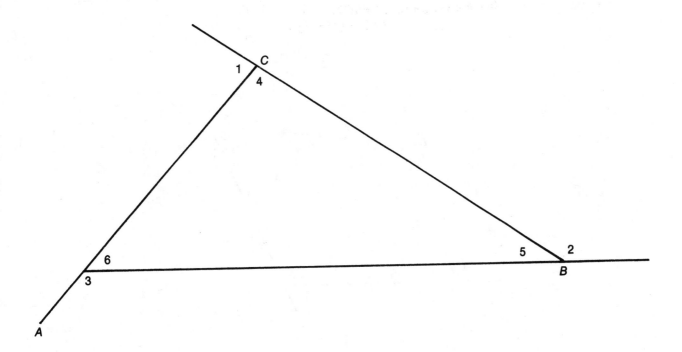

**Lesson 5-8**
# Sum of the Measures of the
# Exterior Angles of a Convex Quadrilateral

## *Directions for the Teacher:*

Draw a picture of a convex quadrilateral on the chalkboard or on a blank transparency. Extend sides and label angles as indicated below.

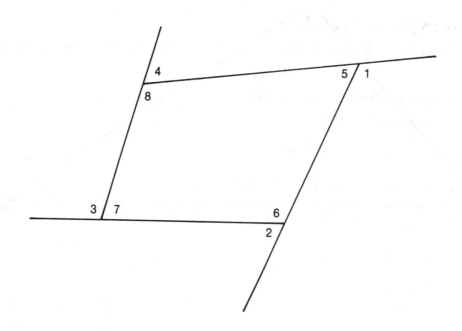

Tell the students you would like to find $m\angle 1 + m\angle 2 + m\angle 3 + m\angle 4$. Ask them to predict the sum. Next lead them through this argument.

$$(m\angle 1 + m\angle 5) + (m\angle 2 + m\angle 6) + (m\angle 3 + m\angle 7) + (m\angle 4 + m\angle 8) = 180° + 180° + 180° + 180°$$
$$(m\angle 1 + m\angle 2 + m\angle 3 + m\angle 4) + (m\angle 5 + m\angle 6 + m\angle 7 + m\angle 8) = 180° + 180° + 180° + 180°$$
$$m\angle 1 + m\angle 2 + m\angle 3 + m\angle 4 + 360° = 360° + 360°$$
$$m\angle 1 + m\angle 2 + m\angle 3 + m\angle 4 = 360°$$

Point out that $\angle 1$, $\angle 2$, $\angle 3$, and $\angle 4$ are exterior angles. Mention that these exterior angles are formed by extending one side of the original quadrilateral and there is an exterior angle at each vertex of the quadrilateral. Compare the results with the results of Lesson 5-7.

## Lesson 5-9
# Sum of the Measures of the
# Exterior Angles of Polygons

## *Materials Needed:*

One copy of each of the following pages for each student: pages 288, 289, and 290.

## *Directions for the Teacher:*

Distribute the worksheets. For parts I and II, you may want to review Lessons 5–7 and 5–8.

### Correct Answers for Worksheet 5–9–1:

I. $m\angle 1 + m\angle 2 + m\angle 3 = 360°$

II. $m\angle 1 + m\angle 2 + m\angle 3 + m\angle 4 = 360°$

III. $m\angle 1 + m\angle 2 + m\angle 3 + m\angle 4 + m\angle 5 = 360°$

IV. $m\angle 1 + m\angle 2 + m\angle 3 + m\angle 4 + m\angle 5 + m\angle 6 = 360°$

# WORKSHEET 5-9-1
## Sum of the Measures of the
## Exterior Angles of Polygons

**Part I.**

Using the information derived from Lesson 5-7, find the sum of the measures of the angles.

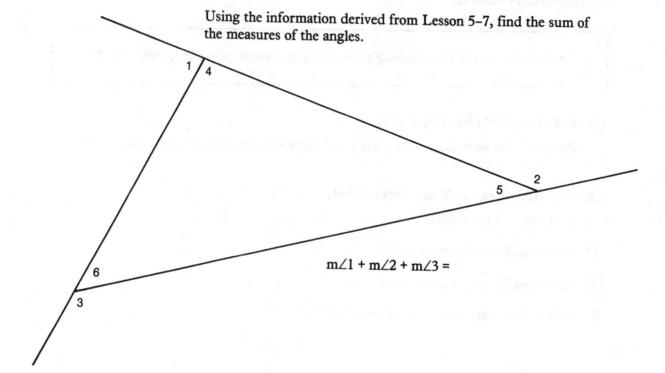

$m\angle 1 + m\angle 2 + m\angle 3 =$

**Part II.**

Using the information derived from Lesson 5-8, find the sum of the measures of the angles.

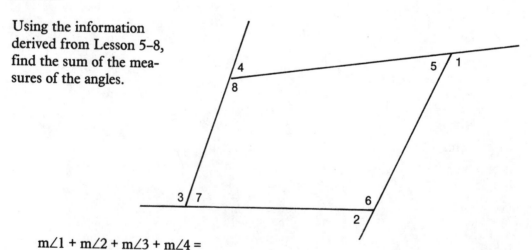

$m\angle 1 + m\angle 2 + m\angle 3 + m\angle 4 =$

*(continued)*

*Visualized Geometry*

# WORKSHEET 5-9-1
## Sum of the Measures of the
## Exterior Angles of Polygons *(continued)*

Predict the sum of the measures of the angles.

**Part III.**

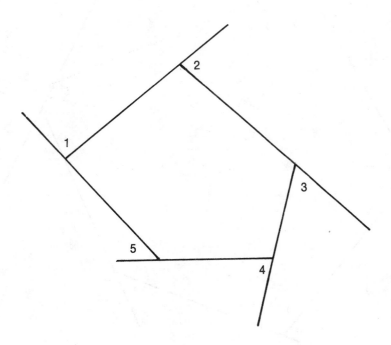

m∠1 + m∠2 + m∠3 + m∠4 + m∠5 =

*(continued)*

*Visualized Geometry*

# WORKSHEET 5-9-1
## Sum of the Measures of the
## Exterior Angles of Polygons *(continued)*

Predict the sum of the measures of the angles.

**Part IV.**

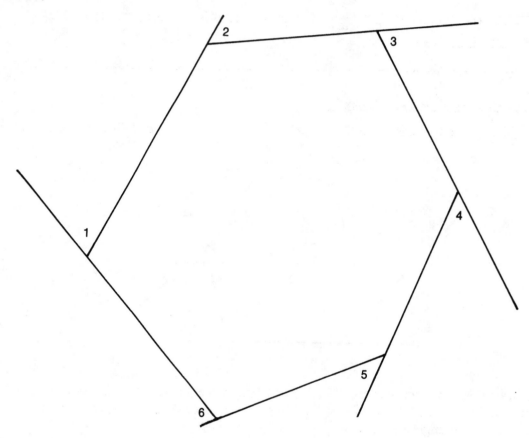

m∠1 + m∠2 + m∠3 + m∠4 + m∠5 + m∠6 =

*Visualized Geometry*

# Lesson 5–10
# Measures of Central Angles

## *Materials Needed:*

One copy of each of the following pages for each student: page 296, 297, 298, and 299.
One transparency of page 295.

## *Directions for the Teacher:*

Place the transparency on the overhead projector and draw the following angle.

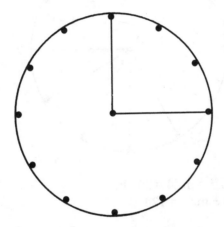

Indicate that any angle with its vertex at the center of a circle is called a central angle. Ask the students about the measure of the angle pictured. They should say that the measure is 90°. Erase that angle and draw the following picture.

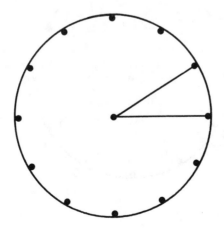

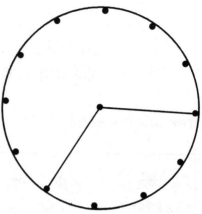

Ask them about the measure of this angle. They should respond that the measure is 30°. (It is one third as big as a right angle). Erase that angle and draw the following picture and ask about the measure of this angle.

They should respond 120°. If they are unable to do this, draw in the following radii and label the angles and points as follows.

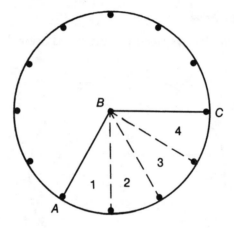

Indicate that m∠1 = m∠2 = m∠3 = m∠4 = 30° but
m∠ABC = m∠1 + m∠2 + m∠3 + m∠4 = 120°

Erase the information written on your transparency and label the points as follows.

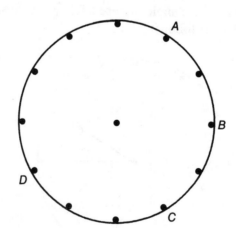

Next, as your students watch you place your index finger on point *A* and trace along the circle to *B* and continue to *C*. Tell them this path is called an arc and is written $\overset{\frown}{ABC}$. Now trace from *A* to *D* to *C* and tell them this arc is written $\overset{\frown}{ADC}$. Emphasize the need for three letters in denoting an arc. Mention that in both cases above, the endpoints were *A* and *C*, but there were two distinctly different arcs. Tell them you want to teach them to measure arcs. Suggest that they think about breaking the circle up into 360 arcs all the same length. Tell them that the measure of each of these small arcs is said to be 1°. Now erase what was written on the transparency and tell them you have twelve dots "equally spaced" on the circle. Pick out two successive dots on the circle and tell them that the measure of the short arc is 30° ($\frac{1}{12} \cdot 360°$). Now label points on the transparency as shown.

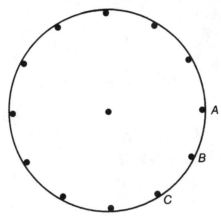

Next argue that m $\overset{\frown}{ABC}$ = 30° + 30° = 60°.

Finally, erase what is on the transparency and label the following dots and direct their attention to $\overset{\frown}{ABC}$.

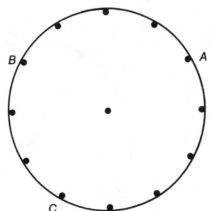

Tell them you want to find m $\overset{\frown}{ABC}$. Move your finger along the arc, counting as you go (shown below).

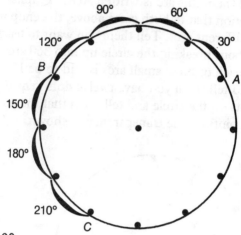

Tell them m $\overset{\frown}{ABC}$ = 210°.

Pass out the worksheets and provide assistance as needed.

## Correct Answers for Worksheet 5–10–1:

1a. 60°
 b. 150°
 c. 30°
 d. 120°
 e. 90°

2a. 120°
 b. 150°
 c. 270°
 d. 270°
 e. 240°
 f. 90°

3a.

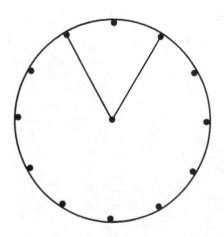

b.

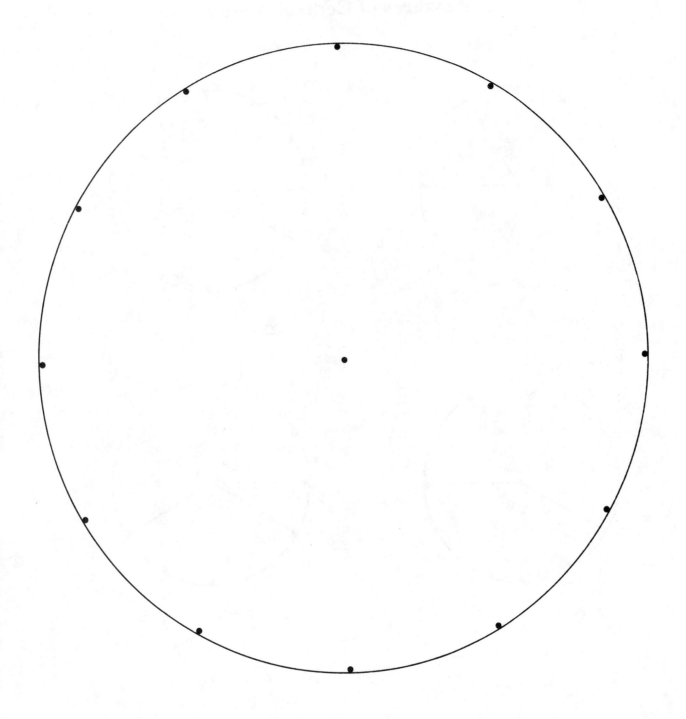

*Visualized Geometry*

Name: _____ Date: _____

# WORKSHEET 5–10–1
## Measures of Central Angles

1. Find the measures of the angles.

a.

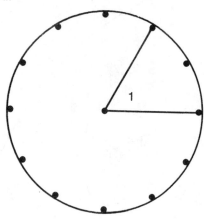

m∠1 =

c.

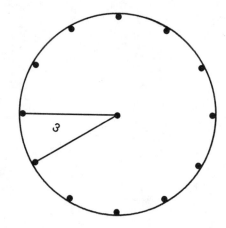

m∠3 =

b.

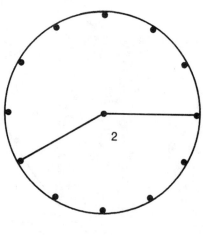

m∠2 =

d.

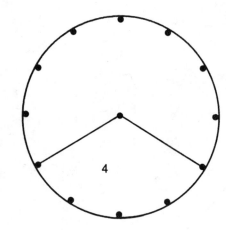

m∠4 =

*(continued)*

*Visualized Geometry*

# WORKSHEET 5–10–1
## Measures of Central Angles *(continued)*

e.

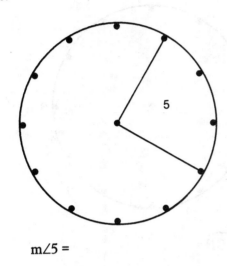

m∠5 =

2. Find the measures of the arcs.

a.

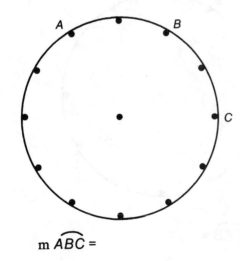

m $\widehat{ABC}$ =

b.

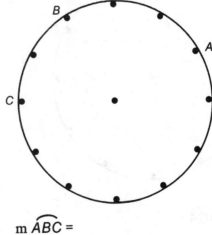

m $\widehat{ABC}$ =

*(continued)*

*Visualized Geometry*

# WORKSHEET 5–10–1
## Measures of Central Angles *(continued)*

c.

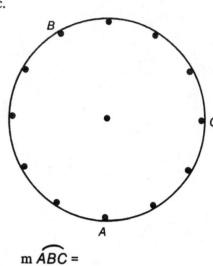

m $\overparen{ABC}$ =

e.

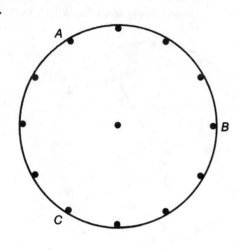

m $\overparen{ACB}$ =

d.

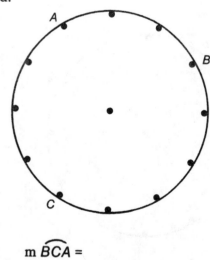

m $\overparen{BCA}$ =

f.

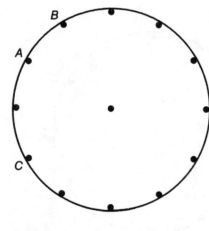

m $\overparen{CAB}$ =

*(continued)*

*Visualized Geometry*

# WORKSHEET 5-10-1
## Measures of Central Angles (*continued*)

3. Draw a central angle with the given measure.

a. 60°

b. 150°

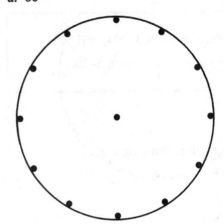

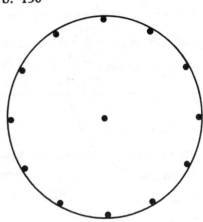

## Lesson 5–11
# Measures of Inscribed Angles

### *Materials Needed:*

One copy of each of the following pages for each student: page 303, 304, and 305.
One transparency of page 295. (This is the transparency used in Lesson 5–10.)

### *Directions for the Teacher:*

Place the transparency on the overhead projector. Draw the following angle.

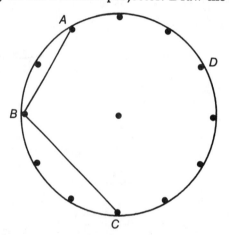

Indicate that an angle in which the vertex is on the circle and which has two other points on the circle is called an inscribed angle. Tell your students that $\overset{\frown}{ADC}$ is the intercepted arc. Suggest that, in general, the intercepted arc is that part of the circle which is "between" the two rays. Ask them about m $\overset{\frown}{ADC}$. (They should respond 210°.) Label the center of the circle $O$ and draw in radii $\overline{OA}$, $\overline{OB}$ and $\overline{OC}$. Label the angles as shown. Tell them that you want to find m∠$ABC$. Point out that m∠$ABC$ = m∠4 + m∠2 and that you intend to find m∠4 and m∠2. Direct their attention to △$OBC$.

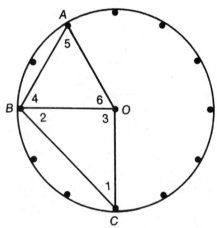

Mention that $OC = OB$ so that $\triangle OBC$ is an isosceles triangle and $m\angle 1 = m\angle 2$. Also

$$m\angle 1 + m\angle 2 + m\angle 3 = 180°, \text{ but}$$
$$m\angle 3 = 90°, \text{ so}$$
$$m\angle 1 + m\angle 2 + 90° = 180°, \text{ or}$$
$$m\angle 1 + m\angle 2 = 90°, \text{ and}$$
$$2m\angle 2 = 90°, \text{ and}$$
$$m\angle 2 = 45°.$$

In a similar way show that $m\angle 4 = 60°$, but
$$m\angle ABC = m\angle 2 + m\angle 4$$
$$= 45° + 60°$$
$$= 105°.$$

Distribute the worksheets and provide individual assistance as needed.

## Correct Answers for Worksheet 5–11–1:

1a. 60°          3a. 90°
  b. 120°          b. 180°

2a. 60°          4a. 120°
  b. 120°          b. 240°

5.

|  | m∠ABC | Measure of intercepted arc |
|---|---|---|
| Class example | 105° | 210° |
| Problem 1 | 60° | 120° |
| Problem 2 | 60° | 120° |
| Problem 3 | 90° | 180° |
| Problem 4 | 120° | 240° |

**6.**

| m∠ABC | Measure of intercepted arc |
|:---:|:---:|
| 48° | 96° |
| 68° | 136° |
| 17° | 34° |
| 151° | 302° |

7a.

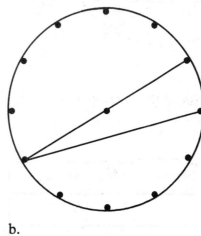

c.

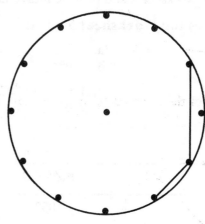

b.

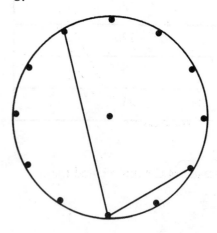

(There are a variety of possible correct answers for problem 7.)

When the worksheets are completed, state the following generalization.

**The measure of an inscribed angle is one half of the measure of the intercepted arc.**

# WORKSHEET 5-11-1
## Measures of Inscribed Angles

1.

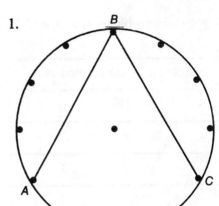

a. m∠ABC =
b. The measure of the intercepted arc
   is _____ .

2.

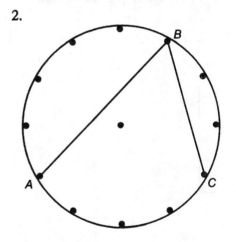

a. m∠ABC =
b. The measure of the intercepted arc
   is _____ .

3.

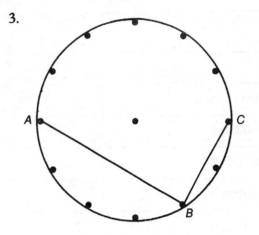

a. m∠ABC =
b. The measure of the intercepted arc
   is _____ .

4.

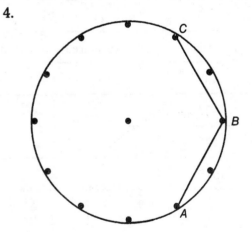

a. m∠ABC =
b. The measure of the intercepted arc
   is _____ .

*(continued)*

*Visualized Geometry*

# WORKSHEET 5-11-1
## Measures of Inscribed Angles *(continued)*

5. Complete the following table using the information you got from problems 1, 2, 3, and 4.

| | m∠ABC | Measure of intercepted arc |
|---|---|---|
| Class example | 105° | 210° |
| Problem 1 | | |
| Problem 2 | | |
| Problem 3 | | |
| Problem 4 | | |

6. Examine the table above for a relationship between the measure of an inscribed angle and the measure of the corresponding intercepted arc. Then complete the table below.

| m∠ABC | Measure of intercepted arc |
|---|---|
| 48° | |
| 68° | |
| 17° | |
| 151° | |

*(continued)*

# WORKSHEET 5-11-1
## Measures of Inscribed Angles *(continued)*

7. Draw a picture of an inscribed angle with the indicated measure.

a. 15°

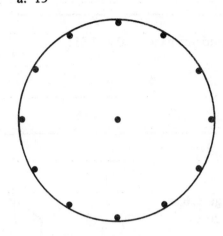

c. 135°

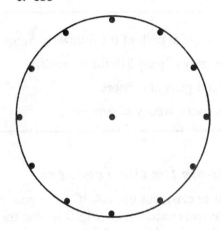

b. 75°

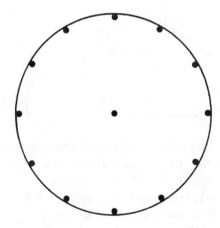

## Lesson 5–12
# Bisectors of the Angles of a Triangle

### *Materials Needed:*

One copy of each of the following pages for each student: pages 310 and 311.

One copy of page 310 for yourself.

Several pairs of scissors.

One transparency of page 309.

### *Directions for the Teacher:*

Prior to class, cut out △ABC from your copy of page 310. As the students watch, fold △ABC so that the fold line goes through *A* so that $\overline{AC}$ and $\overline{AB}$ match in direction. Here is what it should look like.

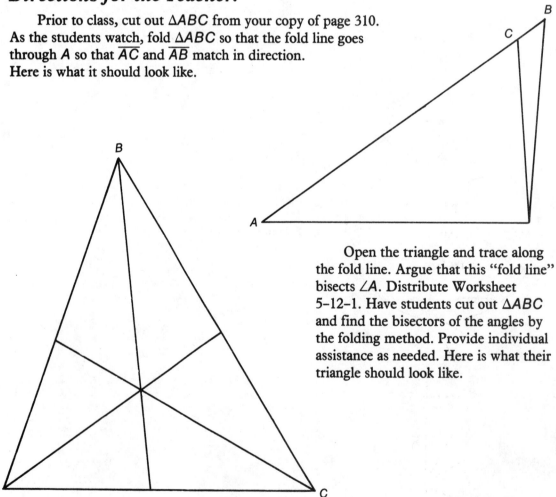

Open the triangle and trace along the fold line. Argue that this "fold line" bisects ∠A. Distribute Worksheet 5–12–1. Have students cut out △ABC and find the bisectors of the angles by the folding method. Provide individual assistance as needed. Here is what their triangle should look like.

Place the transparency on the overhead projector. Label point *D* as shown below, draw $\overline{AD}$, and argue that $\angle BAD \cong \angle DAC$ because the intercepted arcs are the same size. Indicate that $\overline{AD}$ (actually $\overrightarrow{AD}$) bisects $\angle A$ of the original triangle.

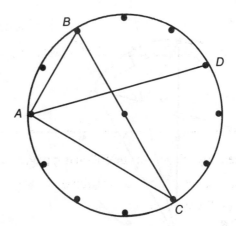

Find bisectors of the other angles by first finding midpoints of the appropriate arcs.

**Correct Answers for Transparency 5–12–1:**

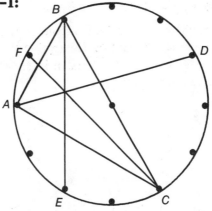

Distribute Worksheet 5–12–2 and provide individual assistance as needed.

**Correct Answers for Worksheet 5–12–2:**

1.

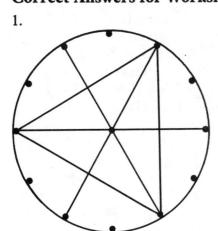

2.

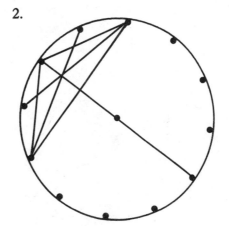

3.

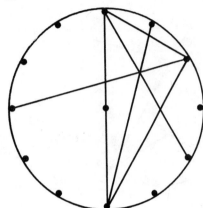

4.

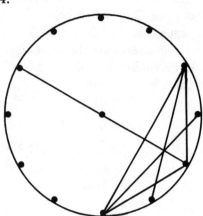

Find the bisectors of the angles of △*ABC*.

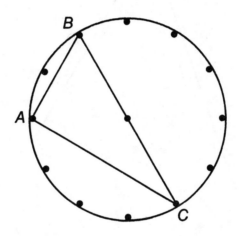

Name: _____ Date: _____

# WORKSHEET 5-12-1
## Bisectors of the Angles of a Triangle

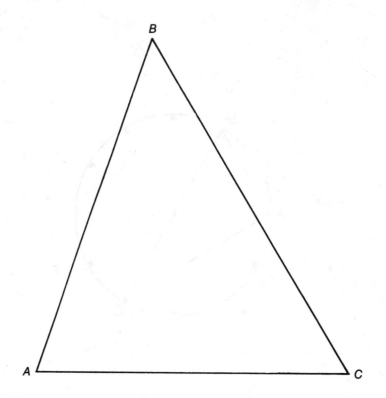

310    *Visualized Geometry*

Name: _____ Date: _____

# WORKSHEET 5–12–2
## Bisectors of the Angles of a Triangle

Find the bisectors of the angles of the triangles pictured below.

1.

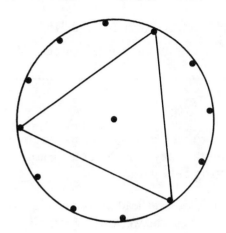

3.

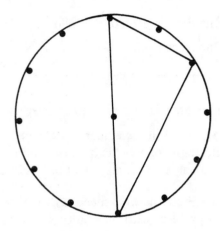

2.

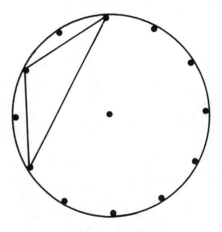

4.

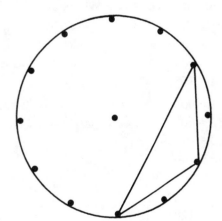

*Visualized Geometry*

## Lesson 5-13
# Measures of Angles in Cyclic Quadrilaterals

## *Materials Needed:*

One copy of each of the following pages for each student: pages 314 and 315.

One transparency of page 314. (Note that this is also a student worksheet page.)

## *Directions for the Teacher:*

In this lesson the students are expected to discover that the sum of the measures of opposite angles of a cyclic quadrilateral is 180°. To do this they must find the measures of inscribed angles. You may want to briefly review Lesson 5-11 with them.

Distribute the worksheets. Put the transparency on the overhead projector. Go through the first problem with the students. Direct them to complete the worksheets. Provide individual assistance as needed.

### Correct Answers for Worksheet 5-13-1:

1. $m\angle 1 = 75°$
   $m\angle 2 = 105°$
   $m\angle 3 = 105°$
   $m\angle 4 = 75°$

2. $m\angle 1 = 90°$
   $m\angle 2 = 60°$
   $m\angle 3 = 90°$
   $m\angle 4 = 120°$

3. $m\angle 1 = 60°$
   $m\angle 2 = 105°$
   $m\angle 3 = 120°$
   $m\angle 4 = 75°$

4. $m\angle 1 = 60°$
   $m\angle 2 = 75°$
   $m\angle 3 = 120°$
   $m\angle 4 = 105°$

5. $m\angle 1 = 120°$
   $m\angle 2 = 90°$
   $m\angle 3 = 60°$
   $m\angle 4 = 90°$

6. $m\angle 1 = 45°$
   $m\angle 2 = 150°$
   $m\angle 3 = 135°$
   $m\angle 4 = 30°$

7a. $m\angle 1 + m\angle 3 = 180°$
   b. $m\angle 2 + m\angle 4 = 180°$
   c. The sum of the measures of opposite angles of a cyclic quadrilateral is 180°. (The angles are supplementary.)

After the worksheets have been completed, you should emphasize that this only holds in cyclic quadrilaterals, not all quadrilaterals. To establish this draw a picture like the following on the blackboard.

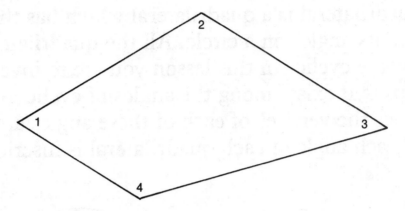

Point out that in this case m∠1 + m∠3 < 180° and m∠2 + m∠4 > 180° and the students should be able to tell this by inspection.

Name: _____ Date: _____

# WORKSHEET 5-13-1
## Measures of Angles in Cyclic Quadrilaterals

A cyclic quadrilateral is a quadrilateral which has the vertices of all four of its angles on a circle. All the quadrilaterals pictured below are cyclic. In this lesson you are to investigate relationships that exist among the angles of cyclic quadrilaterals. Since the vertices of each of these angles are all points on a circle, each angle of each quadrilateral is inscribed in the circle.

1.

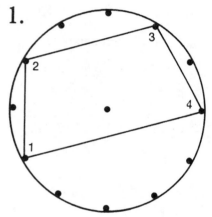

m∠1 =
m∠2 =
m∠3 =
m∠4 =

3.

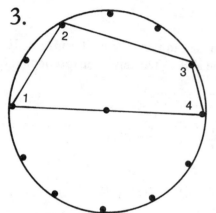

m∠1 =
m∠2 =
m∠3 =
m∠4 =

2.

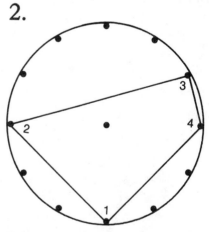

m∠1 =
m∠2 =
m∠3 =
m∠4 =

4.

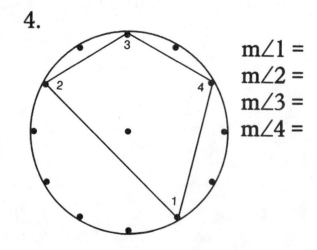

m∠1 =
m∠2 =
m∠3 =
m∠4 =

*(continued)*

*Visualized Geometry*

## WORKSHEET 5-13-1
### Measures of Angles in Cyclic Quadrilaterals *(continued)*

5.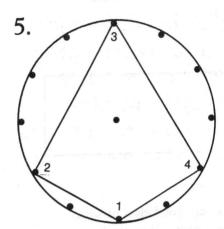

m∠1 =
m∠2 =
m∠3 =
m∠4 =

6.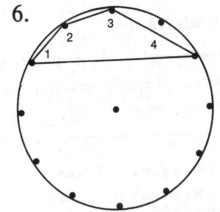

m∠1 =
m∠2 =
m∠3 =
m∠4 =

7. In each of the problems above, ∠1 and ∠3 are opposite angles and ∠2 and ∠4 are opposite angles.

a. In each case, what is the sum of the measures of ∠1 and ∠3?

b. In each case, what is the sum of the measures of ∠2 and ∠4?

c. State a generalization about opposite angles of cyclic quadrilaterals.

     *Visualized Geometry*

## Lesson 5–14
# Measures of Angles That Intersect Circles

### *Materials Needed:*

One copy of page 320 for each student.

One transparency of page 319.

### *Directions for the Teacher:*

This is a difficult lesson. You may want to use it with only a very good class or with only a select group of students in a more standard class. Place the transparency on the overhead projector. Direct the students' attention to problem 1a. Draw in the chord and label the angles as illustrated below.

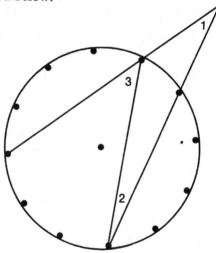

Go through the following argument.

$m\angle 3 = 45°$ (one half the measure of the intercepted arc)

$m\angle 2 = 15°$ (one half the measure of the intercepted arc)

$m\angle 3 = m\angle 1 + m\angle 2$ (measure of exterior angle is the sum of measures of remote interior angles)

$m\angle 1 = m\angle 3 - m\angle 2$

$\quad\quad = 45° - 15°$

$\quad\quad = 30°$

Proceed to problem 1b. Again, draw in the chord and label the angles as shown.

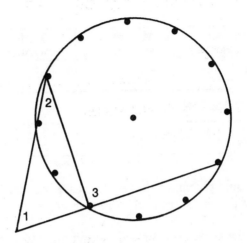

Go through the argument below.

$$m\angle 3 = 90°$$
$$m\angle 2 = 30°$$
$$m\angle 3 = m\angle 1 + m\angle 2$$
$$m\angle 1 = m\angle 3 - m\angle 2$$
$$= 60°$$

Proceed in a similar way with problem 1c.

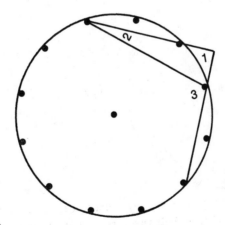

$$m\angle 3 = 105°$$
$$m\angle 2 = 15°$$
$$m\angle 3 = m\angle 1 + m\angle 2$$
$$m\angle 1 = m\angle 3 - m\angle 2$$
$$= 105° - 15°$$
$$= 90°$$

Next, complete the table (problem 2). The arcs referred to are the two arcs intercepted by the sides of the angles.

| Problem | Measure of bigger arc | Measure of smaller arc | Difference in measures of arcs | m∠1 |
|---------|----------------------|------------------------|--------------------------------|------|
| 1a. | 90° | 30° | 60° | 30 |
| 1b. | 180° | 60° | 120° | 60 |
| 1c. | 210° | 30° | 180° | 90 |

The students should recognize that in each case the measure of the original angle is one half the difference of the measures of the intercepted arcs.

Distribute the worksheet. Provide individual assistance as needed.

## Correct Answers for Worksheet 5-14-1:

1a. 75°
  b. 60°
  c. 45°

2.

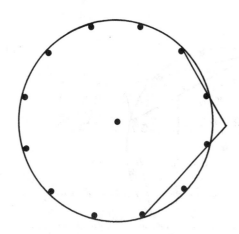

(Other orientations are possible.)

1. Find the measure of the angle.

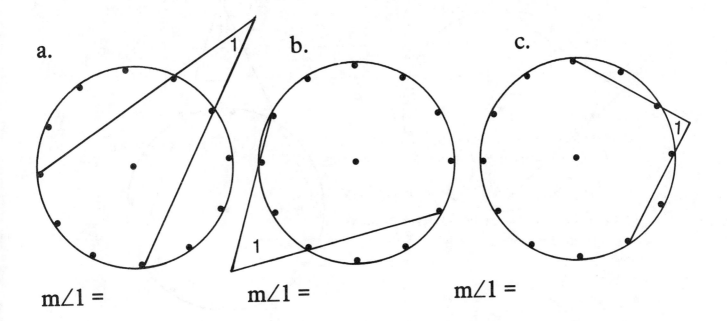

a.        b.        c.

m∠1 =       m∠1 =       m∠1 =

| Problem | Measure of bigger arc | Measure of smaller arc | Difference in measures of arcs | m∠1 |
|---------|----------------------|------------------------|-------------------------------|-----|
| 1a. | | | | |
| 1b. | | | | |
| 1c. | | | | |

*Visualized Geometry*

# WORKSHEET 5-14-1
## Measures of Angles That Intersect Circles

1. Use the generalization made in class to find m∠1.

a.

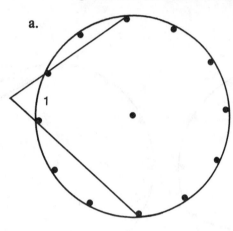

m∠1 =

c.

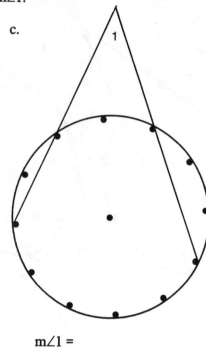

m∠1 =

b.

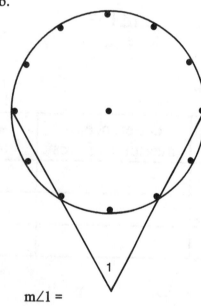

m∠1 =

2. Draw a picture of an angle with the following properties: the vertex of the angle is outside the circle, the angle intersects the circle in four points, and the measure of the angle is 105°.

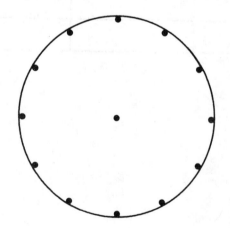

*Visualized Geometry*

# Lesson 5–15
# Measures of Angles with Vertices Inside Circles

## *Materials Needed:*

One copy of page 325 for each student.

One transparency of page 324.

## *Directions for the Teacher:*

Like Lesson 5–14, this lesson is difficult and you may want to use it only with a very good class or with a select group of students in a more standard class. Place the transparency on the overhead projector. Direct the students' attention to problem 1a. Draw in the chord and label the angles as illustrated here.

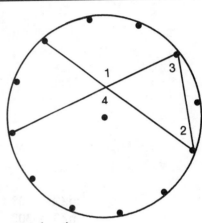

Go through the following argument.

m∠2 = 45° (one half the measure of the intercepted arc)

m∠3 = 75° (one half the measure of the intercepted arc)

m∠1 = m∠2 + m∠3 (measure of exterior angle is sum of measures of remote interior angles)

m∠1 = 45° + 75°

     = 120°

Proceed to problem 1b. Again draw in the chord and label the angles as shown below.

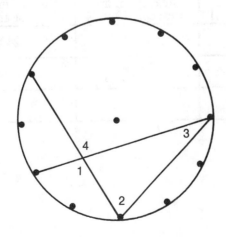

Go through the following argument.

$$m\angle 2 = 75°$$
$$m\angle 3 = 30°$$
$$m\angle 1 = m\angle 2 + m\angle 3$$
$$= 75° + 30°$$
$$= 105°$$

Proceed with problem 1c in a similar way.

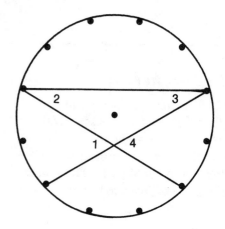

$$m\angle 2 = 30°$$
$$m\angle 3 = 30°$$
$$m\angle 1 = m\angle 2 + m\angle 3$$
$$= 30° + 30°$$
$$= 60°$$

Next proceed to the table. Point out that in each case, $\angle 4$ is the angle which is vertical to $\angle 1$. Here is what the completed table should look like.

| Problem | Measure of arc intercepted by $\angle 1$ | Measure of arc intercepted by $\angle 4$ | Sum of measures of arcs | $m\angle 1$ |
|---------|-----------------|-----------------|-----------------|------|
| 1a. | 90° | 150° | 240° | 120° |
| 1b. | 60° | 150° | 210° | 105° |
| 1c. | 60° | 60° | 120° | 60° |

The students should recognize that in each case the measure of an angle with its vertex inside a circle is one half the sum of the measures of the arcs intercepted by the angle and the angle vertical to it.

Distribute the worksheet. Provide individual assistance as needed.

## Correct Answers for Worksheet 5–15–1:

1a. 150°
  b. 45°
  c. 60°

2.

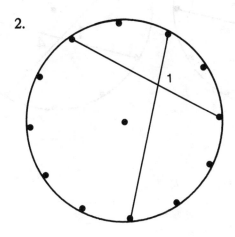

(Other answers are possible.)

## 1. Find the measure of ∠1.

a.

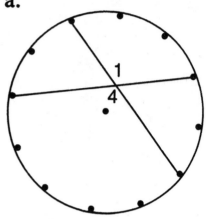

b.

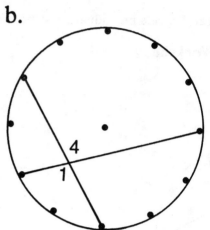

c.

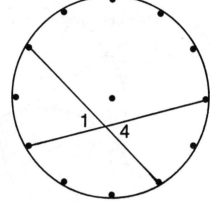

## 2. Complete the table.

| Problem | Measure of arc intercepted by ∠1 | Measure of intercepted by ∠4 | Sum of measures of arcs | m∠1 |
|---------|----------------------------------|------------------------------|-------------------------|------|
| 1a. | | | | |
| 1b. | | | | |
| 1c. | | | | |

*Visualized Geometry*

# WORKSHEET 5-15-1
## Measures of Angles with Vertices Inside Circles

1. Use the generalization made in class to find the m∠1.

a.

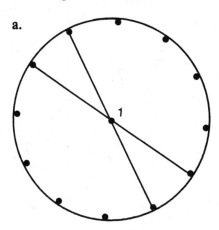

m∠1 =

c.

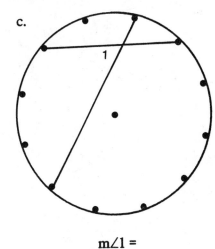

m∠1 =

b.

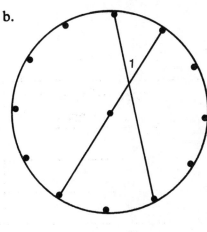

m∠1 =

2. Draw a picture of an angle with the following properties: the vertex of the angle is inside the circle, the angle intersects the circle in four points, and the measure of the angle is 105°.

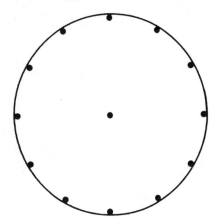

# WORKSHEET 8-15-1
## Measures of Angles with Vertices Inside Circles

Use the generalization made in class to find the $m\angle$.

$m\angle 1 =$

$m\angle 2 =$

$m\angle 3 =$

2. Draw a picture of an angle with the following properties: the vertex of the angle is inside the circle, the angle intersects the circle in four points, and the measure of the angle is 35°.

# CHAPTER 6

# Congruence and Line Symmetry

## Comments and Suggestions

In a standard high school geometry course, congruence is the geometric relation which receives the most attention. However, most geometry textbooks proceed almost immediately to a formal interpretation of congruence without the necessary informal intuitive development of the topic. It is hard to prove that two figures are congruent if you do not know what it means for two figures to be congruent. In this chapter, students initially learn about the congruency of two figures by tracing one of these figures on a blank transparency and fitting this copy on the other figure. Then they proceed to identify congruent figures by looking at dot paper pictures and finally, they draw a figure congruent to a pictured dot paper figure. In Lesson 6–4, students learn the SSS congruence relationship by examining triangles which are formed by strips of paper or cardboard. They also learn that the SSSS congruence relationship does not hold for quadrilaterals.

Line symmetry is motivated with paper-folding activities. Eventually students are required to find symmetry lines for dot paper figures and to complete figures given portions of those figures together with symmetry lines.

# Lesson 6-1
# Review of Congruence Concepts

## *Materials Needed:*

One copy of each of the following pages for each student: pages 331 and 332.

One transparency of each of the following pages: pages 329 and 330.

One blank transparency and one overhead projector pen for each student.

## *Directions for the Teacher:*

This is a brief but important review of Lesson 1-2. Place the first transparency on your overhead projector. Read the statement at the top of the page and discuss it briefly. Your discussion should center around what a copy is, how you can copy a figure on a blank transparency and what it means for the copy to fit on the other figure.

On your blank transparency trace triangle I of problem 1. Then slide this transparency so that the copy of triangle I fits on triangle II. Conclude that the triangles are congruent. Proceed in a similar way with problem 2. This time you must turn the transparency (copy) around to make the copy of triangle I fit on triangle II. Continue with problem 3. This time you must turn the transparency over to make the copy of triangle I fit on triangle II. Place the second transparency on the overhead projector and go on to problem 4. This time the copy of triangle I will not fit on triangle II so the triangles are not congruent. Proceed in a similar way with problems 5 and 6. In both cases the quadrilaterals are congruent. For problem 6 the transparency must be turned over.

## Correct Answers for Transparencies 6-1-1 and 6-1-2:

1. yes                    4. no
2. yes                    5. yes
3. yes                    6. yes

Distribute the worksheets. Provide individual assistance as needed.

## Correct Answers for Worksheet 6-1-1:

1. yes                    4. yes
2. yes                    5. yes
3. no                     6. yes

Two figures are congruent if a copy of one can be made to fit on the other.

1. Is triangle I congruent to triangle II?

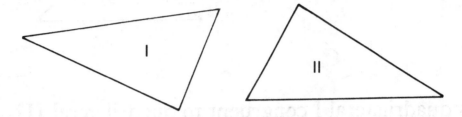

2. Is triangle I congruent to triangle II?

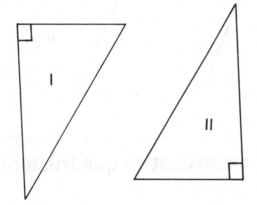

3. Is triangle I congruent to triangle II?

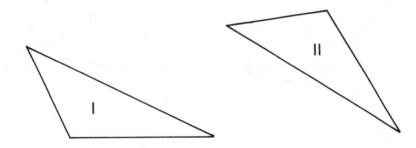

     *Visualized Geometry*

4.  Is triangle I congruent to triangle II?

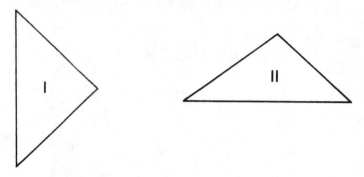

5.  Is quadrilateral I congruent to quadrilateral II?

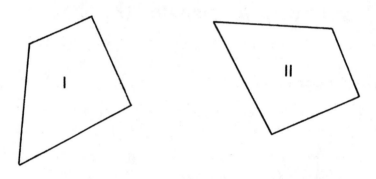

6.  Is quadrilateral I congruent to quadrilateral II?

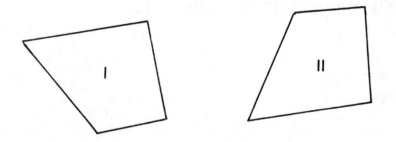

           *Visualized Geometry*

# WORKSHEET 6-1-1
## Review of Congruence Concepts

Use a blank transparency to find out whether the figures are congruent.

1. Is triangle I congruent to triangle II?

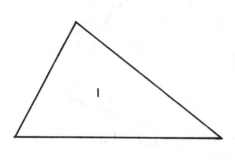
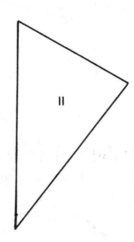

2. Is triangle I congruent to triangle II?

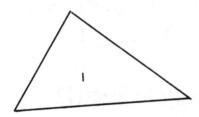
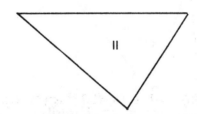

3. Is triangle I congruent to triangle II?

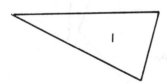

*(continued)*

*Visualized Geometry*

# WORKSHEET 6-1-1
## Review of Congruence Concepts (continued)

4. Is quadrilateral I congruent to quadrilateral II?

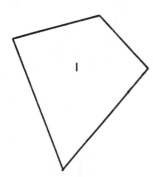
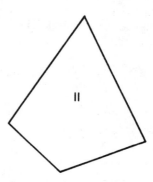

5. Is quadrilateral I congruent to quadrilateral II?

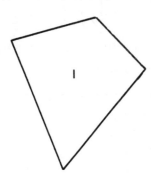
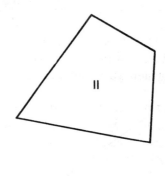

6. Is quadrilateral I congruent to quadrilateral II?

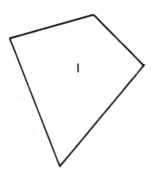
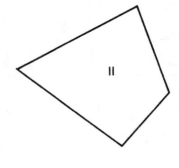

**Lesson 6-2**
# Congruence Correspondences

## *Materials Needed:*

> One copy of each of the following pages for each student: pages 335, 337, 338, and 339.
>
> One transparency of each of the following pages: pages 335 and 336. (Note: Page 335 is also a student worksheet page.)

## *Directions for the Teacher:*

Put the first transparency on the overhead projector. Briefly review the concept of congruence introduced in Lesson 6-1. Specifically mention that two figures are congruent when a copy of one figure exactly fits on the second figure. Indicate that in this lesson a more formal view of congruence will be developed. Go through the discussion involving $\triangle ABC$ and $\triangle DEF$. The students should immediately see that these triangles are congruent.

Place the second transparency on the projector. Try to get your students to "see" that the quadrilaterals are actually congruent. If some students really have difficulty with this idea, copy quadrilateral *ABCD* on a blank transparency and show that this copy exactly fits on quadrilateral *FGHE*. Proceed with the discussion on the transparency.

Distribute the worksheets. Provide individual assistance as needed. Again expect the students to "see" the congruence involved, but for those students who have significant difficulty with this approach, allow them to copy one figure on a blank transparency and check to see if it matches the second figure.

### Correct Answers for Worksheet 6-2-2:

1. $\triangle ABC \cong \triangle EFD$, $\triangle ABC \cong \triangle GIH$, $\triangle ABC \cong \triangle KJL$, $\triangle ABC \cong \triangle OMN$

2a. yes
 b. $\triangle ABC \cong \triangle EDF$

3a. no
 b. does not apply

4a. yes
 b. rectangle *ABCD* $\cong$ rectangle *HEFG*

(There are several correct answers for problem 4b, each of which can be expressed in several ways. All the distinct correct answers include: rectangle *ABCD* $\cong$ rectangle *HEFG*, rectangle *ABCD* $\cong$ rectangle *EHGF*, rectangle *ABCD* $\cong$ rectangle *FGHE*, and rectangle *ABCD* $\cong$ rectangle *GFEH*.)

5a. no
  b. does not apply

6a. no
  b. does not apply

7a. yes
  b. trapezoid $ABCD \cong$ trapezoid $FGHE$

8a. yes
  b. trapezoid $ABCD \cong$ trapezoid $GHEF$

(The congruences indicated in problems 1, 2b, 4b, 7b, and 8b can be expressed in several different ways, but each of these ways still defines the same congruence relationship. For example, the congruence relationship in problem 2 can be stated $\triangle ABC \cong \triangle EDF$, $\triangle BCA \cong \triangle DFE$, $\triangle CAB \cong \triangle FED$, $\triangle CBA \cong \triangle FDE$, etc. Each of these establishes the correspondence $A \leftrightarrow E$, $B \leftrightarrow D$, and $C \leftrightarrow F$.)

# WORKSHEET/TRANSPARENCY 6-2-1
## Congruence Correspondences

The symbol "≅" is read "is congruent to." When this symbol is used it is agreed the order in which the letters representing the vertices of a triangle are written indicates the correspondence.

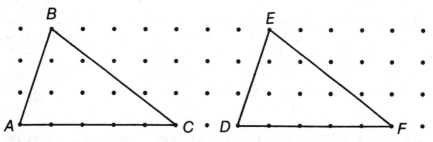

The two triangles are congruent and we indicate this by writing

$$\triangle ABC \cong \triangle DEF.$$

This defines the correspondence between the vertices as

$$A \longleftrightarrow D,$$
$$B \longleftrightarrow E, \text{ and}$$
$$C \longleftrightarrow F.$$

The following congruences of corresponding parts are implied.

$$\angle A \cong \angle D \qquad\qquad \overline{AB} \cong \overline{DE}$$
$$\angle B \cong \angle E \qquad\qquad \overline{AC} \cong \overline{DF}$$
$$\angle C \cong \angle F \qquad\qquad \overline{BC} \cong \overline{EF}$$

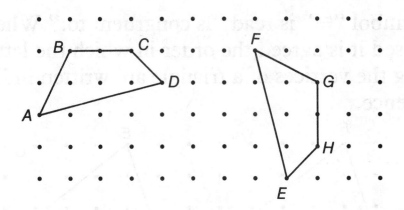

Note that the two quadrilaterals are congruent with the correspondence between vertices of

$$A \longleftrightarrow F$$
$$B \longleftrightarrow G$$
$$C \longleftrightarrow H$$
$$D \longleftrightarrow E.$$

In this situation we write quadrilateral $ABCD \cong$ quadrilateral $FGHE$. The implied congruences are as follows:

$$\angle A \cong \angle F \qquad \overline{AB} \cong \overline{FG}$$
$$\angle B \cong \angle G \qquad \overline{BC} \cong \overline{GH}$$
$$\angle C \cong \angle H \qquad \overline{CD} \cong \overline{HE}$$
$$\angle D \cong \angle E \qquad \overline{DA} \cong \overline{EF}$$

# WORKSHEET 6-2-2
## Congruence Correspondences

1. Triangle *ABC* is congruent to each of the other triangles pictured below. Write a congruence statement which establishes the correspondence.

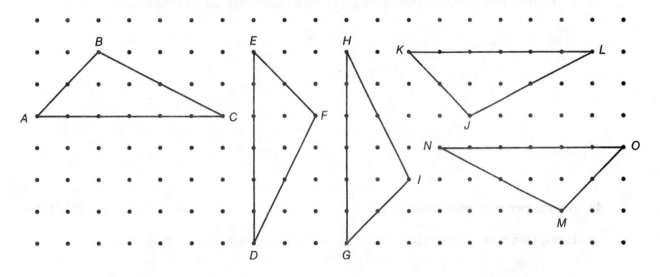

2a. Are the two triangles congruent?

b. If yes, then write a congruence statement which establishes the correspondence.

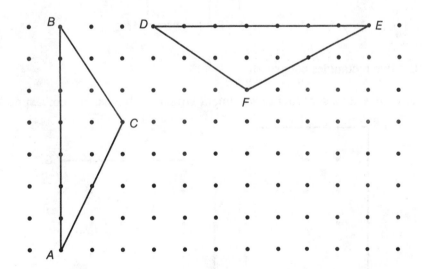

*(continued)*

         *Visualized Geometry*

# WORSHEET 6-2-2
## Congruence Correspondences *(continued)*

**3a.** Are the two triangles congruent?

  **b.** If yes, then write a congruence statement which establishes the correspondence.

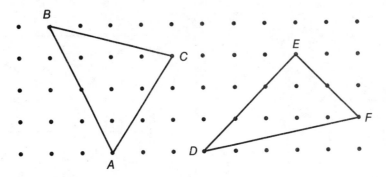

**4a.** Are the two rectangles congruent?

  **b.** If yes, then write a congruence statement which establishes the correspondence.

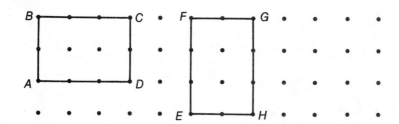

**5a.** Are the two rectangles congruent?

  **b.** If yes, then write a congruence statement which establishes the correspondence.

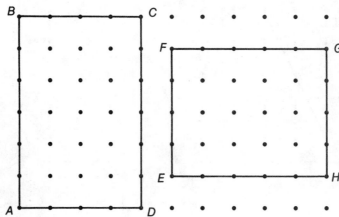

*(continued)*

# WORKSHEET 6-2-2
## Congruence Correspondences *(continued)*

6a. Are the parallelograms congruent?

b. If yes, then write a congruence statement which establishes the correspondence.

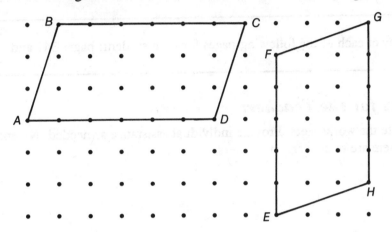

7a. Are the trapezoids congruent?

b. If yes, then write a congruence statement which establishes the correspondence.

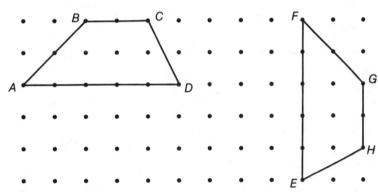

8a. Are the trapezoids congruent?

b. If yes, then write a congruence statement which establishes the correspondence.

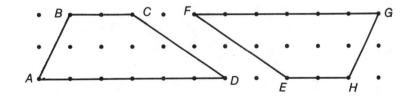

## Lesson 6–3
# Drawing Congruent Figures

### *Materials Needed:*

One copy of each of the following pages for each student: pages 341 and 342.

### *Directions for the Teacher:*

Distribute the worksheets. Provide individual assistance as needed. No answers are given since there are many correct answers.

# WORKSHEET 6-3-1
## Drawing Congruent Figures

1. On the dot paper below, draw a triangle congruent to the one pictured.

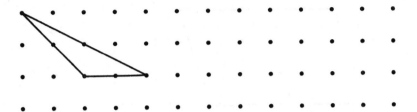

2. On the dot paper below, draw a quadrilateral congruent to the one pictured.

3. On the dot paper below, draw a rectangle congruent to the one pictured.

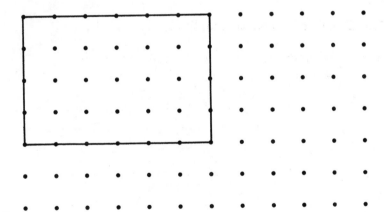

*(continued)*

Name: _____ Date: _____

# WORKSHEET 6-3-1
## Drawing Congruent Figures *(continued)*

4. On the dot paper below, draw a parallelogram congruent to the one pictured.

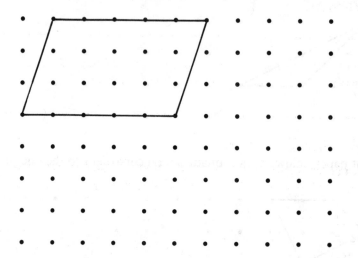

5. On the dot paper below, draw a pentagon congruent to the one pictured.

 *Visualized Geometry*

# Lesson 6-4
# The Triangle SSS Relationship

## *Materials Needed:*

The strips which were originally in the Appendix (on pages 425, 427, 429, and 431) and which have been used in several previous lessons.

## *Directions for the Teacher:*

Make up six packets with each packet consisting of four fasteners, two strips labeled "a," one strip labeled "b," one strip labeled "c," and one strip labeled "d."

The purpose of this lesson is to demonstrate that two triangles are congruent when the three sides of one triangle are congruent to the three sides of the other triangle (SSS), and that two quadrilaterals are not necessarily congruent when the four sides of one quadrilateral are congruent to the four sides of another quadrilateral. Break your class into six groups and give each group one packet of materials. Tell your students that all the pieces with the same label are the same length. Tell your students to take the two pieces labeled "a" and the piece labeled "b" and put them together using the fasteners. Pair up the groups and ask them to compare triangles. They should conclude (with your help) that the triangles are congruent.

Next, tell them to take this triangle apart and to make a new triangle with pieces labeled "a," "b," and "c." Again, ask the groups to compare triangles. Again, they should conclude that the two triangles are congruent although this time they may need to turn one of the triangles over to show they match. Proceed in a similar way with pieces labeled "b," "c," and "d." Again they should conclude that the two triangles are congruent. Then write the following on the chalkboard or on a blank transparency.

**When three sides of one triangle are congruent to the three sides of another triangle, then the triangles are congruent.**

Mention that this is often called the side, side, side (SSS) congruency relationship.

Next, ask each group to make a quadrilateral using pieces labeled "a," "b," "c," and "d." Have them do this by attaching piece "a" to piece "b," piece "b" to piece "c," piece "c" to piece "d," and finally piece "d" to piece "a." Now pair the groups and ask them to compare quadrilaterals. They should conclude that the quadrilaterals may be congruent but they do not necessarily have to be congruent. Emphasize that the quadrilaterals are not rigid like the triangles were. Then, on the chalkboard or a transparency, write the following.

**When four sides of one quadrilateral are congruent to four sides of another quadrilateral, the quadrilaterals may or may not be congruent.**

## Lesson 6–5
# Symmetry Lines by Paper-Folding Methods

### *Materials Needed:*

One copy of page 346 for each student and one copy of that page for yourself.

One pair of scissors for each student.

### *Directions for the Teacher:*

Prior to class, cut out the rectangle from page 346. Begin class by telling the students that when a plane figure has a line of symmetry, the parts of the figure on opposite sides of the line of symmetry "match." Indicate that one way to tell whether a figure has a line of symmetry is to cut out the figure and fold along the potential line of symmetry. If the two parts match, the fold line is a line of symmetry. Fold your rectangle as indicated below.

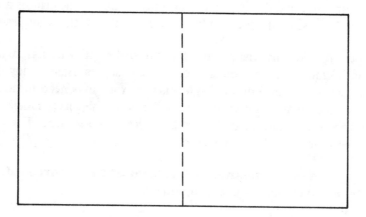

Emphasize that the two "halves" of the rectangle match, which means the fold line is a line of symmetry for the rectangle. Now fold as indicated below.

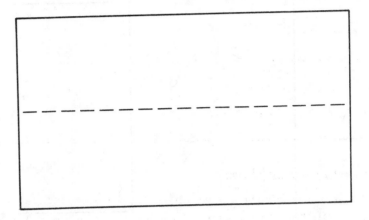

Students should agree that this is another line of symmetry for the rectangle. Now ask them if they think the rectangle has any other lines of symmetry. Someone will probably suggest that a diagonal may be a line of symmetry. If no one makes that suggestion, suggest that possibility yourself. Now fold the rectangle along a diagonal.

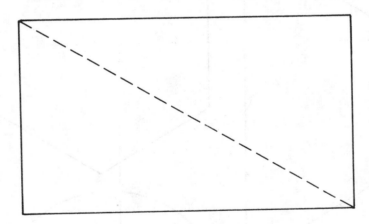

They should see that even though the resulting triangles are congruent, they do not match relative to the fold line. This means that a diagonal is not a symmetry line for a rectangle.

Now pass out the worksheet. Have students cut out the figures and fold to find lines of symmetry.

### Correct Answers for Worksheet 6–5–1:

1. Figure I has two symmetry lines (already completed).

2. Figure II has four symmetry lines.

3. Figure III has three symmetry lines.

4. Figure IV has six symmetry lines.

5. Figure V has zero symmetry lines.

6. Figure VI has many (an infinite number of) symmetry lines.

# WORKSHEET 6–5–1
## Symmetry Lines by Paper-Folding Methods

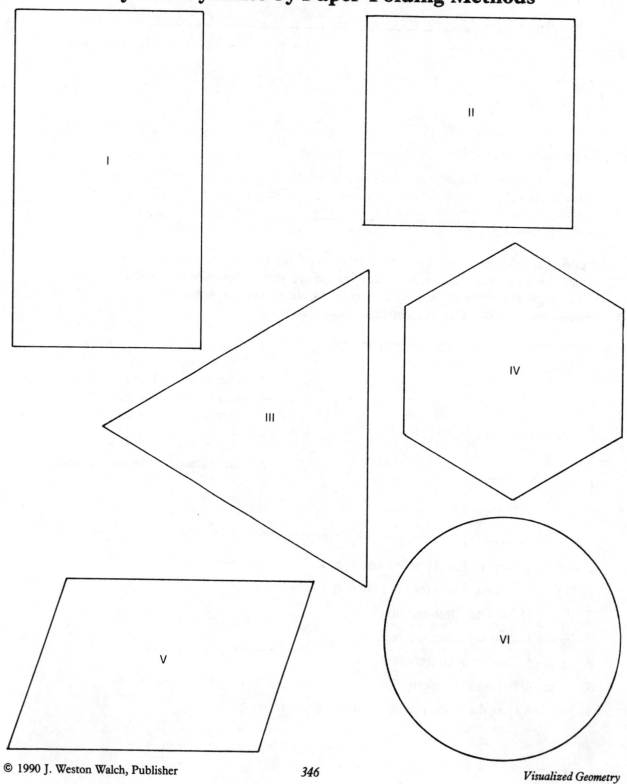

## Lesson 6-6
# Finding Lines of Symmetry in Dot Paper Pictures

### *Materials Needed:*

One copy of each of the following pages for each student: pages 350 and 351.

One transparency of page 349.

### *Directions for the Teacher:*

Briefly review the concept of a line of symmetry (Lesson 6–5). Place the transparency on the overhead projector and consider problem 1. With your students' help, draw in the lines of symmetry. (There are two lines of symmetry, one vertical and one horizontal.) Proceed to problem 2. With student assistance, complete the figure as shown below.

2.

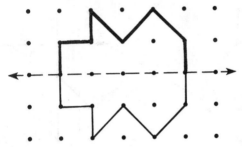

Distribute copies of the worksheets. Provide individual assistance as needed.

### Correct Answers for Worksheet 6-6-1:

1.

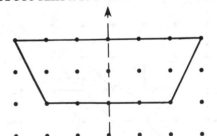

2.

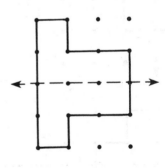

3.

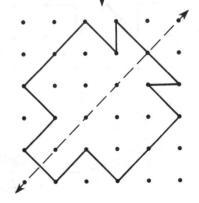

4.

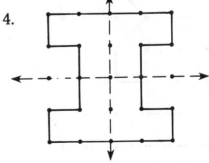

5.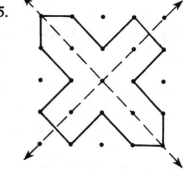

6.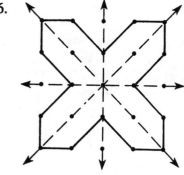

7.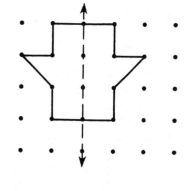

8.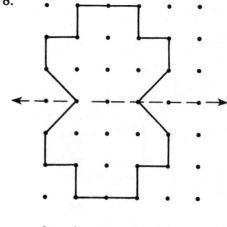

9.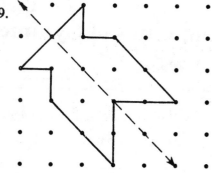

10.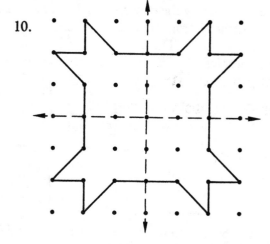

11.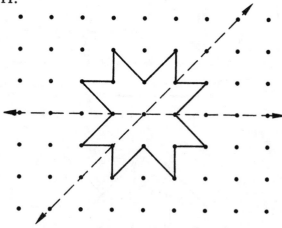

1. Find all symmetry lines.

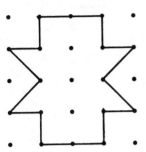

2. Complete the figure so the given line is a symmetry line for the completed figure.

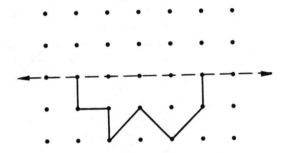

*Visualized Geometry*

# WORKSHEET 6-6-1
## Finding Lines of Symmetry in Dot Paper Pictures

Find *all* lines of symmetry.

1.
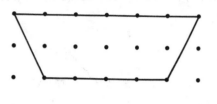

4.
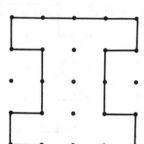

2.
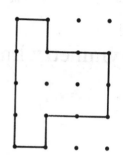

5.
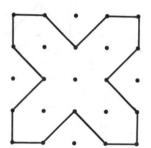

3.
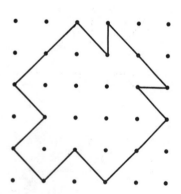

6.
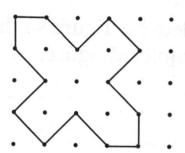

*(continued)*

*Visualized Geometry*

# WORKSHEET 6-6-1
## Finding Lines of Symmetry in
## Dot Paper Pictures (continued)

Complete the figure so that each dashed line is a line of symmetry for the completed figure.

7.

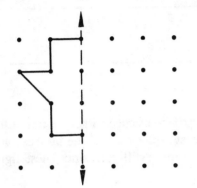

10.

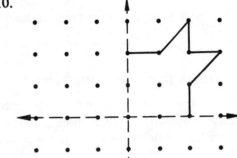

8.

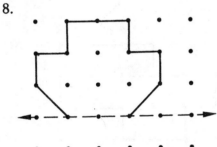

11.

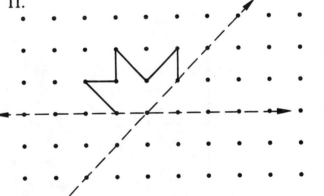

9.

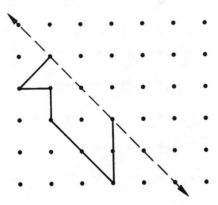

## Lesson 6-7
# Separating a Figure into Two Congruent Parts

### Materials Needed:

One copy of page 353 for each student.

### Directions for the Teacher:

Briefly review the concept of congruence. Distribute the worksheet. Provide individual assistance as needed. The first three problems are fairly easy, since each of the figures has a symmetry line. However, the last three problems are much more difficult, since these figures do not have a line of symmetry.

### Correct Answers for Worksheet 6-7-1:

1.

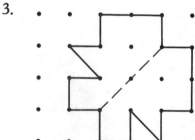

2.

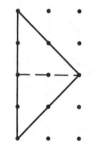

3.

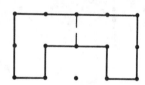

4.

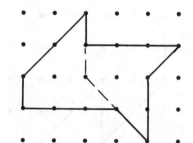

5.

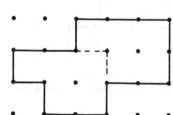

6.

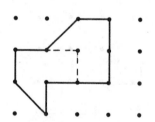

# WORKSHEET 6-7-1
## Separating a Figure into Two Congruent Parts

Show how you could cut the pictured region into two smaller congruent regions. (Problems 1 and 4 are done for you.)

1.
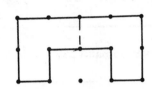

4.
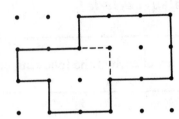

2.
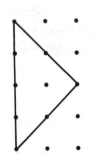

5.
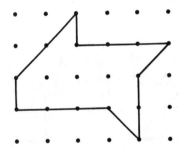

3.
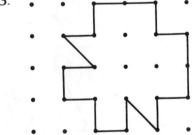

6.

## Lesson 6-8
# Noncongruent Triangles and Squares on Dot Paper

## *Materials Needed:*

One copy of each of the following pages for each student: pages 356 and 357.

## *Directions for the Teacher:*

Briefly review the meaning of the words *acute*, *obtuse*, *right*, *scalene*, *isosceles*, and *equilateral* in the context of triangles. Distribute the worksheet. Provide individual assistance as needed.

### Correct Answers for Worksheet 6-8-1:
I.
1a.       c.       e.       g.

b.       d.       f.       h.

(Students' answers will vary because the triangles need not be listed in the order shown above.)

2. g, h
3. e, f
4. a, b, c, d
5. d, e, f
6. a, b, c, g, h
7. There are none.

II.
1a.      b.      c.

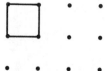

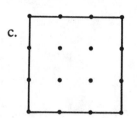

**Correct Answers for Worksheet 6-8-1** *(continued)*:

1d.

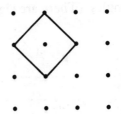

e.

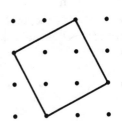

Name: _____ Date: _____

# WORKSHEET 6-8-1
## Noncongruent Triangles and Squares on Dot Paper

I. Using only the nine dots, form all possible noncongruent triangles. (There are eight of them.)

1a.    c.    e.    g.

b.    d.    f.    h.

2. Which of these triangles are acute triangles?

3. Which of these triangles are obtuse triangles?

4. Which of these triangles are right triangles?

5. Which of these triangles are scalene triangles?

6. Which of these triangles are isosceles triangles?

7. Which of these triangles are equilateral triangles?

II. Using only the 16 dots, form all possible noncongruent squares.

1a.    b.    c.

*(continued)*

*Visualized Geometry*

# WORKSHEET 6-8-1
## Noncongruent Triangles and Squares on
## Dot Paper *(continued)*

d.

. . . .

. . . .

. . . .

. . . .

e.

. . . .

. . . .

. . . .

. . . .

     *Visualized Geometry*

# Lesson 6–9
# Paper Cutting and Predictions

## *Materials Needed:*

One copy of each of the following pages for each student: pages 359, 360, 361, and 362.

One pair of scissors and sixteen pieces of $8\frac{1}{2}$ " x 11" paper.

## *Directions for the Teacher:*

Take a piece of $8\frac{1}{2}$ " x 11" paper and fold and cut it as shown below. (In most cases, the folded edge or edges of the paper will be on the left or at the top, and in all cases, the folded edge will be indicated by the darker boundary.)

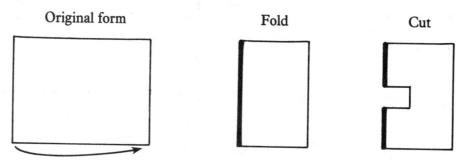

Original form          Fold          Cut

Now ask the students to predict what the piece of paper will look like when it is unfolded. After a short discussion, unfold and show them.

Distribute the worksheets. Direct the students' attention to problem 1. Take a new piece of paper and fold and cut it as shown. Tell the students to make a rough sketch of what the paper will look like when it is unfolded. Then unfold the paper. Proceed in a similar way with the other problems, each time using a new piece of $8\frac{1}{2}$ " x 11" paper.

Name: _____   Date: _____

# WORKSHEET 6-9-1
## Paper Cutting and Predictions

Predict what the paper will look like when it is folded, cut, and unfolded.

| Original form | Fold | Cut | Your prediction |

1.

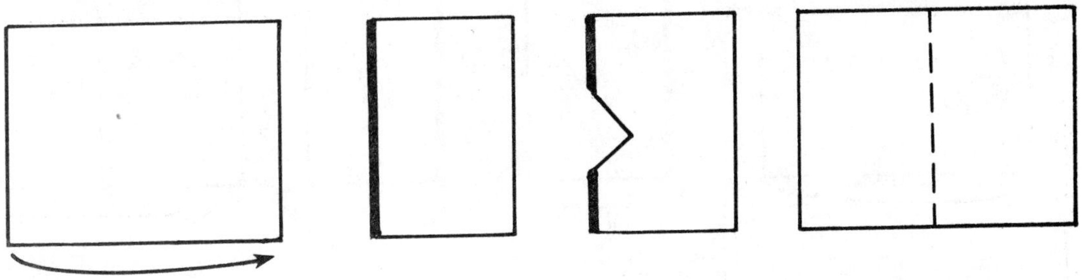

2.

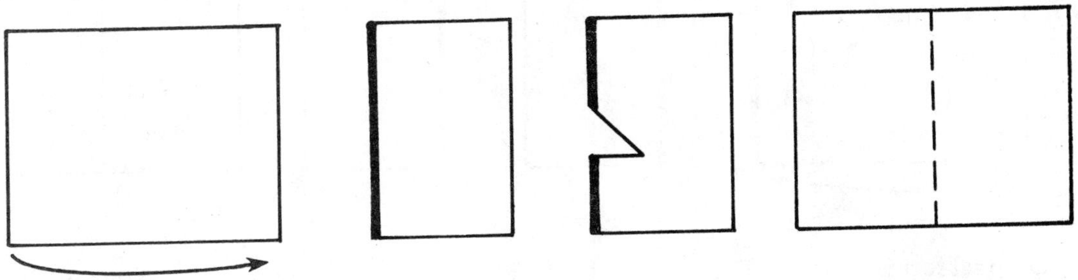

3.

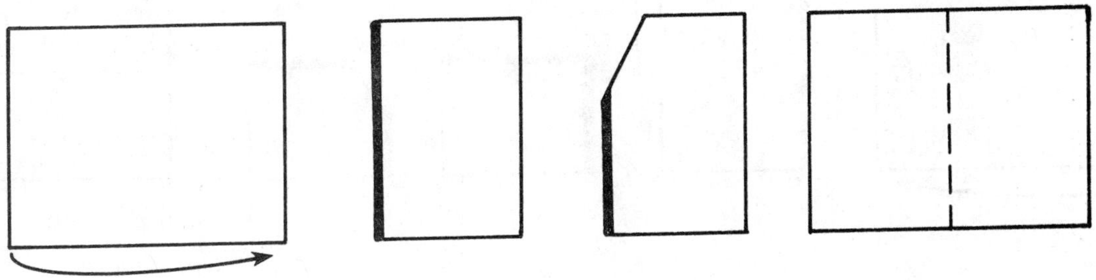

(continued)

*Visualized Geometry*

# WORKSHEET 6–9–1
## Paper Cutting and Predictions *(continued)*

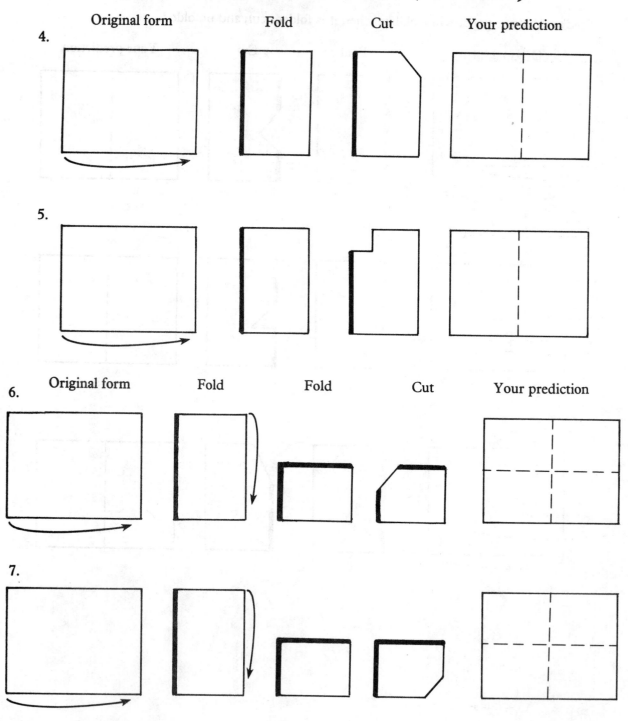

*(continued)*

# WORKSHEET 6-9-1
## Paper Cutting and Predictions *(continued)*

| Original form | Fold | Fold | Cut | Your prediction |
|---|---|---|---|---|

8.

9.

10.

11.

*(continued)*

# WORKSHEET 6-9-1
## Paper Cutting and Predictions (continued)

| Original form | Fold | Fold | Cut | Your prediction |
|---|---|---|---|---|

12.

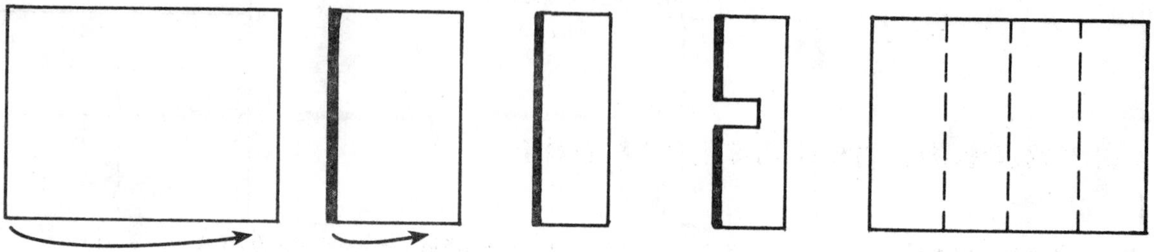

13.

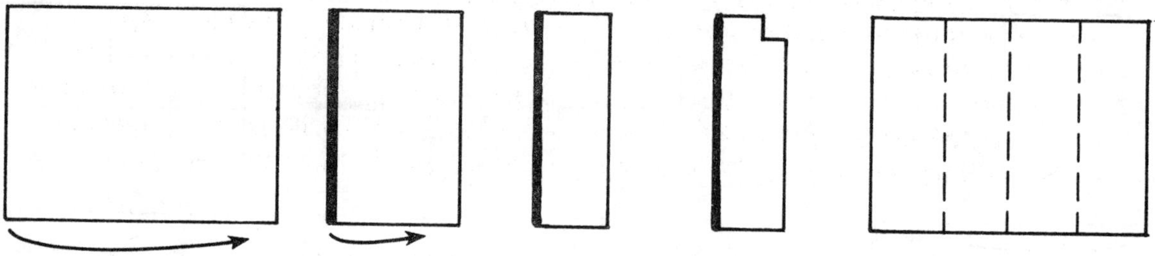

14.

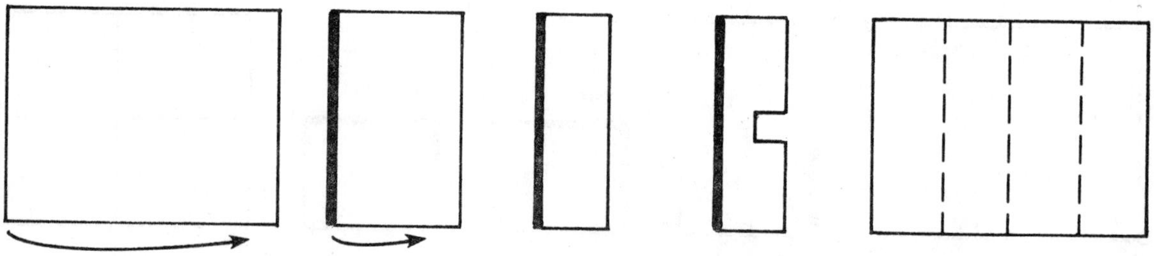

15.

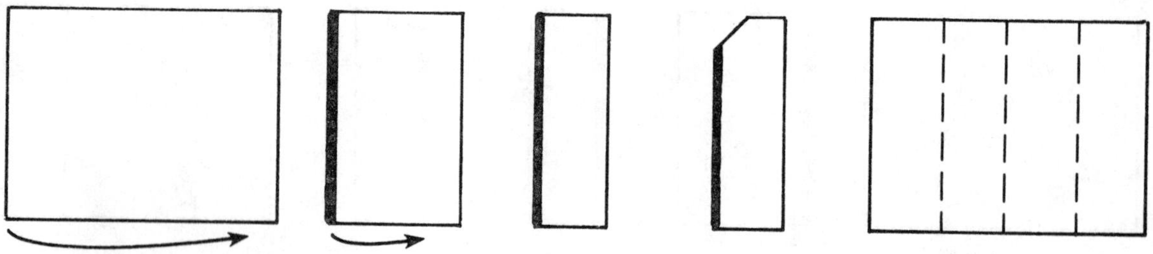

(continued)

*Visualized Geometry*

# CHAPTER 7

# Similarity

## Comments and Suggestions

In the opinion of the authors, similarity is a topic which is very poorly taught in the standard curriculum. Middle school mathematics textbooks and high school geometry textbooks ordinarily include a page or two devoted to an informal interpretation of similarity. Those students who do not proceed to high school geometry do not have enough experience in mathematics so they can make everyday applications of similarity, while high school geometry students are not satisfactorily prepared to study this topic in a formal way. This book contains 11 lessons designed to give students a firm intuitive understanding of this concept. Those students who master these lessons will be prepared to make everyday applications of similarity and to study the topic in a more formal way in high school geometry.

In Lesson 7–8, students learn to construct a figure similar to a given one on dot paper. This is a significantly higher-level task than simply identifying similar figures. In Lesson 7–9, students learn about areas of similar figures and specifically find that if the similarity ratio between two figures is $\frac{a}{b}$ is then the area ratio is $\left(\frac{a}{b}\right)^2$.

Lesson 7–1
# Definition of Similarity

## *Materials Needed:*

> One copy of page 366 for yourself.
>
> One meterstick (or yardstick).

## *Directions for the Teacher:*

Prior to class, cut out the triangle and the quadrilateral from the copy of page 366. Place the triangle on the overhead projector. Turn the projector so that the light from the projector hits the chalkboard perpendicularly. Put a dot on the chalkboard corresponding to each vertex. Turn off the projector and use a straightedge to "construct" the triangle. Label the vertices *A*, *B*, and *C*. Move the projector farther away from the chalkboard and turn it on. Again place dots corresponding to the vertices. Turn off the projector and "construct" this triangle. Label the vertices *D*, *E*, and *F*. The chalkboard should look something like the following.

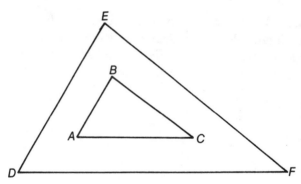

Tell the students that △*ABC* and △*DEF* are similar. Ask them to compare ∠*A* and ∠*D*, ∠*B* and ∠*E*, and ∠*C* and ∠*F*. They should conclude that these pairs of angles are congruent. Indicate that these pairs of angles are called corresponding angles. As the students watch, measure the lengths of the sides of the triangles. With a calculator, calculate the following ratios.

$$\frac{AB}{DE} \ , \ \frac{BC}{EF} \ , \ \frac{AC}{DF}$$

These ratios should be equal (or close to it).

Proceed with the quadrilateral in a similar manner. This time the chalkboard picture will look like the following.

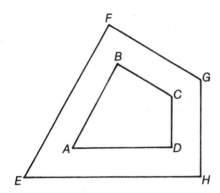

Tell the students that quadrilateral *ABCD* is similar to quadrilateral *EFGH*. As they watch, measure the lengths of sides and calculate the ratios below.

$$\frac{AB}{EF} \quad , \quad \frac{BC}{FG} \quad , \quad \frac{CD}{GH} \quad , \quad \frac{AD}{EH}$$

Again the ratios should be the same. Point out that $\angle A \cong \angle E$, $\angle B \cong \angle F$, $\angle C \cong \angle G$, and $\angle D \cong \angle H$.

Next, discuss what it means for two polygons to be similar. The discussion should include the following three points.

a. There is a correspondence between vertices of the two polygons which establishes corresponding sides and angles.

b. Corresponding angles are congruent.

c. The ratios of lengths of corresponding sides are equal.

Point out to the students that if two polygons are similar they have the same shape.

# Lesson 7-1-1
## Teacher Copy Page

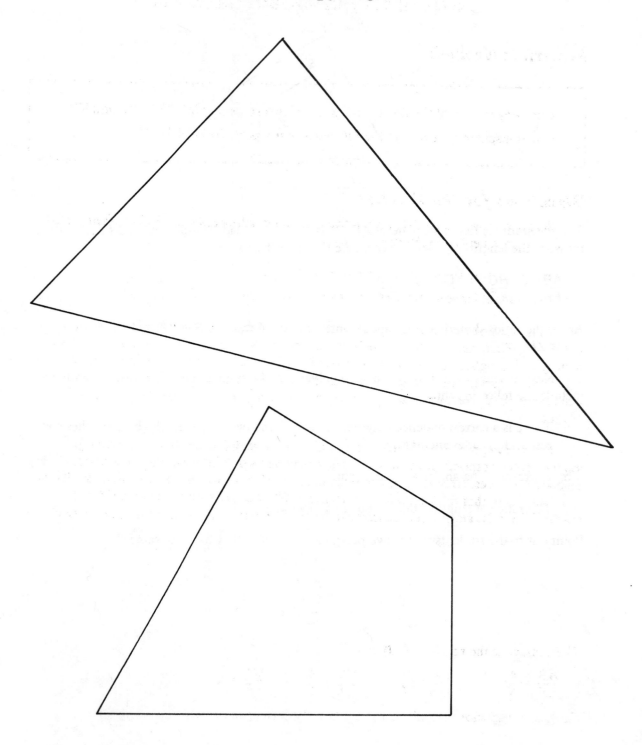

 *Visualized Geometry*

## Lesson 7-2
# Similarity of Quadrilaterals

## *Materials Needed:*

One copy of each of the following pages for each student: pages 372, 373, and 374.

One transparency of each of the following pages: pages 370 and 371.

## *Directions for the Teacher:*

Briefly review Lesson 7–1. Emphasize that two quadrilaterals are similar when there is a correspondence between vertices such that

  a. corresponding angles are congruent and

  b. the ratios of lengths of corresponding sides are equal.

Place the first transparency on the overhead projector. Direct the students' attention to problem 1. First, mention that since both quadrilaterals are rectangles, each angle in these rectangles is a right angle and any correspondence between vertices would produce pairs of congruent angles (since they are all right angles). Then point out that a correspondence has been established. Next calculate the ratios (each one is $\frac{1}{2}$) and conclude that the rectangles are similar.

Proceed to problem 2. Mention that since all the angles in each rectangle are right angles, any correspondence that would be determined would result in the congruence of corresponding angles. Indicate that you must next establish a correspondence. Mention that you must do this so that the long sides of rectangle *ABCD* correspond to the long sides of rectangle *EFGH*. Establish such a correspondence. There are many possibilities, but here is one.

$$A \leftrightarrow F$$
$$B \leftrightarrow G$$
$$C \leftrightarrow H$$
$$D \leftrightarrow E$$

Then calculate the ratios listed below.

$$\frac{AB}{EF} = \frac{4}{5} \qquad \frac{BC}{GH} = \frac{3}{4} \qquad \frac{CD}{HE} = \frac{4}{5} \qquad \frac{DA}{EF} = \frac{3}{4}$$

Conclude that since the ratios are not equal, the rectangles are not similar.

Proceed in a similar way to problem 3. Here is a way the correspondence can be made. (It can be made in other ways.)

$$A \leftrightarrow F$$
$$B \leftrightarrow G$$
$$C \leftrightarrow H$$
$$D \leftrightarrow E$$

Then calculate the ratios listed below.

$$\frac{AB}{FG} = \frac{3}{2} \qquad \frac{BC}{GH} = \frac{6}{4} \qquad \frac{CD}{HE} = \frac{3}{2} \qquad \frac{DA}{EF} = \frac{6}{4}$$

Conclude that the two rectangles are similar.

Since the opposite sides of a rectangle are congruent it is not necessary to look at all four of the ratios of lengths of corresponding sides. It is sufficient to look at only two ratios, as long as two adjacent sides of one rectangle are compared to corresponding sides of the other rectangle. For instance, looking at the ratios $\frac{AB}{FG}$ and $\frac{BC}{GH}$ would allow a conclusion to be drawn on similarity of two rectangles (or two parallelograms). This "shortcut" does not work with general quadrilaterals.

Place the second transparency on your projector. Ask the students if they think the quadrilaterals (problem 4) are similar. They should say "No." Appropriate reasons for this response include:

a. The quadrilaterals are not the same shape. ("I can tell by just looking.")

b. All the angles in quadrilateral *ABCD* are right angles but, for example, $\angle E$ in the second quadrilateral is not a right angle. There is no way to establish a correspondence between vertices so that the angle which corresponds to $\angle E$ is congruent to $\angle E$.

Of course, other explanations are possible.

Proceed to problem 5. The students should conclude that the quadrilaterals are not similar because

a. they are not the same shape,

b. since,

$$\frac{AB}{EF} = \frac{2}{5} \qquad \frac{BC}{FG} = \frac{2}{4} \qquad \frac{CD}{GH} = \frac{2}{5} \qquad \frac{DA}{HE} = \frac{2}{4} \text{,}$$

the ratios of lengths of "corresponding" sides are not equal.

Distribute the worksheet. Provide individual assistance as needed.

## Correct Answers for Worksheet 7-2-1:

1. Quadrilaterals *EFGH*, *MNOP*, and *QRST* are similar to square *ABCD*.

2a. no
 b. (does not apply)

3a. yes
 b. $\frac{1}{2}$, $\frac{2}{4}$, or $\frac{3}{6}$

4a. no
 b. (does not apply)

5a. yes
 b. $\frac{2}{1}$ or $\frac{6}{3}$

6a. no
 b. (does not apply)

7. yes

1.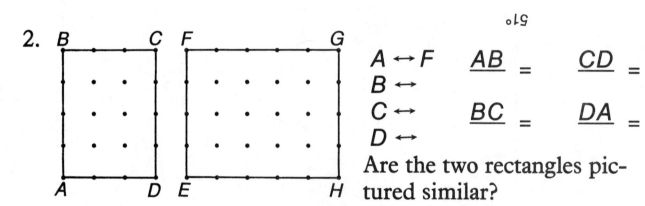

$A \leftrightarrow E$    $\dfrac{AB}{EF} =$    $\dfrac{CD}{GH} =$

$B \leftrightarrow F$

$C \leftrightarrow G$    $\dfrac{BC}{FG} =$    $\dfrac{DA}{HE} =$

$D \leftrightarrow H$

Are the two rectangles pictured similar?

2.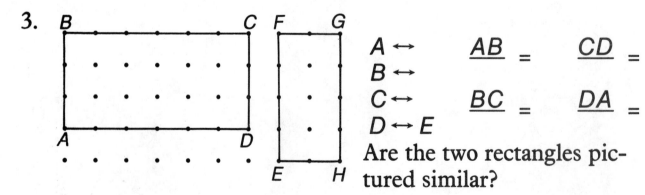

$A \leftrightarrow F$    $\dfrac{AB}{\quad} =$    $\dfrac{CD}{\quad} =$

$B \leftrightarrow$

$C \leftrightarrow$    $\dfrac{BC}{\quad} =$    $\dfrac{DA}{\quad} =$

$D \leftrightarrow$

Are the two rectangles pictured similar?

3.

$A \leftrightarrow$    $\dfrac{AB}{\quad} =$    $\dfrac{CD}{\quad} =$

$B \leftrightarrow$

$C \leftrightarrow$    $\dfrac{BC}{\quad} =$    $\dfrac{DA}{\quad} =$

$D \leftrightarrow E$

Are the two rectangles pictured similar?

*Visualized Geometry*

4.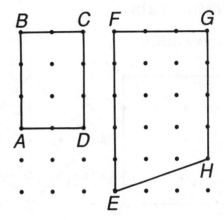

Are the two quadrilaterals pictured similar? Why or why not?

5.

Are the quadrilaterals pictured similar? Why or why not?

*Visualized Geometry*

# WORKSHEET 7-2-1
## Similarity of Quadrilaterals

1. Write "S" in each quadrilateral which is similar to square *ABCD*.

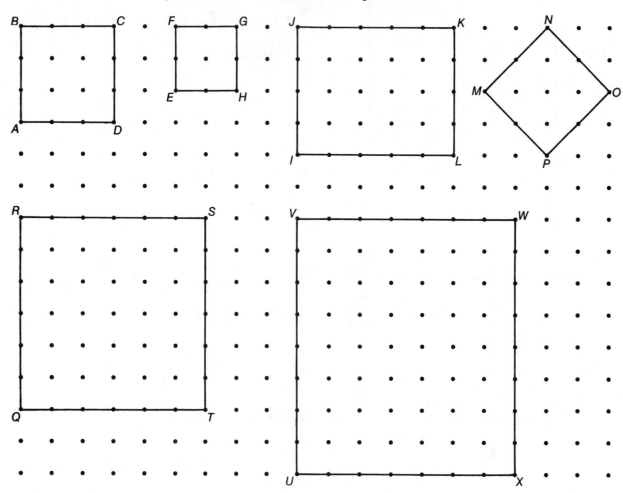

2a. Is rectangle *ABCD* similar to parallelogram *EFGH*? _____

b. If yes, give the ratio of length of a side of rectangle *ABCD* to the length of a corresponding side of quadrilateral *EFGH*. _____

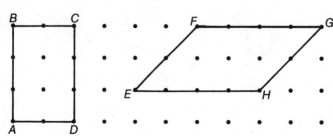

*(continued)*

# WORKSHEET 7-2-1
## Similarity of Quadrilaterals (*continued*)

3a. Is rectangle *ABCD* similar to rectangle *FGHE*? _____

 b. If yes, give the ratio of the length of a side in rectangle *ABCD* to the length of a corresponding side of rectangle *FGHE*. _____

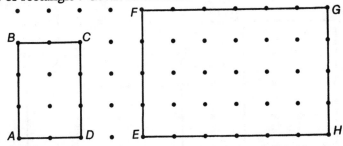

4a. Is rectangle *ABCD* similar to rectangle *FGHE*? _____

 b. If yes, give the ratio of the length of a side in rectangle *ABCD* to the length of a corresponding side of rectangle *FGHE*. _____

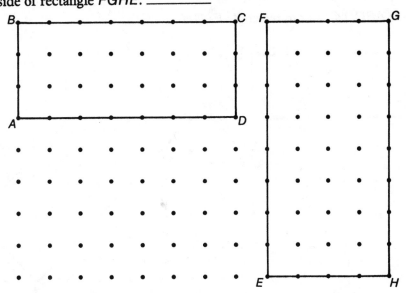

5a. Is rectangle *ABCD* similar to rectangle *FGHE*? _____

 b. If yes, give the ratio of the length of a side in rectangle *ABCD* to the length of a corresponding side of rectangle *FGHE*. _____

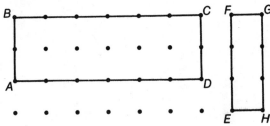

*(continued)*

       *Visualized Geometry*

# WORKSHEET 7-2-1
## Similarity of Quadrilaterals *(continued)*

6a. Is rectangle *ABCD* similar to rectangle *EFGH*? _____

  b. If yes, give the ratio of the length of a side in rectangle *ABCD* to the length of a corresponding side of rectangle *EFGH*. _____

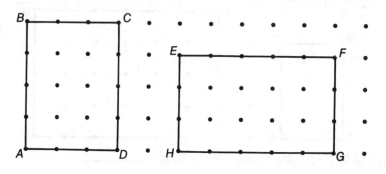

7. Is rectangle *ABCD* similar to rectangle *EFGH*? _____

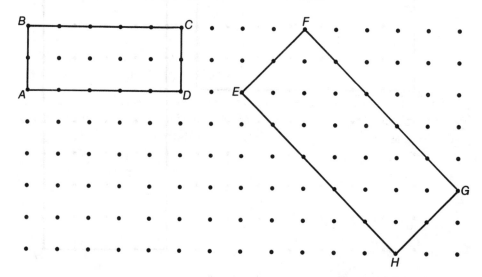

374

*Visualized Geometry*

## Lesson 7-3
# Ratios of Lengths of Segments

## *Materials Needed:*

One copy of page 378 for each student.

One transparency of page 377.

## *Directions for the Teacher:*

Place the transparency on the overhead projector. Direct the students' attention to problem 1a. If they can see $\frac{AB}{CD} = \frac{1}{2}$, proceed. If not, label the midpoint of $\overline{CD}$ as shown.

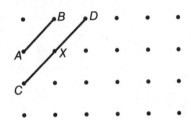

Argue that $\overline{CX} \cong \overline{XD} \cong \overline{AB}$, which means that $\overline{AB}$ is half as long as $\overline{CD}$. Conclude that $\frac{AB}{CD} = \frac{1}{2}$. Proceed in a similar way with problem 1b. Students should conclude that $\overline{EF}$ is three times as long as $\overline{GH}$, so $\frac{EF}{GH} = \frac{3}{1}$. In problem 1c you may need to label points as shown below.

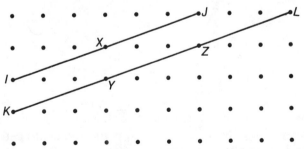

Lead the students to conclude that $\overline{IJ}$ is 2 "units" long and $\overline{KL}$ is 3 "units" long, so the ratio of their lengths is $\frac{2}{3}$.

Next, consider problem 1d. If the students can find the required ratios proceed with the next pair of segments. If they cannot, label the points as shown.

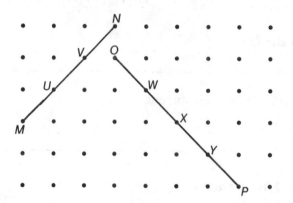

Argue that $\overline{MU}$ and $\overline{OW}$ are the same length (congruent) as are several other pictured segments. Point out that $\overline{MN}$ is 3 "units" long and $\overline{OP}$ is 4 "units" long so the required ratio is $\frac{3}{4}$. In problem 1e label the points as shown.

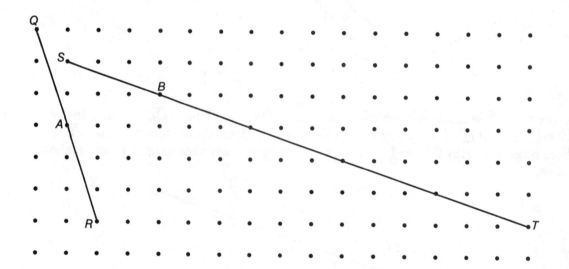

Argue the $\overline{QA}$ is the same length as (congruent to) $\overline{SB}$. You may need to observe that you could get from $Q$ to $A$ by going down 3 and over 1, while you could get from $S$ to $B$ by going down 1 and over 3. This makes the lengths of $\overline{QA}$ and $\overline{SB}$ the same. Conclude that $\overline{QR}$ is 2 "units" long while $\overline{ST}$ is 5 "units" long. This means that the ratio $\frac{QR}{ST}$ is $\frac{2}{5}$.

Distribute the worksheet. Provide individual assistance as needed.

**Correct Answers for Worksheet 7-3-1:**

1. $\frac{2}{3}$   2. $\frac{3}{2}$   3. $\frac{1}{2}$   4. $\frac{4}{3}$

# Find the ratios of lengths of segments.

1a.

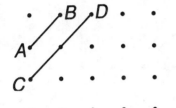

$$\frac{AB}{CD} =$$

c.

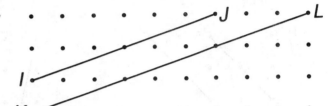

$$\frac{IJ}{KL} =$$

b.

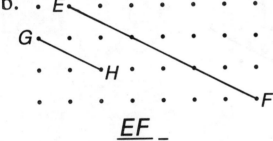

$$\frac{EF}{GH} =$$

d.

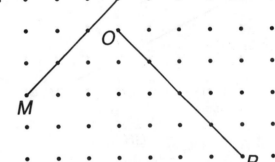

$$\frac{MN}{OP} =$$

e.

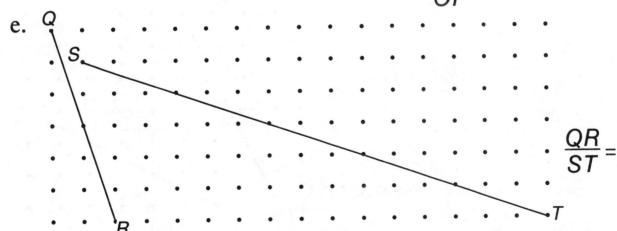

$$\frac{QR}{ST} =$$

*Visualized Geometry*

Name: _____ Date: _____

# WORKSHEET 7-3-1
## Ratio of Lengths of Segments

Find the ratios of lengths of segments.

1.

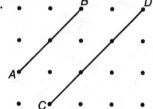

$$\frac{AB}{CD} =$$

3.

$$\frac{IJ}{KL} =$$

2.

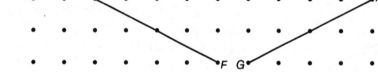

$$\frac{EF}{GH} =$$

4.

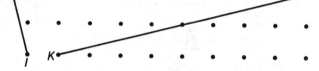

$$\frac{MN}{OP} =$$

*Visualized Geometry*

# Lesson 7-4
# Similarity of Triangles

## *Materials Needed:*

One copy of each of the following pages for each student: pages 383 and 384.

One transparency of each of the following pages: pages 381 and 382.

## *Directions for the Teacher:*

Briefly review the concept of similarity. Emphasize that if two triangles are similar then there is a correspondence between vertices so that

a. corresponding angles are congruent and
b. the ratios of lengths of corresponding sides are equal.

Place the first transparency on the overhead projector. Direct the students' attention to problem 1. They should immediately conclude that the two triangles are not similar because $\triangle ABC$ has a right angle and $\triangle DEF$ does not. In problem 2, $\angle A \cong \angle D$, $\angle B \cong \angle E$, and $\angle C \cong \angle F$. Calculate the ratios of lengths of sides using the technique developed in Lesson 7-3. For each pair of corresponding sides, the ratio of the lengths will simplify to $\frac{2}{3}$. The class should conclude that for problem 2, $\triangle ABC$ is similar to $\triangle DEF$.

Next, examine problem 3. This time the correspondence is not so obvious. Point out that $\angle A$ is the largest angle in $\triangle ABC$ and $\angle E$ is the largest angle in $\triangle DEF$, so $A$ must correspond to $E$. Similarly $\angle B$ and $\angle F$ are the smallest angles, so $B$ and $F$ must correspond. Then write

$$A \leftrightarrow E$$
$$B \leftrightarrow F$$
$$C \leftrightarrow D.$$

Next, calculate the ratios of corresponding sides.

$$\frac{AB}{EF} = \frac{9}{6} \qquad\qquad \frac{BC}{FD} = \frac{3}{2} \qquad\qquad \frac{AC}{ED} = \frac{6}{4}$$

$$= \frac{3}{2} \qquad\qquad\qquad\qquad\qquad\qquad = \frac{3}{2}$$

Conclude that the two triangles are similar.

Place the second transparency on the overhead projector. Establish the correspondence

$$A \leftrightarrow D$$
$$B \leftrightarrow F$$
$$C \leftrightarrow E.$$

From the ratios

$$\frac{AB}{DF} = \frac{8}{16} \qquad \frac{BC}{FE} = \frac{3}{6} \qquad \frac{AC}{DE} = \frac{1}{2}$$

$$= \frac{1}{2} \qquad \qquad = \frac{1}{2}$$

conclude that triangle *ABC* is similar to triangle *DFE*.

Distribute the worksheets. Provide individual assistance as needed.

## Correct Answers for Worksheet 7–4–1:

1a. yes

  b. $\frac{2}{3}$

2a. yes

  b. $\frac{3}{1}$

3a. no

  b. (does not apply)

4a. yes

  b. $\frac{4}{3}$

5a. yes

  b. $\frac{2}{1}$

6a. yes

  b. $\frac{1}{1}$

  c. yes

*Note:* When two figures are similar and the ratio of the lengths of corresponding sides is $\frac{1}{1}$, the two figures are also congruent. The relationship between congruence and similarity will be discussed in detail in Lesson 7–11.

1. 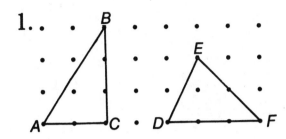 Is △ABC similar to △DEF? _____

2.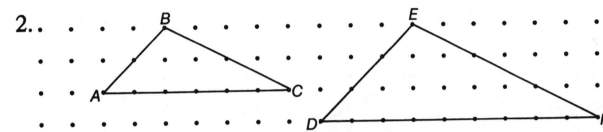

   a. Find the ratios of lengths of sides.

   $$\frac{AB}{DE} = \qquad \frac{BC}{EF} = \qquad \frac{AC}{DF} =$$

   b. Is △ABC similar to △DEF? _____

3.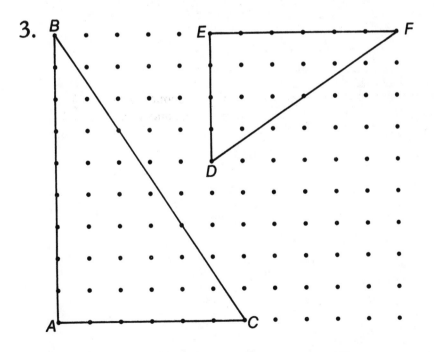

   Is △ABC similar to △EFD? _____

       *Visualized Geometry*

4.

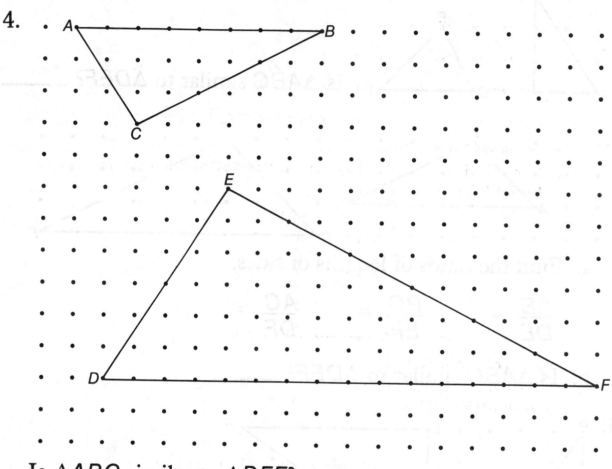

Is △*ABC* similar to △*DFE*? _____

# WORKSHEET 7-4-1
## Similarity of Triangles

1.

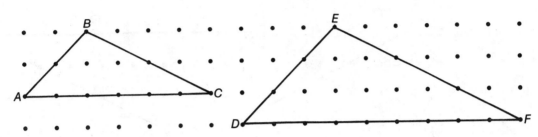

   a. Are the two triangles similar? _____

   b. If yes, what is the ratio of the length of a side of $\triangle ABC$ with the length of a corresponding side of $\triangle DEF$? _____

2.

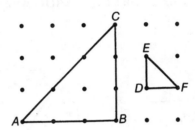

   a. Are the two triangles similar? _____

   b. If yes, what is the ratio of the length of a side of $\triangle ABC$ with the length of a corresponding side of $\triangle FDE$? _____

3.

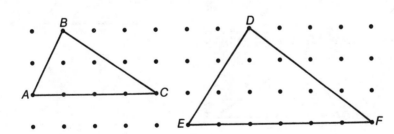

   a. Are the two triangles similar? _____

   b. If yes, what is the ratio of the length of a side of $\triangle ABC$ with the length of a corresponding side of $\triangle EDF$? _____

*(continued)*

*Visualized Geometry*

# WORKSHEET 7–4–1
## Similarity of Triangles (*continued*)

4.

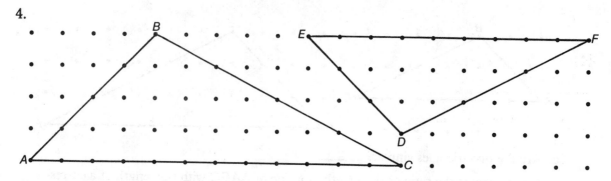

    a. Are the two triangles similar? _____

    b. If yes, what is the ratio of the length of a side of $\triangle ABC$ with the length of a corresponding side of $\triangle EDF$? _____

5.  a. Are the two triangles similar? _____

    b. If yes, what is the ratio of the length of a side of $\triangle ABC$ with the length of a corresponding side of $\triangle EFD$? _____

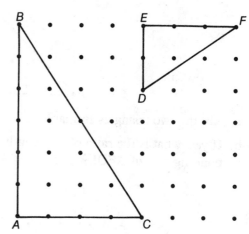

6.

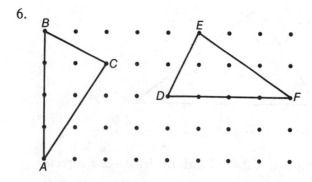

    a. Are the two triangles similar? _____

    b. If yes, what is the ratio of the length of a side of $\triangle ABC$ with the length of a corresponding side of $\triangle FDE$? _____

    c. Are the two triangles congruent? _____

*Visualized Geometry*

## Lesson 7-5
# Similarity of Rectangles
# Using Diagonal Properties

## *Materials Needed:*

One copy of page 389 for each student.

One ruler, a blank transparency, an overhead projector pen, and two pieces of unlined $8\frac{1}{2}''$ x 11'' paper for each student.

Several metersticks or yardsticks.

One transparency of page 388.

## *Directions for the Teacher:*

Distribute two pieces of unlined $8\frac{1}{2}''$ x 11'' paper and one ruler to each student. Read the following directions, allowing time for students to complete each activity before you proceed to the next direction.

a.  Take one blank sheet of paper and turn it so that one of the long sides is along the bottom of your paper. Take a meterstick or yardstick and draw a diagonal from the lower left corner to the upper right corner, as shown below.

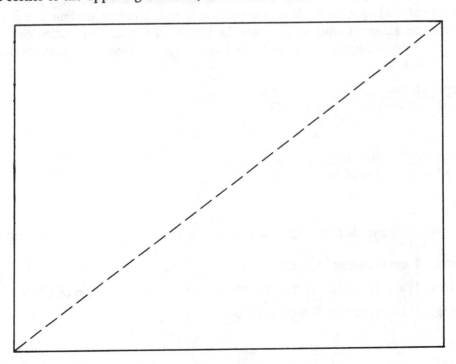

b. Take the other blank sheet of paper and carefully fold it in half so the fold line intersects the longest sides. Tear (or cut) along the fold line.

c. Take one of these halves and turn it so one of the long sides is along the bottom of your desk. Use your ruler to draw a diagonal from the lower left corner to the upper right corner.

d. Take the other half and fold and tear it as described in "b."

e. Take one of the pieces (fourths) and draw a diagonal as indicated in "a." Be sure that a long side is along the bottom of your desk and the diagonal is drawn from the lower left corner to the upper right corner.

f. Take the other of these pieces (fourths) and fold and tear as in "b." This gives two eighths. As before, draw a diagonal for one of the eighths.

g. Take the other eighth and fold it and tear as described in "b." Discard one of these pieces (sixteenths) and draw a diagonal on the other one as before.

Now each student should have five rectangular sheets of paper (the page that you gave them, together with the four they got by tearing), each with a diagonal drawn in. Direct them to label the largest piece, "I"; the second-largest piece, "II"; the third-largest piece, "III"; the fourth-largest piece, "IV"; and finally the smallest piece, "V."

Briefly review the process used to get the various pieces and point out (demonstrate) that each side of rectangle I is twice as long as a corresponding side of rectangle III. Argue that this indicates that rectangle I and rectangle III are similar. Point out (demonstrate) rectangle II and rectangle IV are similar and rectangle III and rectangle V are similar because in each case a side of the larger rectangle is twice as long as a corresponding side of the smaller rectangle. Also point out (demonstrate) that rectangle I and rectangle V are similar because a side of the larger rectangle is four times as long as a corresponding side of the smaller rectangle. Have the students measure the lengths of the sides of rectangles I and II. Show that the ratio of the lengths of "corresponding" sides of these rectangles are not equal. Illustrate this as below.

$$\frac{\text{length of short side of rectangle I}}{\text{length of short side of rectangle II}} = \frac{8\frac{1}{2} \text{ in.}}{5\frac{1}{2} \text{ in.}}$$
$$\approx 1.54$$

$$\frac{\text{length of long side of rectangle I}}{\text{length of long side of rectangle II}} = \frac{11 \text{ in.}}{8\frac{1}{2} \text{ in.}}$$
$$\approx 1.30$$

Mention that this shows that rectangle I and rectangle II are not similar. Then point out that

a. rectangle I and rectangle IV are not similar,

b. rectangle II and rectangle III are not similar,

c. rectangle II and rectangle V are not similar,

d.  rectangle III and rectangle IV are not similar, and

e.  rectangle IV and rectangle V are not similar.

You may need to calculate some more ratios to convince the students that these statements are actually true.

Next, place the transparency on the overhead projector. Direct the students to place the pieces on top of each other as are shown on the transparency. Ask them what they see. (When the diagonals "line up" the rectangles are similar, but when the diagonals do not "line up," as in the case of rectangle I and rectangle II, the rectangles are not similar.)

Distribute a copy of page 389 to each student. Note that each student will need a blank transparency and an overhead projector pen. Provide individual assistance as needed. Point out that no cutting or tearing is needed and that similarity is to be determined by comparisons of diagonals.

## Correct Answers for Worksheet 7-5-1:

1. Rectangles *NOPM* and *UVWX* are similar to rectangle *ABCD*.

# Transparency 7-5-1

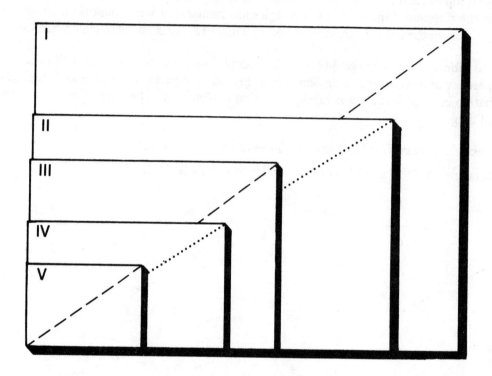

*Visualized Geometry*

Name: _____          Date: _____

# WORKSHEET 7-5-1
## Similarity of Rectangles Using Diagonal Properties

1. Make a copy of rectangle *ABCD* on your transparency and draw in a diagonal. Draw a "corresponding" diagonal for each of the other rectangles and use the technique involving diagonals to find out which rectangles are similar to rectangle *ABCD*. Write "S" in each rectangle which is similar to rectangle *ABCD*.

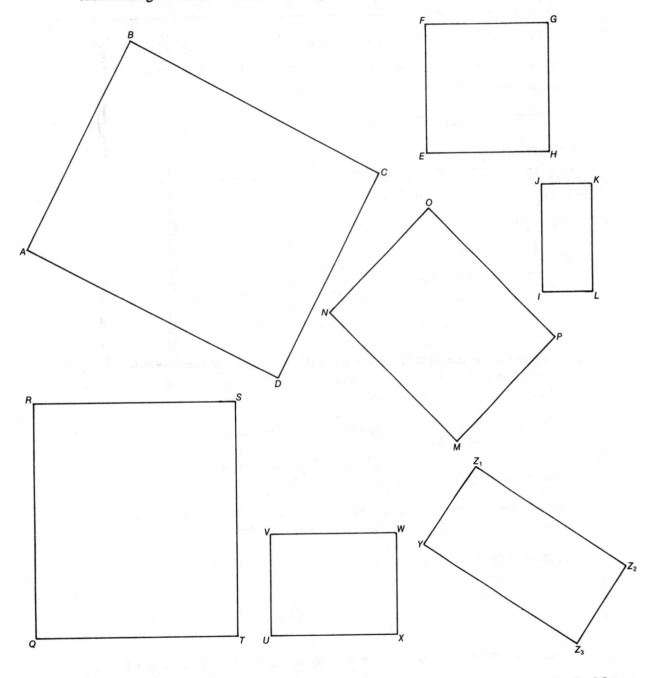

# Lesson 7–6
# Similarity of Parallelograms
# Using Diagonal Properties

## *Materials Needed:*

One copy of each of the following pages for each student: pages 392 and 393.

One blank transparency and an overhead projector pen for each student.

One transparency of page 391.

## *Directions for the Teacher:*

Place the transparency on the overhead projector. With the students' assistance proceed through the three problems there.

## Correct Answers for Transparency 7-6-1:

1. $\frac{AE}{AB} = \frac{1}{2}$    $\frac{AG}{AD} = \frac{3}{6} = \frac{1}{2}$    $\frac{GF}{DC} = \frac{1}{2}$    $\frac{EF}{BC} = \frac{3}{6} = \frac{1}{2}$    yes

2. $\frac{AE}{AB} = \frac{3}{4}$    $\frac{AG}{AD} = \frac{6}{8} = \frac{3}{4}$    $\frac{GF}{DC} = \frac{3}{4}$    $\frac{EF}{BC} = \frac{6}{8} = \frac{3}{4}$    yes

3. $\frac{AE}{AB} = \frac{1}{2}$    $\frac{AG}{AD} = \frac{2}{5}$    $\frac{GF}{DC} = \frac{1}{2}$    $\frac{EF}{BC} = \frac{2}{5}$    no

Some students may notice that when any two ratios are found to be not equal (as in problem 3), the figures cannot be similar and any remaining ratios need not be found. They are correct and should be rewarded for their insight.

Now for each problem draw diagonals $\overline{AF}$ and $\overline{AC}$. Ask the students what they notice. They should say that when the parallelograms are similar, the diagonals "line up" and when they are not similar the diagonals do not "line up." Of course this is exactly what happened when similar rectangles were investigated (Lesson 7–5).

Distribute the worksheets. Note that each student will need a blank transparency and an overhead projector pen. Provide individual assistance as needed.

## Correct Answers for Worksheet 7-6-1:

1a. yes
 b. no
 c. yes
 d. no

2. Parallelogram *EFGH* and parallelogram *NOPM* are similar to parallelogram *ABCD*.

1.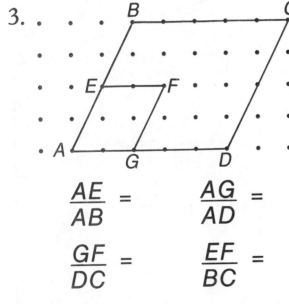

$$\frac{AE}{AB} = \qquad \frac{AG}{AD} =$$

$$\frac{GF}{DC} = \qquad \frac{EF}{BC} =$$

Is quadrilateral *ABCD* similar
to quadrilateral *AEFG*?

2.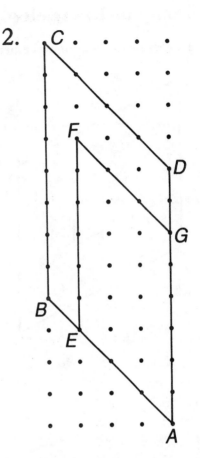

$$\frac{AE}{AB} = \qquad \frac{AG}{AD} =$$

$$\frac{GF}{DC} = \qquad \frac{EF}{BC} =$$

Is quadrilateral *ABCD* similar
to quadrilateral *AEFG*?

3.

$$\frac{AE}{AB} = \qquad \frac{AG}{AD} =$$

$$\frac{GF}{DC} = \qquad \frac{EF}{BC} =$$

Is quadrilateral *ABCD* similar
to quadrilateral *AEFG*?

     *Visualized Geometry*

# WORKSHEET 7–6–1
## Similarity of Parallelograms Using Diagonal Properties

1. Use diagonals to determine whether the parallelograms are similar.

a.

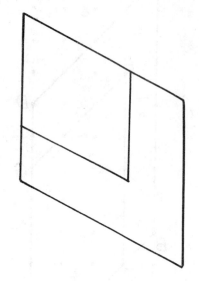

Yes _____      No _____

b.

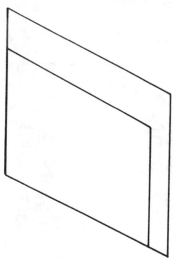

Yes _____      No _____

c.

Yes _____      No _____

d.

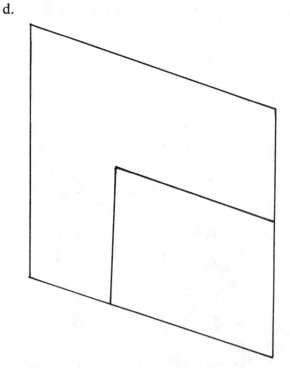

Yes _____      No _____

*(continued)*

*Visualized Geometry*

# WORKSHEET 7-6-1
## Similarity of Parallelograms Using
## Diagonal Properties *(continued)*

2. Make a copy of parallelogram *ABCD* on your blank transparency and draw in a diagonal. Draw a "corresponding" diagonal for each of the other parallelograms and use the technique involving diagonals to find out which parallelograms are similar to parallelogram *ABCD*. Write "S" in each parallelogram which is similar to parallelogram *ABCD*.

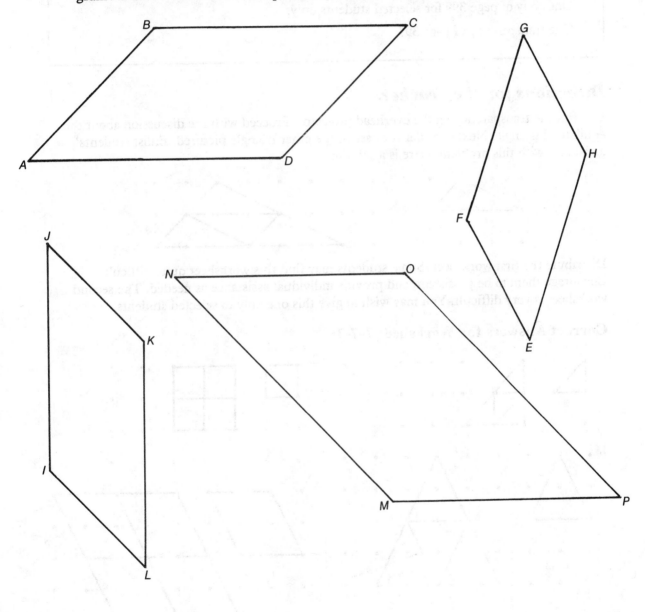

# Lesson 7-7
# Making Larger Similar Figures

## Materials Needed:

One copy of page 398 for each student.

One copy of page 399 for selected students only.

One transparency of page 397.

## Directions for the Teacher:

Put the transparency on the overhead projector. Proceed with the discussion about the equilateral triangle. Next consider the case of the other triangle pictured. Enlist students' assistance with this problem. Here is a solution.

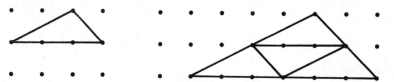

Distribute the first worksheet. Some students may find this worksheet quite difficult. Encourage them to be persistent, and provide individual assistance as needed. The second worksheet is very difficult. You may wish to give this one only to selected students.

## Correct Answers for Worksheet 7-7-1:

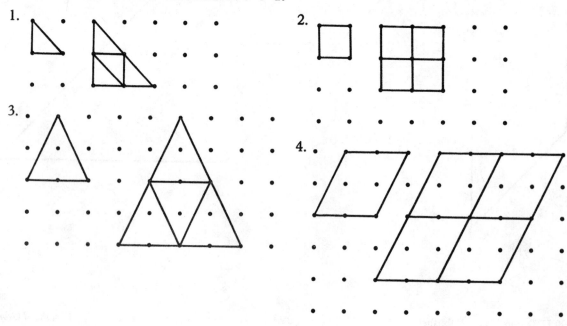

5.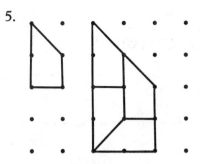

7.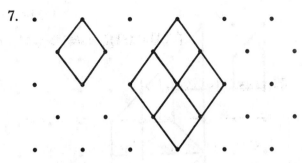

6.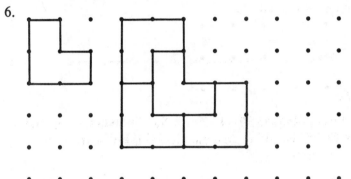

## Correct Answers for Worksheet 7–7–2:

1.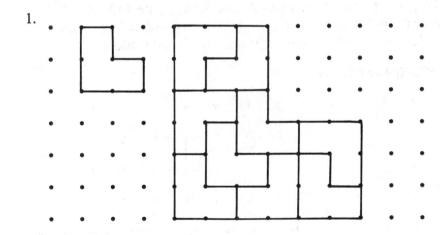

2.

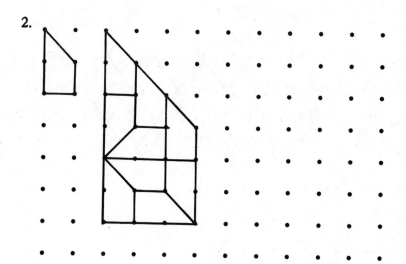

It is often possible to use four "copies" of a figure to make another figure which is similar to the original figure. For example, the picture below shows how to use four copies of an equilateral triangle to make a figure similar to the original equilateral triangle.

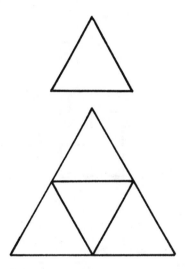

Use the dot paper (which is provided) to help you use four copies of the triangle to make a triangle similar to the one pictured.

397    *Visualized Geometry*

# WORKSHEET 7-7-1
## Making Larger Similar Figures

Make a figure similar to the one pictured by using four copies of the figure.

1.

5.

2.

6.

3.

7.

4.

# WORKSHEET 7-7-2
## Making Larger Similar Figures

Make a figure similar to the one pictured by using nine copies of the figure.

1.

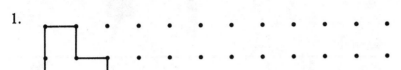
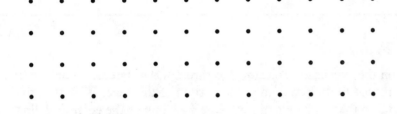

2.

*Visualized Geometry*

# Lesson 7-8
# Drawing Similar Figures
# Using the Similarity Ratio

## *Materials Needed:*

> One copy of each of the following pages for each student: pages 403 and 404.
>
> One transparency of page 402.

## *Directions for the Teacher:*

Put the transparency on the overhead projector. Go through the statements on the first part of the transparency. Proceed to the problem at the bottom of the page. With the students' help, construct $\triangle ABC$ so that each side of $\triangle ABC$ is $\frac{2}{3}$ as long as the corresponding side of $\triangle DEF$. Be sure to label the vertices of this triangle appropriately. One possible solution follows.

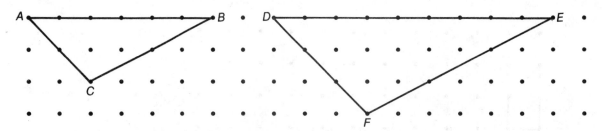

Distribute the worksheets. Provide individual assistance as needed. The solutions to worksheet problems are not unique.

## Possible Correct Answers for Worksheet 7-8-1:

1.

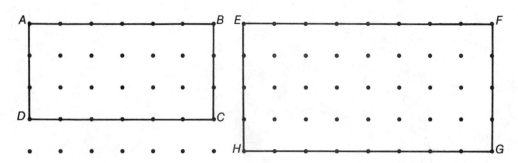

2.

3.

4.

5.

6.

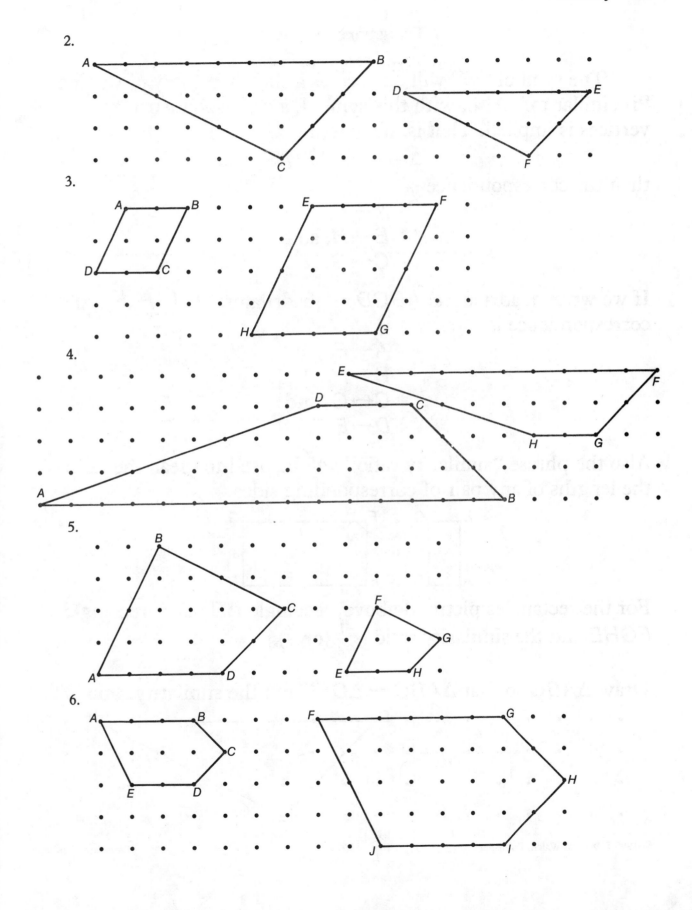

The symbol "~" will be used as a shorthand way of writing "is similar to." Also, with this symbol, a correspondence of vertices is implied. That is, if we write

$$\triangle ABC \sim \triangle FHG,$$

then the correspondence is

$$A \longleftrightarrow F,$$
$$B \longleftrightarrow H, \text{ and}$$
$$C \longleftrightarrow G.$$

If we write quadrilateral $ABCD \sim$ quadrilateral $FHGE$ then the correspondence is

$$A \longleftrightarrow F,$$
$$B \longleftrightarrow H,$$
$$C \longleftrightarrow G, \text{ and}$$
$$D \longleftrightarrow E.$$

Also the phrase "similarity ratio" will be used to mean the ratio of the lengths of any pair of corresponding sides.

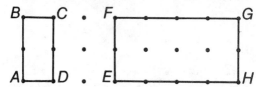

For the rectangles pictured above, rectangle $ABCD \sim$ rectangle $FGHE$ and the similarity ratio is $\frac{1}{2}$ (or $\frac{2}{4}$).

Draw $\triangle ABC$ so that $\triangle ABC \sim \triangle DEF$ and the similarity ratio is $\frac{2}{3}$.

Name: _____ Date: _____

# WORKSHEET 7-8-1
## Drawing Similar Figures Using the Similarity Ratio

1. Draw rectangle *ABCD* so that rectangle *ABCD* ~ rectangle *EFGH* and the similarity ratio is $\frac{3}{4}$.

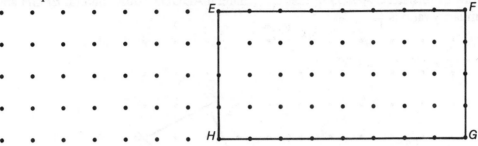

2. Draw $\triangle ABC$ so that $\triangle ABC \sim \triangle DEF$ and the similarity ratio is $\frac{3}{2}$.

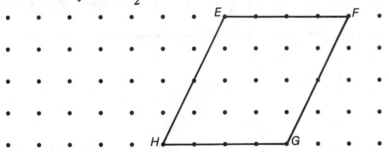

3. Draw parallelogram *ABCD* so that parallelogram *ABCD* ~ parallelogram *EFGH* and the similarity ratio is $\frac{1}{2}$.

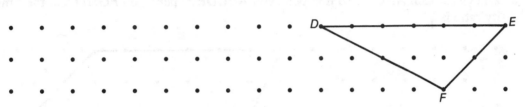

4. Draw trapezoid *ABCD* so that trapezoid *ABCD* ~ trapezoid *EFGH* and the similarity ratio is $\frac{3}{2}$.

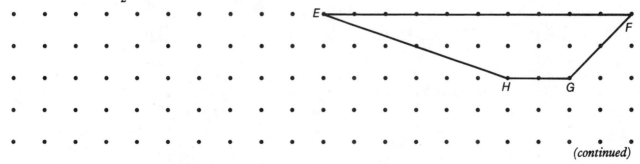

*(continued)*

                   *Visualized Geometry*

# WORKSHEET 7-8-1
## Drawing Similar Figures Using
## the Similarity Ratio (continued)

5. Draw quadrilateral *ABCD* so that quadrilateral *ABCD* ~ quadrilateral *EFGH* and the similarity ratio is $\frac{2}{1}$.

6. Draw pentagon *ABCDE* so that pentagon *ABCDE* ~ pentagon *FGHIJ* and the similarity ratio is $\frac{1}{2}$.

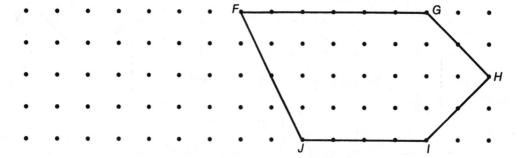

## Lesson 7-9
# The Similarity Ratio and the Area Ratio of Similar Figures

## *Materials Needed:*

One copy of each of the following pages for each student: pages 408, 409, and 410.

One transparency of page 407.

## *Directions for the Teacher:*

Place the transparency on the overhead projector. Direct the students' attention to problem 1. As a result of their experiences in Lesson 7-8, they should be readily able to identify the similarity ratio ($\frac{1}{2}$). Encourage them to "recognize" that the rectangle on the right is "made up" of four rectangles, each of which is congruent to the rectangle on the left. Thus help them conclude that the area ratio is $\frac{1}{4}$. In problem 2, they should be able to identify the similarity ratio ($\frac{3}{2}$). However, they may have a little difficulty finding the area ratio. If they do struggle, point out that the triangle on the left is "made up" of 9 small right triangles while the triangle on the right is "made up" of 4 small right triangles. Help them conclude that the area ratio is $\frac{9}{4}$.

Distribute the worksheets. Provide individual assistance as needed. The students should discover that if the similarity ratio is $\frac{a}{b}$ then the area ratio is $(\frac{a}{b})^2$.

### Correct Answers for Worksheet 7-9-1:

1a. $\frac{1}{2}$      4a. $\frac{5}{2}$

 b. $\frac{1}{4}$       b. $\frac{25}{4}$

2a. $\frac{1}{3}$      5a. $\frac{3}{2}$

 b. $\frac{1}{9}$       b. $\frac{9}{4}$

3a. $\frac{4}{1}$      6a. $\frac{2}{3}$

 b. $\frac{16}{1}$       b. $\frac{4}{9}$

7.

| Problem number | Similarity ratio | Area ratio |
|:---:|:---:|:---:|
| 1 | $\frac{1}{2}$ | $\frac{1}{4}$ |
| 2 | $\frac{1}{3}$ | $\frac{1}{9}$ |
| 3 | $\frac{4}{1}$ | $\frac{16}{1}$ |
| 4 | $\frac{5}{2}$ | $\frac{25}{4}$ |
| 5 | $\frac{3}{2}$ | $\frac{9}{4}$ |
| 6 | $\frac{2}{3}$ | $\frac{4}{9}$ |

8.

| Similarity ratio | Area ratio |
|:---:|:---:|
| $\frac{5}{2}$ | $\frac{25}{4}$ |
| $\frac{4}{3}$ | $\frac{16}{9}$ |
| $\frac{2}{3}$ | $\frac{4}{9}$ |
| $\frac{5}{4}$ | $\frac{25}{16}$ |

1a. What is the similarity ratio?

 b. What is the area ratio?

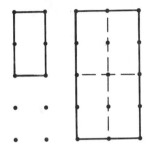

2a. What is the similarity ratio?

 b. What is the area ratio?

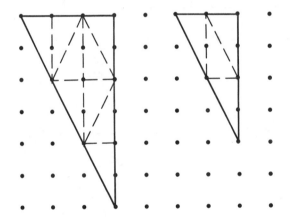

         *Visualized Geometry*

# WORKSHEET 7-9-1
## The Similarity Ratio and the Area Ratio of Similar Figures

1. The two squares are similar.
   a. What is the similarity ratio?
   b. What is the area ratio?

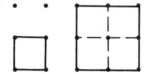

2. The two triangles are similar.
   a. What is the similarity ratio?
   b. What is the area ratio?

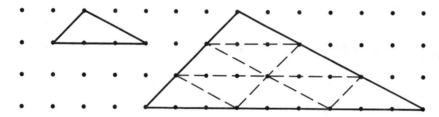

3. The two parallelograms are similar.
   a. What is the similarity ratio?
   b. What is the area ratio?

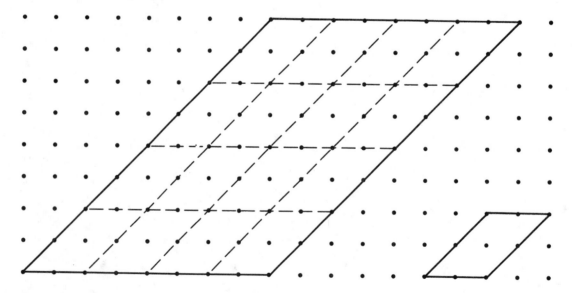

*(continued)*

     *Visualized Geometry*

# WORKSHEET 7-9-1
## The Similarity Ratio and the Area Ratio
## of Similar Figures *(continued)*

4. The squares are similar.

   a. What is the similarity ratio?

   b. What is the area ratio?

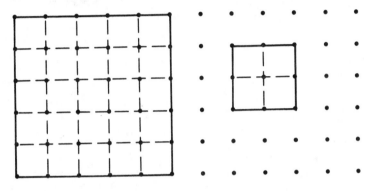

5. The triangles are similar.

   a. What is the similarity ratio?

   b. What is the area ratio?

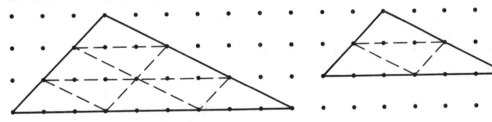

6. The parallelograms are similar.

   a. What is the similarity ratio?

   b. What is the area ratio?

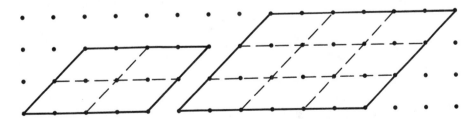

*(continued)*

*Visualized Geometry*

# WORKSHEET 7-9-1
## The Similarity Ratio and the Area Ratio
## of Similar Figures *(continued)*

7. Using the information from problems 1–6, complete the table below. (The first one is done for you.)

| Problem number | Similarity ratio | Area ratio |
|---|---|---|
| 1 | $\frac{1}{2}$ | $\frac{1}{4}$ |
| 2 | | |
| 3 | | |
| 4 | | |
| 5 | | |
| 6 | | |

8. Carefully examine the table above. Now try to complete the table below.

| Similarity ratio | Area ratio |
|---|---|
| $\frac{5}{2}$ | |
| $\frac{4}{3}$ | |
| | $\frac{4}{9}$ |
| | $\frac{25}{16}$ |

 *Visualized Geometry*

# Lesson 7–10
# Similarity Involving Equilateral Triangles, Squares, and Circles

## *Materials Needed:*

One transparency of each of the following pages: pages 413, 414, and 415.

## *Directions for the Teacher:*

The purpose of this lesson is to convince the students that any pair of equilateral triangles is similar, any pair of squares is similar, and any pair of circles is similar.

Place the first transparency on the overhead projector. Direct the students' attention to problem I. Point out that the use of special (isometric) dot paper allows for the drawing of equilateral triangles. They should conclude that the triangles are similar and the similarity ratio is $\frac{3}{2}$. Proceed to problem II. Below the problem write

$$GH = HI = GI$$
$$\text{and}$$
$$JK = KL = JL.$$

Justify these statements by emphasizing that the triangles are equilateral. Then write and argue that

$$\frac{GH}{JK} = \frac{HI}{KL} = \frac{GI}{JL}\ .$$

Also, argue that all of the angles of both equilateral triangles are congruent, so $\triangle GHI \sim \triangle JKL$.

Next, read the conclusion.

Place the second transparency on the overhead projector. Direct the students' attention to problem 1. They should conclude that the squares are similar and the similarity ratio is $\frac{3}{4}$. Proceed to problem II. Below the problem write

$$IJ = JK = KL = IL$$
$$\text{and}$$
$$MN = NO = OP = MP.$$

Justify these statements by emphasizing that the quadrilaterals are actually squares. Then write

$$\frac{IJ}{MN} = \frac{JK}{NO} = \frac{KL}{OP} = \frac{IL}{MP}.$$

Also, argue that all of the angles of a square are right angles, so square *IJKL* ~ square *MNOP*. Next, read the conclusion.

Place the third transparency on the projector. Point out that intuitively speaking, two figures are similar when they have the "same shape." Mention that all equilateral triangles have the "same shape" and all squares have the "same shape" so the conclusions previously described are reasonable. Indicate that any two circles have the "same shape" so they are similar, which means that the two circles pictured are similar. Similarity ratios previously referred to the ratios of the lengths of corresponding sides of similar figures. Point out that since a circle does not have a side in the same sense as quadrilaterals have sides, in this case some other type of ratio must be established. Suggest that the ratio of the length of a radius of one circle to the length of a radius of the other circle is reasonable. Conclude that in this case the similarity ratio is $\frac{1}{2}$. Finally, read the conclusion.

I.

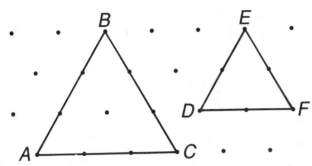

a. Triangle *ABC and* △*DEF* are both equilateral triangles. Are these triangles similar?

b. If yes, what is the similarity ratio?

II.

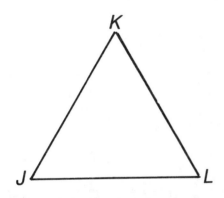 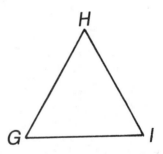

Triangle *GHI and* △*JKL* are both equilateral triangles. Show that these triangles are similar.

III. *Conclusion*

Any two equilateral triangles are similar.

     *Visualized Geometry*

I.

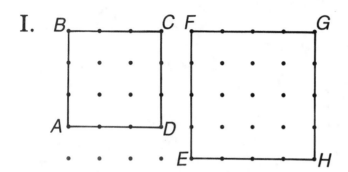

   a. Quadrilateral *ABCD* and quadrilateral *EFGH* are both squares. Are these squares similar?

   b. If yes, what is the similarity ratio?

II.

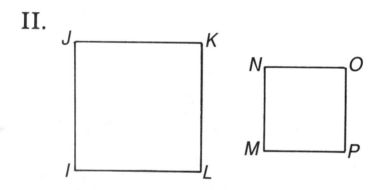

Quadrilateral *IJKL* and quadrilateral *MNOP* are both squares. Are these squares similar?

III. *Conclusion*

Any two squares are similar.

 *Visualized Geometry*

I.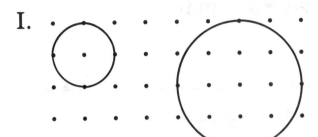

   a. Are the two circles similar?

   b. If yes, what is the similarity ratio?

## II. *Conclusion*

Any two circles are similar.

          *Visualized Geometry*

# Lesson 7–11
# Congruence and Similarity

## *Materials Needed:*

One copy of each of the following pages for each student: pages 419 and 420.
One transparency of page 418.

## *Directions for the Teacher:*

Distribute the worksheets and provide individual assistance as needed.

### Correct Answers for Worksheet 7–11–1:

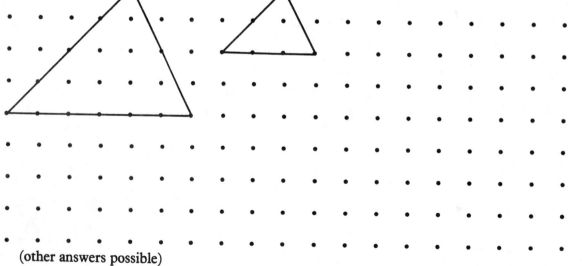

1a.                                        • (other answers possible)

b. The triangles are congruent.

2a.                                        (other answers possible)

b. yes, $\frac{1}{1}$

3.

(other answers possible)

4. not possible

The purpose of this lesson is to investigate the relationships between congruency and similarity. After the worksheets have been completed, lead a discussion concerning these two relations. After the students have expressed themselves, place the transparency on the overhead projector. Go through each item carefully, justifying with problems 1–4 if necessary.

**If two figures are congruent, then they are similar and the similarity ratio is $\frac{1}{1}$. If two figures are similar and the similarity ratio is $\frac{1}{1}$, then they are congruent.**

**It is possible to have two figures which are similar but not congruent. The requirement is that the figures have a similarity ratio different from $\frac{1}{1}$.**

**It is impossible to have two figures which are congruent but not similar.**

*Visualized Geometry*

# WORKSHEET 7-11-1
## Congruence and Similarity

1a. Draw a triangle which is similar to the one pictured and such that the similarity ratio is $\frac{1}{1}$.

b. What do you notice about these triangles?

2a. Draw a picture of a quadrilateral which is congruent to the one pictured.

b. Are these quadrilaterals similar? If yes, what is the similarity ratio?

3. Draw a picture (if possible) of a triangle which is similar to the pictured triangle but not congruent to it.

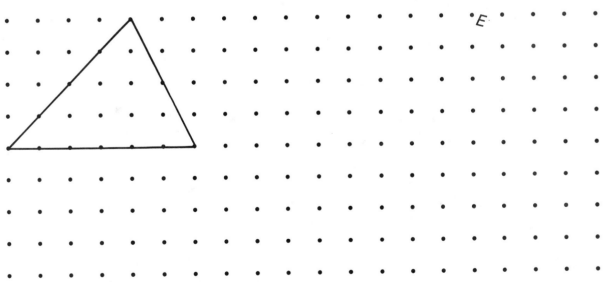

*(continued)*

# WORKSHEET 7-11-1
## Congruence and Similarity *(continued)*

4. Draw a picture (if possible) of a triangle which is congruent to the triangle pictured but not similar to it.

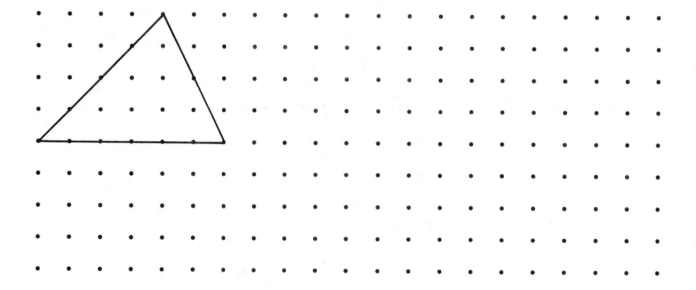

# Appendix

*Visualized Geometry*

*Visualized Geometry*

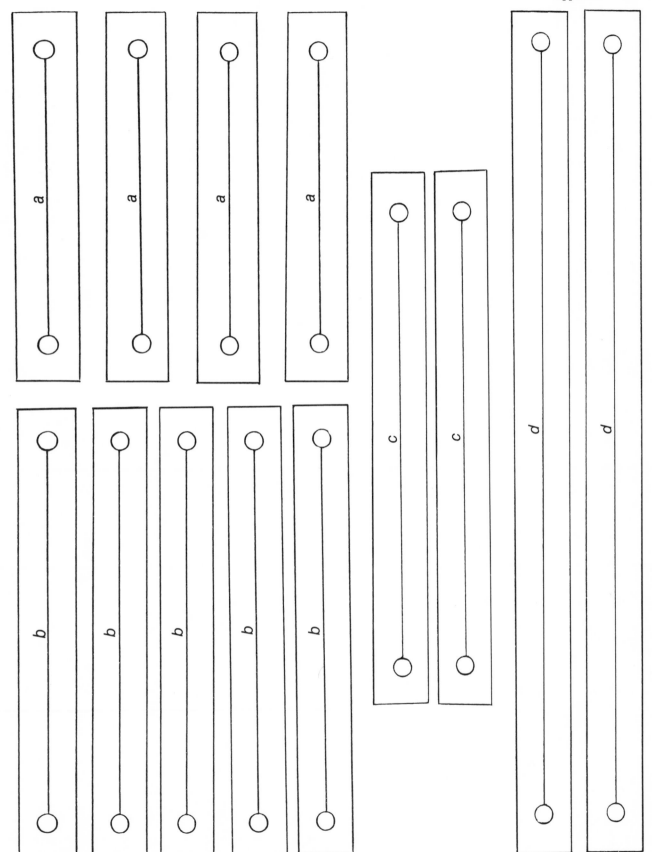

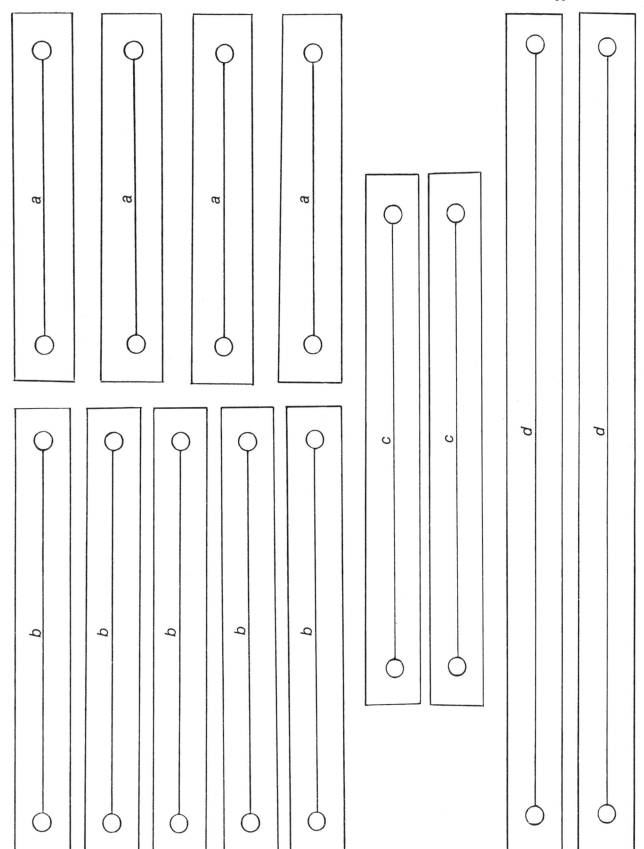

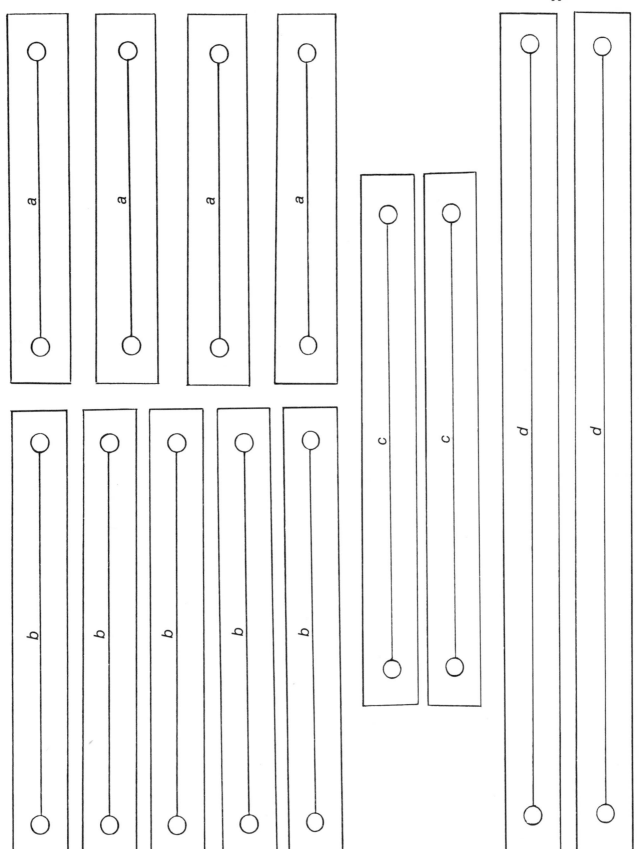